The Little Red Hen
(Makes a Pizza)

The Little

RETOLD BY

Philemon Sturges

ILLUSTRATED BY

Amy Walrod

RED HEN (MAKES A PIZZA)

PUFFIN BOOKS

To the ducks, the cats, the furry dogs, and especially to
the beautiful Red Hen at Studio Goodwin-Sturges—P.S.

To John, with love and thanks,
and thanks to Philemon—A.W.

PUFFIN BOOKS
Published by the Penguin Group
Penguin Putnam Books for Young Readers,
345 Hudson Street, New York, New York 10014, U.S.A.
Penguin Books Ltd, 80 Strand, London, WC2R ORL, England
Penguin Books Australia Ltd, 250 Camberwell Road, Camberwell, Victoria 3124, Australia
Penguin Books Canada Ltd, 10 Alcorn Avenue, Toronto, Ontario, Canada M4V 3B2
Penguin Books (N.Z.) Ltd, 182–190 Wairau Road, Auckland 10, New Zealand
Penguin Books Ltd, Registered Offices: Harmondsworth, Middlesex, England

First published in the United States of America by Dutton Children's Books,
a division of Penguin Putnam Books for Young Readers, 1999
Published by Puffin Books, a division of Penguin Putnam Books for Young Readers, 2002

38 39 40

Text copyright © Philemon Sturges, 1999
Illustrations copyright © Amy Walrod, 1999
All rights reserved
CIP Data is available.

ISBN 0-525-45953-7
Puffin Books ISBN 978-0-14-230189-0

Manufactured in China

T

he Little Red Hen had eaten the
last slice of her tasty loaf of bread. She'd sipped
a cup of chickweed tea and taken her nap. Now she was
hungry again. So she scratched through her cupboard and
spied a can of tomato sauce.

Why don't I make a lovely little pizza? she said to herself.

She rummaged through her pan drawer. There were bread pans, cake pans, muffin pans, frying pans—all kinds of pans— but not one single pan was large and round and flat.

"Cluck," she said. "I need a pizza pan."

She stuck her head out the window. "Good morning," she called. "Does anybody have a pizza pan?"

"Very well, then, I'll fetch one myself," said the Little Red Hen. So she went to the hardware store. She bought a pizza pan, a large mixing bowl, a pizza slicer, and . . . some other stuff.

When she got home, she opened the cupboard.

She saw beans and rice,

sugar and spices,

jars of jam,      and jars of honey,

and even pickled eggplant
—but no flour.

"Cluck," she said. "I need flour."

She stuck her head out the window. "Hello," she said. "Who'll run to the store and get me some flour?"

"Very well, then, I'll fetch some myself," said the Little Red Hen. So she went to the supermarket. She bought some flour, some salt, some oil, and . . . some other stuff.

When she got home, she opened the fridge.

"Cluck," she said. "There's cream cheese, blue cheese, string cheese, and Swiss cheese . . . but no mozzarella!" So . . .

She stuck her head out the window. "Excuse me," she said. "Who will go to the store and buy me some mozzarella?"

So the Little Red Hen went to the delicatessen. She bought

some mozzarella, pepperoni, and olives;

 some mushrooms, onions, and garlic;

a can of eight small anchovies; and . . .

some other stuff. But no pickled eggplant.

When she got home, the Little Red Hen put on her apron and stuck her head out the window. "Good afternoon," she said. "Who will help me make some pizza dough?"

"Not I," said the duck.

"Not I," said the dog.

BISCUITS

"Not I," said the cat.

"Very well, then, I'll make it myself," said the Little Red Hen.

So she put the flour and some other stuff into her mixing bowl
and stirred and mixed and mixed and kneaded and kneaded and
pounded until she had a big ball of pizza dough.

After the dough rose, the Little Red Hen rolled it flat and
folded it and rolled it again and spun it around her head
several times.

When the dough was just right, she tossed it way up in the air one last time for good luck and put it in her pizza pan.

Then she stuck her head out the window. "Excuse me," she said. "Who will help me make the topping?"

"Not I," said the duck.

"Not I," said the dog.

"Not I," said the cat.

"Very well, then, I'll make it myself," said the Little Red Hen.

So she chopped and grated and grated and sliced. Next she opened her can of tomato sauce and spread it all over the pizza dough. On top of that, she put some grated mozzarella, some sliced pepperoni, some chopped olives, some mushrooms, some onions and garlic, eight small anchovies, and . . . some other stuff. But no pickled eggplant.

The Little Red Hen looked at her pizza. It looked just right. She put it in the oven and sat down to sip a cup of chickweed tea.

Pretty soon a delicious smell drifted from the oven. It filled the room and floated out the window.

My lovely little pizza must be ready, she thought.

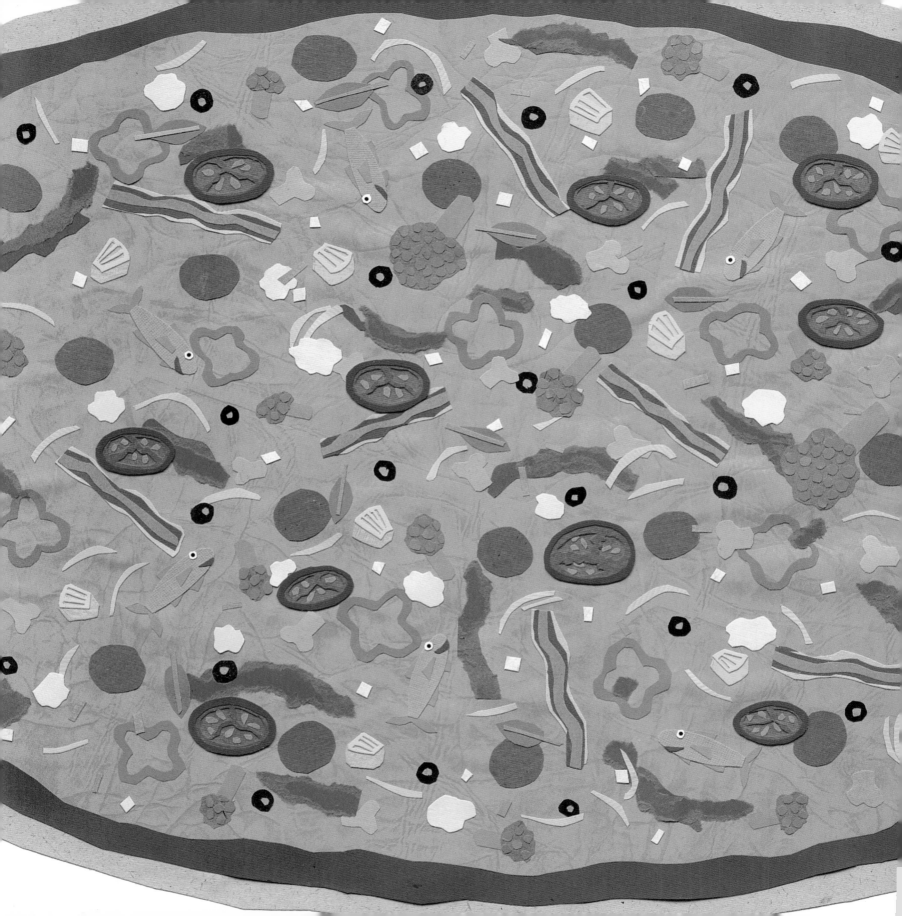

It was lovely, but it was not little.

So she stuck her head out the window. "Good evening," she said. "Would anybody like some pizza?"

Can you guess what the duck said?

Can you guess what the dog said??

Can you guess what the cat said???

They all said, "YES!" of course.

ISCUITS

(But the cat scraped most of the topping off his share!)
When the pizza was all gone, the Little Red Hen made herself
another cup of chickweed tea.

Then she asked, "Who will help me do the dishes?"
Now can you guess what the duck, the dog, and the cat ach said?

They each said,

"I will."

And they did.

Errata, Corrigenda, et Addenda

7   *for* The Hylton A. Thomas Collection University Gallery
    read The Hylton A. Thomas Collection, University Gallery

8   Add at bottom: In all cases the catalogue entry directly faces the picture discussed;
    when an artist is represented by more than one example, his biography continues
    in the left column of the succeeding pages.

9   *for* the Hon. Luis A. Ferre *read* the Hon. Luis A. Ferré

11 *for* Maratta *read* Maratti

28 under Ref.: *for* "Del Todeschine ...," *read* "Del Todeschini ...,"

38 *for* Victor-Amédée *read* Victor-Amadeus

45 *for* Barry Flannegan *read* Barry Hannegan

72 *for* eslewhere *read* elsewhere

80 under Ex Coll.: *for* 1960 *read* 1860

82 *for* Edward Dummond Libbey *read* Edward Drummond Libbey

88 under Ex Coll.: *for* Jacob Haimann *read* Jacob Heimann

104 *for* Ca Dolfin *read* Ca' Dolfin; *for* Archepiscopal *read* Archiepiscopal;
    under Ref.: add no. 221C to Pallucchini and Piovene entry

106 under Ref.: add no. 105 to Pallucchini and Piovene entry

108 *for* Archepiscopal *read* Archiepiscopal

124 *for* McSwiny *read* McSwinny

136 under lender add, The Christina N. and Swan J. Turnblad Memorial Fund

138 *for* Bood *read* Book

150 under lender add, The Christina N. and Swan J. Turnblad Memorial Fund

164 *for* Pannini *read* Panini

168 under Ref.: *for* "German Schoo" *read* "German School"

176 under Ex Coll.: *for* Torolonia *read* Torlonia

180 *for* Forli *read* Forlì

184 *for* Chigi Palazzo Chigi, 1780–86); *read* Chigi (Palazzo Chigi, 1780–86),;
    under media add "oil on paper mounted on canvas"

188 *for* via de' Cerociferi *read* via de' Crociferi

191 the catalogue illustration is reversed

194 under Ref.: *for* "Designi Giovanile ..." *read* "Disegni Giovanile ..."

198 Since the catalogue photograph has been printed the picture has been cleaned
    revealing that $5\frac{1}{2}$ inches have been added at the top and $1\frac{5}{8}$ inches at the bottom.

200 *for* Trasteverina *read* Trasteverina

202 under Ex Coll.: *for* Palazzo Parisani Ascoli *read* Palazzo Parisani, Ascoli

204 *for* Giampaolo *read* Gianpaolo

224 *for* Trinita *read* Trinità

230 The sentence reading: "The attribution (oral) is due to Professor Chiarini."
    should be placed at the end of the catalogue entry.

242 *for* Beautiful aurora *read* Beautiful Aurora

Technical Note Addenda

247 under 2. *for* w. 0.061 *read* w. 0.061 M; under 4. *for* crimson latke *read* crimson lake

249 The following additions should be made parenthetically to the Summary chart:

F.   Guardi

lead white (basic lead carbonate) $2PbCO_3 \cdot Pb(OH)_2$
bone black $C + Ca_3(PO_4)_2$
ultramarine (lapis lazuli) $3Na_2O \cdot 3Al_2O_3 \cdot 6SiO_2 \cdot 2Na_2S$
green earth (glauconite) Fe, Mg, Al, K hydrosilicate
vermilion (mercuric sulfide) HgS
red lead (tetroxide of lead) Pb_3O_4
red ochre (hydrated iron oxide) $Fe_2O_3 \cdot nH_2O$
crimson lake, unidentified organic dye
Naples yellow (lead antimoniate) $Pb_3[SbO_4]_2$
raw sienna (hydrated iron oxide) $Fe_2O_3 \cdot H_2O$
Van Dyck brown, bituminous earth
burnt sienna (iron oxide) Fe_2O_3

Cavallucci

lead white (basic lead carbonate) $2PbCO_2 \cdot Pb(OH)_2$
bone black $C + Ca_3(PO_4)_2$
Naples yellow (lead antimoniate) $Pb_3[SbO_4]_2$
yellow ochre (hydrated iron oxide) $Fe_2O_3 \cdot H_2O$
red ochre (hydrated iron oxide) $Fe_2O_3 \cdot nH_2O$
burnt sienna (iron oxide) Fe_2O_3

PAINTING IN ITALY IN THE EIGHTEENTH CENTURY

ROCOCO TO ROMANTICISM

Under the high patronage of

The Honorable Richard M. Nixon
President of the United States

The Honorable Giuseppe Saragat
President of the Republic of Italy

Domenico Corvi, Allegory of Painting. Walters Art Gallery, Baltimore

PAINTING IN ITALY
IN THE EIGHTEENTH CENTURY:
ROCOCO TO ROMANTICISM

Edited by John Maxon and Joseph J. Rishel, Chicago, 1970

An exhibition organized by

The Art Institute of Chicago,

The Minneapolis Institute of Arts,

and The Toledo Museum of Art

The Art Institute of Chicago
September 19–November 1, 1970

The Minneapolis Institute of Arts
November 24, 1970–January 10, 1971

The Toledo Museum of Art
February 7–March 21, 1971

Committee of Honor

The Honorable Egidio Ortona
Ambassador of Italy to the United States, Washington, D.C.

The Honorable Graham A. Martin
Ambassador of the United States to Italy, Rome

Dr. Bartolomeo Attolico
Cultural Counselor, Embassy of Italy, Washington, D.C.

Wells Stabler
Deputy Chief of Mission, Embassy of the United States, Rome

Russell L. Harris
Cultural Attaché, Embassy of the United States, Rome

Professor Giuseppe Cardillo
Italian Institute of Culture, New York

Giuseppe Avitabile
Consul General of Italy, Chicago

Mario Anziano
Acting Consul of Italy, Cleveland

Professor Bruno Molajoli
*Direzione Generale delle Antichità e Belle Arti
Ministero della Pubblica Istruzione, Rome*

Professor Mario Salmi
*v. Presidente del Consiglio Superiore delle Antichità e Belle Arti,
Rome*

Professor Italo Faldi
*Director, Galleria Nazionale d'Arte Antica, Palazzo Corsini,
Rome*

Giovanni Agnelli
President, The Fiat Company, Rome

Harold Boeschenstein
President, The Toledo Museum of Art

Clinton Morrison
Chairman of the Board, Minneapolis Society of Fine Arts

Frank H. Woods
President, The Art Institute of Chicago

Lenders to the Exhibition

Professor Giuliano Briganti, Rome
Dr. Franco Di Castro, Rome
Walter P. Chrysler Jr., New York
Mr. and Mrs. Paul H. Ganz, New York
Dr. Mina Gregori, Florence
Hampton Court Palace, Lent by Gracious Permission of Her Majesty Queen Elizabeth II
Mr. and Mrs. Milton J. Lewine, New York
D. C. Miller, Palo Alto
Mrs. John S. Pillsbury, Sr., Crystal Bay, Minnesota
Professor Caesar Pinnau, Hamburg-Blankenese
Francesco Molinari Pradelli, Bologna
Private Collection, Milan
Private Collections, U.S.A.
Samuel Pryor Reed, New York
David E. Rust, Washington, D.C.
Suida-Manning Collection, New York

Accademia Nazionale di San Luca, Rome
Albright-Knox Art Gallery, Buffalo
Allen Memorial Art Museum, Oberlin College, Ohio
Art Gallery of Ontario, Toronto
The Art Institute of Chicago
Barber Institute of Fine Arts, University of Birmingham, England
The Brooklyn Museum, Brooklyn
City Art Museum of Saint Louis
The Cleveland Museum of Art
P. & D. Colnaghi & Co. Ltd., London
E. B. Crocker Art Gallery, Sacramento
The Detroit Institute of Arts
M. H. de Young Memorial Museum, San Francisco (Gift of the Samuel H. Kress Foundation)
Galleria Nazionale d'Arte Antica, Rome
Galleria Nazionale d'Arte Antica, Rome (on deposit at the Chamber of Deputies)

Galleria Nazionale d'Arte Antica, Rome (on deposit in Villa d'Este, Tivoli)
Galleria Palatine, Palazzo Pitti, Florence
Gripsholm Castle, Sweden
Hamburger Kunsthalle
Kunsthistorisches Museum, Vienna
The Minneapolis Institute of Arts
The Montreal Museum of Fine Arts
Musée des Beaux-Arts, Chambéry (Savoie)
Museo de Arte de Ponce (Luis A. Ferré Foundation), Puerto Rico
Museo di Palazzo Venezia, Rome
Museo e Gallerie Nazionali di Capodimonte, Naples
Museum of Art, Rhode Island School of Design, Providence
Museum of Fine Arts, Boston
Museum of Fine Arts, Springfield, Massachusetts
Muzeum Narodowe, Warsaw
National Collection of Fine Arts, Smithsonian Institution
National Gallery, Prague
Nationalmuseum, Stockholm
Nelson Gallery—Atkins Museum (Samuel H. Kress Collection), Kansas City
Norfolk Museum of Arts and Sciences, Virginia
North Carolina Museum of Art, Raleigh, Samuel H. Kress Collection
Pinacoteca Nazionale, Bologna
Seattle Art Museum, Washington
Norton Simon Foundation, Fullerton, California
The Hylton A. Thomas Collection University Gallery, University of Minnesota, Minneapolis
The Toledo Museum of Art
Virginia Museum of Fine Arts, Richmond
Wadsworth Atheneum, Hartford
Walker Art Gallery, Liverpool
The Walters Art Gallery, Baltimore
Wildenstein and Company, New York

Contents

Page 11   Introduction
           by Ellis K. Waterhouse

17   Piedmont, Liguria, Lombardy
      by Robert L. Manning

45   Venice and the Veneto
      by Barry Hannegan

115   Bologna and Emilia
      by Dwight C. Miller

145   Florence and Tuscany
      by Mina Gregori

163   Rome and the Papal States
      by Anthony M. Clark

217   Naples and Southern Italy
      by Michael W. Stoughton

246   Technical Note
      by Marigene H. Butler

250   Index of Artists

Some six years ago, two of us—Otto Wittmann and Anthony Clark—were discussing with John Maxon exhibitions still to be done in America to illuminate major fields of the history of art. It was agreed that an exhibition to illustrate the 18th century in Italy had never been done. After a number of further discussions we decided to undertake just such an exhibition, which aims to give a fair idea of what happened in pictorial art in the peninsula during one of the crucial centuries of European thought and politics and Italian creativity.

The exhibition is necessarily selective. We have sought to show important works by the major Italian painters of the 18th century. The founding masters of the High Baroque, who died old in the first decades of the century (e.g., Cignani, Luca Giordano, and Maratti), were eliminated, as were such foreign artists as Subleyras, Mengs, and Vernet, whose brilliant (if relatively brief) stays in Italy made them members of native schools in the 18th-century sense. Several artists (Van Wittel, Van Bloemen, and Pecheux) with very long adult careers in Italy, however, are included. Still-life painting is not represented at all; landscape and genre are not fully shown, although shown only slightly more fully than portraiture.

Given the riches of the period, it was thought best both to avoid and to pursue the obvious: avoid it in ignoring small sketches and models, now popular and often better known than the monumental commissions they represent; court the obvious by seeking pictures whose importance is judged not merely by our own contemporary ideas of quality but by the 18th-century's sense of importance, as belonging to the major forms and subjects, or, at least, as particular, intelligent evidences of the artists' careers. The picture of heroic concept, with a grand religious, literary, or historical subject, and often large in format, was still the foundation of the art of painting and of the degree of artistic reputation in the 18th century.

We could not have organized such an exhibition without the complete and amicable cooperation of these officials in Italy and of our Italian museum colleagues charged with the care of the art of that great country. We are equally grateful to those officials and colleagues in other foreign countries as well as to the collectors and museum directors of our own country. Their unfailing generosity has made this exhibition an international effort of scholarly and aesthetic significance.

Of course not all pictures requested could be lent. Some of the most desirable examples—the Melbourne Tiepolo for example—are too large to travel far. Fresco decorations can only be shown photographically (or in models) which limits our representation of the Genoese School. However, the general emphasis on works of art infrequently seen at the expense of the better known schools (such as that of Venice) is the result of the deliberations of the organizers—and any imbalance is their fault.

The major aim of the exhibition, aside from the patent (but so often ignored) one of the pursuit of beauty, is to give the visitor something which approaches a fair notion of what happened in the history of painting throughout Italy during the 18th century. After the visitor has seen the exhibition and read this catalogue, we, the sponsors, hope he will understand our sub-title, *Rococo to Romanticism*, for that is the course which evolved, and in the dissolution of the rococo style and emergence of neoclassicism also came the beginnings of the romantic impulse.

We wish here to thank not only our collaborators in this catalogue but also the following people who helped us materially in our work: Dott. Luisa Becherucci, James M. Brown, Prof. Maria Vittoria Brugnoli-Pace, Charles E. Buckley, Thomas S. Buechner, Henry B. Caldwell, Phillip J. Carlson, David G. Carter, Prof. Raffaello Causa, Dr. M. Chiarini, Dr. Francesco Cosentino, Frederick Cummings, Dr. Bengt Dahlbäck, Allen Davis, James Elliott, Sarah Faunce, the Hon. Luis A. Ferre, John Fleming, Richard E. Fuller, Prof. Cesare Gnudi, Louis Goldenberg, Dr. Alfred Hentzen, Dr. Werner

Hofmann, Hugh Honour, Arnold Jolles, Frank W. Kent, Dr. Friderike Klauner, Dr. Jirí Kotalik, Sherman E. Lee, Michel LaClotte, Prof. Dr. Stanislaw Lorentz, Mino Mallari, Jacques Manoury, Dr. Edward A. Maser, William Mayglothling, Oliver Millar, C.V.O., F.S.A., Dr. Antonio Morassi, Prof. Luigi Pierotta, Richard H. Randall, Jr., Perry T. Rathbone, Daniel Robbins, Frederick B. Robinson, Pierre Rosenberg, Victor D. Spark, Hugh Scrutton, Erich Schleier, Carlo and Marcello Sestieri, Laurence Sickman, Gordon Mackintosh Smith, John R. Spencer, Charles W. Stanford, Jr., Timothy Stevens, Joshua C. Taylor, Rene Taylor, R. M. D. Thesiger, Ian McKibbin White, Margareta Winqvist, William J. Withrow, and Willis F. Woods.

We are particularly indebted to the following members of the staff of The Art Institute of Chicago: Joseph J. Rishel, who was responsible for assembling the loans and the catalogue entries with the assistance of Sandra Grung and Anselmo Carini, to Wallace D. Bradway for handling the many details of transporting the material for this exhibition, and to Marigene H. Butler for her technical research about the paintings.

Charles C. Cunningham
Director
The Art Institute of
Chicago

Anthony M. Clark
Director
The Minneapolis
Institute of Arts

Otto Wittmann
Director
The Toledo
Museum of Art

It is probable that at no time, since that distant age when the Romans raped the Sabines, was the culture of Italy so fragmented as it was during the eighteenth century. When Metternich, in that period of tidying-up after Napoleon, remarked that Italy was "merely a geographical expression", he was giving voice to a point of view which was held by almost everybody in Europe except the Italians themselves. They knew better; and they were right.

This is the reason why it is very well worthwhile to hold an exhibition of Italian painting of the eighteenth century—and also why it has not seriously been attempted before. I say "seriously" because there has been a tendency in the last few years for certain intelligent dealers to hold exhibitions which have almost entirely been made up of small Italian eighteenth-century paintings. There is a simple reason for this—that it was during the eighteenth century in Italy that people with living rooms no bigger than those in which most of us live today for the first time created a demand for small pictures. This growth of a middle class which liked pictures was an aspect of society common to Turin, Genoa, Milan, Venice, Florence, Rome and Naples, and the enormous number of little pictures—which tend to be called *modelli* or *bozzetti*—which are flooding the market today does not indicate any special scrupulousness or fussiness on the part of those who commissioned large pictures or ceiling decorations, but rather a liking on the part of those with modest incomes and modest apartments to have some record of a favorite work of art. Such exhibitions are often pleasant enough, but the spirit which has prompted them has been the line of least resistance, rather than a serious attempt—as has been made in the present exhibition—to give some notion of both the variety and the coherence of Italian painting during the eighteenth century.

There are two complementary changes in what one might call the "art situation" in Italy which distinguish the eighteenth century from the seventeenth—one concerned with the movements of painters from one center (or one country) to another, the second with changes in the pattern of patronage. During the seventeenth century the leading artists, in spite of often tempting invitations, tended to remain on their home ground, and the great bulk of their commissions was from Italian patrons. For instance, both Guercino and Maratta resisted pressing invitations to go to England, and the Court of Charles II in England had to put up with the very small change of Benedetto Gennari and Antonio Verrio—while the amount of diplomatic pressure which had to be exercised by

Louis XIV to get even a brief visit from Bernini to Paris was phenomenal. There was enough work being commissioned from the best artists—and even from what one may call the "second line" of artists—to retain them contentedly at home. But a change in the amount of money available (or, at any rate, expended) for native artistic patronage began to be apparent in the 1690's, and soon two of the major *vedettes* of Italian painting were lured abroad. Luca Giordano went to work for the Spanish Court in 1692, and it was only the death of Carlos II in 1700, with the subsequent outbreak of the War of the Spanish Succession, that led him to return to Naples three years before his death in 1705; and Fratel Pozzo, who had completed his spectacular activities in S. Ignazio in Rome in 1698, was carried off to Vienna in 1703 by the Prince of Liechtenstein. Italian painters began to rely more and more during the eighteenth century on selling easel pictures to rich foreign travellers, especially the English and the Germans, who were flocking to Italy in ever greater numbers. The patronage of contemporary Italian painters—in Genoa, Venice, Bologna, Florence and Rome—of the 5th Earl of Exeter (who died in 1700) was altogether remarkable, and Count Friedrich Christian zu Schaumburg-Lippe provides a German parallel.

During the first quarter of the eighteenth century a number of the ablest Venetian painters—the two Ricci, Pellegrini, Amigoni and Bellucci—found it necessary to seek their fortunes abroad; and when, in the 1740's, the War of the Austrian Succession prevented the British from visiting Venice—which had degenerated by then into little better than a tourist-trap—Canaletto felt forced to come to England, and was followed, a little later, by Zuccarelli. Even Giovanni Battista Tiepolo, who appears to our hindsight as the greatest Italian painter of the century, received his most expansive commissions from Germany or Spain, or from Milan, which was then a dependency of the Empire; and, at the end of his life, he found the situation in Venice so depressing, that he preferred to remain on and die in Spain. The general outlines of the history of Venetian painting during the century are perhaps the only ones which are normally familiar, but one tends to forget the frequent absences of the most notable figures. Soon after Zuccarelli had been elected President of the Venetian Academy of Painters, the Academy had to admit that no one had any idea where he was!

The broad pattern of development in the eighteenth century is more or less the same for all the different Italian centers. By 1700 there had been, almost everywhere, a victory over the High Baroque by what Wittkower has called "High Baroque Classicism." This is epitomized in Rome by the triumph of Maratti over Baciccia, and by the predominance of Carlo Cignani at Bologna. For about a generation this probably remained the "establishment" style, but it was gradually undermined in most places by a style which is now generally called "Italian Rococo"—a name which would have seemed very odd a generation or so ago. As the century wore on this gave way to a proto-neoclassic style, and this, in turn, leads on to full-blown neoclassicism.

This sequence is naturally most clearly to be read in Rome. The direct pupils of Maratti give way to the rococo of Conca, Michele Rocca and Giaquinto. The most seminal proto-neoclassic painter—who will perhaps be the most surprising discovery to many visitors to the Exhibition—was Marco Benefial. Shortly after the middle of the century the stage in Rome seems to be held by the Saxonian, Raphael Mengs, who was hailed by Winckelmann, after the completion of his *Parnassus* ceiling for the Villa Albani in 1761, as the white hope of painting. This at once led to his translation as Court Painter to Madrid, and it was left to another foreigner, this time the Frenchman, Jacques Louis David, to crystallize the neoclassic style, when he completed in Rome in 1785 his *Oath of the Horatii*. After that the stage was set for the invasion of Italy by Napoleon!

The term "rococo" has been so generally—and correctly—associated with the development of style in France and Germany, that it has only become acceptable in the last decade or so to speak of Italian rococo. It is a somewhat tamer style than its northern counterpart, but it is marked by the same symptoms. Its father-figure in Italy is Luca Giordano, and it flowered most brilliantly in Naples in the first third of the eighteenth century. With the advent of the Bourbon Kings in 1734 it fell from grace, at any rate for major enterprises. The Bourbons steadily refrained from employing the best native painters and architects and tended to bring in outsiders with neoclassical leanings—and in this their taste was reinforced by their sponsoring the excavations of Pompeii and Herculaneum. The Palace of Caserta was the greatest neoclassical monument of the century in Italy—just as the greatest rococo monument was at the opposite end of Italy, in Piedmont, Juvarra's palace of Stupinigi.

In Naples the mantle of Giordano fell upon Solimena, and it was Solimena's pupils who were the most profuse purveyors of rococo throughout Italy (in Rome and Turin) and in Madrid. In Naples itself Francesco de Mura and his pupil, Giacinto Diana, carried on the style well into the age of neoclassicism. In Rome Conca and Giaquinto were the leaders of the rococo movement, and Giaquinto worked also in Pisa, Turin and in Spain, while Conca's pupil, Gregorio Guglielmi, carried Italian rococo to Vienna and to St. Petersburg. Perhaps the most elegant of Solimena's pupils, however, was Domenico Antonio Vaccaro, who was primarily an architect and decorator, but had the unique distinction of painting the altarpieces for his own churches. But it is unhappily not possible to transfer to the walls of an exhibition the whole Church of the SS. Concezione di Montecalvario, where the blending of Vaccaro's paintings in pastel shades with his ornamental stuccoes and frames of fanciful curvatures produces the most completely satisfying Neapolitan rococo *ensemble*.

This abundant use of fanciful curves for the frames of altarpieces, or for the limiting edges of ceiling frescoes or ceiling canvases, is a constant element of rococo in all the separate centers of Italy—as it was also in France and Germany. They appear everywhere from Naples to Turin, where the frames designed for Crosato's ceiling paintings at Stupinigi or for a host of painters at the Royal Palace are prodigious. At Genoa, Gregorio de Ferrari and his son Lorenzo, in their frescoes in both churches and palaces, exercise the same ingenuity. It is worth stressing the elaborate shapes of these vast and unexhibitable works, as the small reductions from these designs, made by the artists themselves, are usually set into canvases of a more conventional shape, which are easier to frame. The same bulges and curves appear in rococo architecture, and it is worth quoting the neoclassic Milizia's criticism of Raguzzini's Piazza S. Ignazio at Rome, which is today considered one of the chief masterpieces of the style: "it has been disfigured", says Milizia, "by those ridiculous buildings which look like chests-of-drawers."

There are three classes of painting which receive particular emphasis in all centers of Italy during the eighteenth century—genre, portraiture, and real and fanciful painting of views. During the seventeenth century genre painting had been the particular province of foreigners, mainly Flemish and Dutch, who had filled an increasing demand for what the major patrons regarded as rather a low taste. It is true that, at the very beginning of the century, Caravaggio had painted a few examples of what one might almost call "heroic genre," but the Establishment had managed to banish such things from Rome by the early 1620's. Only at Genoa, where there had long been a tradition of sympathy with northern taste, did native Italian painters, Sinibaldo Scorza and Antonio Travi, establish a genre tradition in the seventeenth century, which was to flower by the turn of the century into the extraordinary personality of Magnasco, who captivated the taste of a number of collectors (perhaps of the more waggish sort?) in Lombardy and Florence as well as Genoa. In the eighteenth century native genre is found everywhere. In Turin there are Olivero and Graneri; in Florence the most attractive side of the work of Giandomenico Ferretti is of this sort. In Lombardy a new note is struck by Todeschini and Ceruti; and, in Bologna, there is the great master of native Italian genre—Giuseppe Maria Crespi. The rather stuffy Bolognese in fact favored the watered classicism of Franceschini, and the chief patrons for Crespi's genre paintings were in fact the most distinguished collectors throughout the whole of Italy in the earlier years of the eighteenth century---Prince Eugene of Savoy, the Grand Duke Ferdinand of Tuscany, and Cardinal Ottoboni at Rome.

Crespi had an influence on Piazzetta in Venice, and, even more, on Pietro Longhi. The taste for the work of Piazzetta, as for that of Tiepolo, was widely diffused in Germany, but Longhi is a much odder character. He is the one Venetian painter of the century whom the Venetians managed to keep to themselves. He was a bit clumsy—but so were they. Longhi's paintings of Venice in the eighteenth century miraculously show a Venice in which the foreign tourists never intrude! If it is possible to pinpoint a native Venetian taste in this century, it is centered on Pietro Longhi.

In Rome there was the still rather mysterious Antonio Amorosi and Pier Leone Ghezzi, and in Naples a group of four or five painters produced for the royal tapestry works a series of designs for *Don Quixote* (now in the Palazzo Reale), which are altogether in the style of Italian genre. The only familiar name among these today is that of Giuseppe Bonito, who, with Gaspare Traversi, produced a number of lower-middle-class genre scenes on the scale of life, which seem to go back to the tradition of Caravaggio. Both also painted rather dreary altarpieces, and Bonito was sufficiently well thought of to end his days as Director of the Naples Academy, but there is no doubt that both these painters show much greater liveliness of spirit and *brio* of paint in these scenes of low-class genre.

Eighteenth-century genre painting in Italy has been a good deal studied in recent years, but the step-child of Italian art-historical research is the portrait. There was a quite astonishing "Exhibition of Italian Baroque Portraits" at the Palazzo Vecchio in Florence in 1911, but this has been followed by almost complete neglect except for the "Mostra del Ritratto storico Napoletano" of 1954. It is, however, a subject of great interest and there is no doubt that portraits were also painted by the chief history painters. But it was regarded as rather a potboiling activity and the biographers of history painters tend to pass over their portrait activities in silence.

There was certainly great curiosity about people's appearance in Rome in the early eighteenth century. The evidence is in the scores of fascinating caricatures by Pier Leone Ghezzi, which have never been properly collected or published; and it is only in recent years that the researches of Anthony Clark have revealed the virtues of Pierleone as a straight portrait painter. Although the "Pittore di Camera" to the Pope (whose portrait he also painted) he does not seem to have had the upper crust of the Vatican as his sitters. Early in the century they went to Giuseppe Passeri and then to Agostino Masucci, and the less fashionable Cardinals were painted by Antonio Lesma and Ludovico David. Trevisani—who had very good patronage as a history painter—seems to have specialized in doing portraits of British visitors who had relations with the exiled Stuarts. In the middle of the century Marco Benefial, whose portraits are only now being identified, had a very good practice, and, from the 1750's onwards, Mengs and Pompeo Batoni became two of the most famous painters (and portrait painters) in Europe—especially for visiting gentlemen and noblemen from the north. In history, as well as in portrait, Batoni's work is the paradigm for the first phase of neoclassicism.

All these Roman painters are masters of the formal portrait (which is what was asked of them) but we can see from the great collection of artists' portraits (many of them self-portraits) in the Accademia di S. Luca in Rome—and, to a lesser extent, from the collection of artists' self-portraits in the Uffizi—that they were all capable of more relaxed and informal experiments. But it is in the north of Italy that we really begin to discern from their portraits what men looked like behind their formal masks. At the beginning of the century Bombelli and Tinelli in Venice, Ghislandi (Fra Galgario) in Bergamo, and Salomone Adler in Milan all show us human beings whose worries we seem able to understand (as if they were distant successors of Lorenzo Lotto). In the next generation Giacomo Ceruti—whose name has perhaps been used in recent years as something of a wastepaper basket!—has left us a gallery of portraits which resemble very much the sitters' descendants today. The same sort of tradition also prevails at Bologna with the splendid portraits of Giuseppe Maria Crespi, whose son, Luigi, and the Gandolfi prolonged the style, in a somewhat watered form, until the close of the century.

In Venice, as usual, the situation was a little different. All the great Venetians produced occasional portraits, but it is probable that Amigoni only took to portraiture with some reluctance after he had come to England—because he could not get enough commissions for history pictures. But he was an admirable portraitist and continued to do portraits in Spain.

In Venice itself, Rosalba, with her pretty crayons, and Bartolommeo Nazari, often with small portraits on copper, suitable for travellers, had a good practice at the bibelot level both with native Venetians and with visitors, while the two Longhis, father and son, continued in demand for the Venetian upper classes until the fall of the Republic.

But the tourists, or rather the "Grand Tourists," liked to bring back home not merely a record of their own faces, but some visible record of the places to which they had travelled. The prettiest fancy of this sort was that of Sir Adam Ferguson who commissioned Zuccarelli to paint for him an "*Et in Arcadia Ego*" scene, which meant in his case "I too have travelled in that ideal landscape." And, although it may seem derogatory to one of the greatest painters, it cannot be denied that Claude was the founder of this "souvenir-landscape" tradition which burgeoned in eighteenth century Italy. It is true that his pictures are souvenirs fit for the best educated princes in the world, but it is perfectly clear that they were the direct ancestors of, for instance, the later works of Corot, which were merely souvenirs for millionaires. The high tone and concentrated poetic content of Claude's pictures had, already in the seventeenth century, been watered down to suit the tastes of the more average traveller by Gaspard Poussin. In Rome this arcadian style was carried on with great success by Orizzonte and Locatelli, and, usually on a more topographical level, by Vanvitelli, Hendrik van Lint and Giovanni Battista Busiri. But, also in Rome, an entirely new kind of *veduta*, specifically apt for the eighteenth century Grand Tourists, was created by two artists who are much nearer to being great masters, Giovanni Battista Panini and the Frenchman, Joseph Vernet (who worked in Rome from 1738 to 1753).

Panini could paint faithful views of buildings, ceremonies and festival occasions to perfection, but he also devised anthologies of Famous Ancient Buildings and Sculptures, set in an appropriate landscape, which had an enormous vogue and were abundantly copied as fittings for Palladian mansions in England. Vernet drew also on the Neapolitan tradition of Salvator Rosa's landscapes and devised romantic views of Mediterranean harbours, often in pairs, which played the same decorative role. In Naples itself a similar school of souvenir-landscape painting flourished, ending with Pietro Fabris and Carlo Bonavia.

But it was in Venice that the landscape of pure fantasy, and also the topographical view, had their greatest success. Venice is so much the most obviously picturesque of Italian cities, so much unlike any other in the world, that travellers wanted to bring home an accurate record of its charms. Such painting was entirely for export. Until the present century—when a certain vogue for his work has been developed among North Italian industrialists—not a single Canaletto of any consequence was to be found in Italy; and Bellotto's greatest successes were in Germany and Poland. The virtues of these two painters are too obvious and too familiar to need comment. More curious is the way in which Venice and the Venetian *terra firma* became the basic subject matter for Italian rococo landscape—for the Roman *campagna*, which is the basis of the Claude tradition, does not lend itself to rococo treatment. Marco Ricci, Zais and Zuccarelli internationalised a kind of back-drop landscape, peopled, as often as not, by *contadine* who look like the ancestresses of the choruses in several of Verdi's operas. But it was from about 1760 onwards that a painter appears who, though barely esteemed in his own lifetime, seems to us today often to add a melancholy poetry—a sort of Venetian echo of Watteau—to a tradition which had never before risen above the level of "society verse." This was Francesco Guardi. His touch is as sparkling and evanescent as that of the best pastry-cook, and the exquisite quality of the surface of his pictures can be only too easily ruined by ironing and heavy varnish, but where it survives it is enchanting. With Guardi it is certainly the case of a great tradition ending in a whimper—but it is a whimper of remarkable charm.

ELLIS K. WATERHOUSE

Corrado Giaquinto
The Visitation (Meeting at the Golden Gate)
Lent by the Montreal Museum of Fine Arts

Piedmont, Liguria, Lombardy

by Robert L. Manning

Bazzani began his studies in his native city Mantua with Giovanni Canti (1653–1716) of Parma, alongside Giovanni Cadioli (1710–67) and Francesco Raineri, called Lo Schivenoglia (1703–85). During his formative years he studied the old masters, particularly the Venetians, Paolo Veronese and the Bassani; he also studied Rubens, Fetti, and Castiglione, who had all worked at the Gonzaga court in Mantua, and was influenced by his contemporaries such as Maffei, Pittoni, Guala, G. A. Guardi, Bencovich, and Magnasco. Highly appreciated during his lifetime, he worked for churches and palaces in Mantua and its surroundings. There his mature style developed around 1740. On the death of Cadioli he succeeded him as director of the Accademia di Belli Arti in Mantua, which had been founded in 1762. Since he was crippled and ailing during his last years, he probably was assisted by Raineri, his former fellow student in the studio of Canti. Bazzani had little influence in Italy, but his paintings had some effect on the later Austrian Baroque painters, particularly Maulpertsch.

REF.: Mantua, *Bazzani*, 1950, Catalogue by Nicola Ivanoff.

I

Death of Sapphira
Canvas: 92.1 x 140 cm.; 36¼ x 55⅛ inches
Allen Memorial Art Museum, Oberlin College
Not signed

DATE: C. 1751–1752

EX COLL.: Edward Hirschler, Vienna (sold April 26, 1900, no. 49 as G. B. Tiepolo); Prince Henry of Bourbon, Vienna (sold April 2, 1906, no. 87 as G. B. Piazzetta); Ernest Lang, Berlin, 1927; Dr. Fritz Haussmann, Berlin, 1930–35; Dr. Hanns Schaeffer, New York, 1943.

REF.: V. Bloch, "La pittura italiana a Berlino," *Vita Artistica*, 1927, p. 178; I. Kunze, "Die Ausstellung Italienischer Malerei des 17 und 18 Jahrhunderts zu Berlin," *Der Cicerone*, XIX, 1927, pp. 379 ff.; H. Voss, "Spätitalienische Gemälde in der Sammlung Dr. Fritz Haussmann," *Zeitschrift für Bildende Kunst*, Dec. 1931, p. 165; G. Delogu, "Pittura italiana del 600 e del 700 nella collezione Haussmann, Berlin," *Emporium*, LXXXII, 1935, p. 331; M. Goering, "Eine Bilderfolge von Bazzani," *Pantheon*, 1938, p. 95; Mantua, *Bazzani*, p. 67 and Fig. 61, illustrated but not exhibited; *Allen Memorial Art Museum Bulletin*, Oberlin College, Winter 1954, no. 50 (this publication coincided with the exhibition *Paintings and Drawings from Five Centuries*, M. Knoedler and Co., New York); A. Pigler, *Barockthemen*, Budapest-Berlin, 1956, I, p. 381; C.

Perina, "Some Unpublished Paintings by Giuseppe Bazzani," *The Art Bulletin*, XLVI, 1964, p. 229; London, *An American University Collection*, Kenwood (London County Council), 1962, cat. no. 14.

Before the subject was correctly identified as the rarely represented *Death of Sapphira*, it was thought to portray *The Apostles Attending the Fainting Virgin*. Taken from the Book of Acts, the story is as follows: Ananias, a Christian of Jerusalem, having noticed the favorable considerations given to those Christians who sold their property and gave the proceeds to the Apostles for distribution among the believers, sold some property and—in conjunction with his wife Sapphira—kept part of the money while pretending to give the entire amount to the Apostles. Reprimanded by Peter for having lied to God, Ananias fell and died suddenly. In ignorance of what had happened, Sapphira appeared later before the Apostles and repeated the same story; Peter therefore prophesied the same doom for her, the scene which Bazzani has chosen to represent in this possibly unique example in Italian art. Artists portraying this biblical episode usually combine the deaths of Ananias and Sapphira in one composition. Perhaps one of the earliest representations of the death of Ananias is the Raphael tapestry cartoon, 1515–16, in the Victoria and Albert Museum, London: whereas, one of the earliest representations of the death of Sapphira alone is probably the painting by Poussin in the Louvre, Paris, executed between 1652 and 1656. Two other representations of the death of Sapphira by French artists are an engraving by Louis Chéron (1660–1713), Le Blanc no. 25, and an oil sketch by Sebastien Leclerc the Younger (1676–1763), Saint-Germain-des-Pres, Paris.

The fact that at the beginning of this century before this painting was correctly identified as an important work by Bazzani, it was attributed to two of the greatest Venetian masters of the 18th-century—first to G.-B. Tiepolo and later to G.-B. Piazzetta—is evidence of its superb quality. Chiara Perina has assigned the date for this painting about 1751–1752, during a period in which "he frees himself from the vestiges of seicento aesthetic" and "compositional schemes are looser, lighter, and the handling of color more precious and subtle. . . ." Other paintings which she relates it to and assigns to the same period are the *Madonna with Santa Chiara* and the *Annunciation* in the parish church at Revere, the *Miracles of Pius V*, San Maurizio, the paintings in Santa Maria della Carita, both in Mantua, and the fifteen oval-shaped paintings depicting the *Mysteries of the Rosary*, originally situated in the intrados of the vaulting of a side altar in the church at Cavriana.

Born in Turin and destined to be its official and most evident artist, Beaumont was sent by his king to Rome in 1716. He briefly visited Bologna on the way to study the works of the elderly and very famous Cignani and, in Rome, studied with Trevisani (*q.v.*) until 1719. Back in Turin, Beaumont executed his first ceiling fresco in the Royal Palace, an *Aurora*. From 1723–31 he was again in Rome under the king's protection and on terms both with Trevisani and Vleughels, director of the French Academy there. In 1725 Beaumont was elected to the Roman Academy. A large pension from his king began in 1722 and the artist was sending a stream of pictures back to the Piedmont: a *Helen* for the Castle of Rivoli, a *Sophonisba* for Palazzo Madama, two altarpieces for the Superga, etc. In July 1731 he returned to Turin, recalled as first painter of the Court of Sardinia.

Turin and Piedmont were, on Beaumont's return, at the peak of Juvara's (from 1714; died 1736) famous architectural constructions and renovations. Prominent "foreign" artists of Rome, Naples and Venice were now involved either intimately (as Giaquinto, 1733; Crosato, 1733, 1740; Nogari 1741–42; de Mura, 1741–42; Guglielmi, 1755; Carle van Loo, 1732 on his return to France from his long Roman training), or by lucrative commissions that were shipped in rather than done on the spot (Solimena, de Mura, Conca, Giaquinto; all the prominent Roman painters of the 1720's and 1730's including such landscapists as Panini and Locatelli; several Bolognese; Amigoni, Sebastiano Ricci). Beaumont is responsible for many of these (his 1737 trip to Venice was probably to the purpose), and several must have presented problems for him since they involved painters less academic or courtly, more authentically rococo (Crosato, de Mura, Guglielmi), than he himself was, or was to become.

Beaumont as head of the royal drawing school, as supervisor of the tapestry works and producer of its main cartoons (from 1731), and as first painter, was kept heavily employed. His painting commissions include many church altarpieces and other canvases for the royal castles. The most important and lovely of his paintings are perhaps the frescoes in the Royal Palace, Turin: the Queen's apartments (1731–33), including the Camera di Lavoro and Gabinetto di Toletta; the Chinese Room (1737); the Armeria Gallery (1738); the Galleria delle Battaglie (by 1748). These eclectic but vivid paintings attempt a judicious amalgam of Bolognese, Roman, Neapolitan, and Venetian tendencies of the end of the first quarter of the century as well as an official and grander rococo style. The freshness and strength of the results and their advantages for vigorous or lovely narrative can be seen in Beaumont's preparations for tapestries.

REF.: Andreina Griseri, *ad voc.*, *Dizionario Biografico degli Italiani*, 7, Rome 1965 (with full bibliography).   A.M.C.

2

The Battle of Pharsalia
Canvas: 101.7 x 80.8 cm.; 40 x 31¾ inches
The Minneapolis Institute of Arts, The John R. van Derlip Fund
Not signed
DATE: *c.* 1745

EX. COLL.: Rose Cumming, New York (as Tiepolo; identified as Beaumont, 1958); Viancini, Venice; Agnew's, London (1969).
VERSIONS: The tapestry cartoon prepared from this sketch by Felice Manassero (3.47 x 3.41 m.) in 1745–46 is at Stupinigi. The tapestry itself, inscribed with Beaumont's name and that of the tapestry weaver Francesco Demignot and the date 1749, is in the Palazzo Reale, Turin (Mob. 1316; 4.95 x 3.05 m.; reproduced in Viale-Ferrero, 1963, p. 8).

REF.: Mercedes Viale-Ferrero, *Arazzi*, in *Mostra del Barocco Piemontese*, Turin, 1963, p. 12, no. 14; do., "Claudio Beaumont and the Turin Tapestry Factory," *The Connoisseur*, (American ed.), December, 1959, pp. 145–151.

Juvara and the Turinese Court made long and careful preparations for a tapestry factory and the need of tapestry wall decorations was a known part of Beaumont's appointment as court painter in 1731. Beaumont prepared several series of tapestries: the *Story of Alexander* (woven 1734–40 *ca.*), of *Caesar* (woven 1741–50), of *Hannibal* (woven 1751–54 with others as late as 1760 and 1778), of *Cyrus* (woven 1750–56). He probably executed his sketches from 1731 and not later than 1748. A group of sketches mainly for narrower scenes are in the Museo Civico, Turin, including two sketches for the *Story of Caesar*. There is only one other sketch for a wide scene known, also in Turin: the *Battle of Cannae* (96 x 162 cm.). The Minneapolis sketch was used, even in the border design, with few changes.   A.M.C.

Descended from a family of Italian decorators, sculptors, and painters who were active in Italy and various parts of Europe from the second half of the 15th century until the beginning of the 19th century, Carlo was born in Scaria but was taken at a very early age to Germany. Apprenticed to the painter Giulio Quaglio (1668–1751), he worked with him in the region of Friuli and Lubiana, and also spent time in Venice and the area of Treviso, After some time at the French Academy in Rome, he was invited to Passau in 1710 and received commissions in Germany, Austria, and Switzerland. Among these were frescoes in the Swiss Abbey of Einsiedeln, in the Belvedere of Prince Eugene of Savoy in Vienna, in the Convent of S. Florian, and in the Castle of Ludwigsburg, Württemberg, where he collaborated with his brother Diego, a sculptor who also worked in decorative stucco relief. After 1736 he returned for the remainder of his life to northern Italy where he executed a cycle of frescoes in the cathedral of Monza, and also worked in Brescia, Lodi, Bergamo, Asti, and Scaria.

REF.: M. Marangoni, *I Carloni*, Florence, 1925; Amalia Barigozzi Brini and Klara Garas, *Carlo Innocenzo Carlone*, Milan, 1967.

3

God the Father Receiving the Madonna of The Immaculate Conception
Canvas: 97.9 x 76.9 cm.; $38\frac{1}{2}$ x $30\frac{1}{4}$ inches
National Collection of Fine Arts, Smithsonian Institution
Not signed

DATE: 1725–1726

EX COLL.: John Gellatly

REF.: *Catalogue of American and European Paintings in the Gellatly Collection*, Washington, D.C., 1945, cat. no. 135 (attributed to G. B. Tiepolo); F. Lechi, "Un elenco di abozzi delle opere di Carlo Carloni," *Arte Lombarda*, X, 1965, pp. 127–128; New York City, *Masters of the Loaded Brush—Oil Sketches from Rubens to Tiepolo*, Exhibition organized by Columbia University Department of Art and Archeology, M. Knoedler and Co., 1967, pp. 44–45, catalogue note by Desmond McRae. Brini and Garas, *op. cit.*, p. 47; ill. no. 11.

This sketch for the decoration of a cupola, showing God the Father receiving the Virgin Immaculate into Heaven, surrounded by hosts of angels and angel *putti* grouped in concentric circles was formerly attributed to Tiepolo (1945), attesting to the high quality of this work. The very convincing attribution to Carlone appears first in publication in Desmond McRae's note pertaining to this painting for the exhibition catalogue *The Loaded Brush*.

In comparing it with the various frescoes published by Brini and Garas in their monograph on Carlone, it has been possible to identify the present composition as the sketch for the fresco decoration in the cupola of the Chapel of the SS. Annunziata del Crocefisso, Como, Italy, executed by Carlone in the years 1725 and 1726. Other scenes represented in this chapel decoration are *Putti with the Emblems of the Virgin*, *Virtue*, *Four Prophets* in the lunettes, the *Education of the Virgin*, and the *Marriage of the Virgin* in two medallions in chiaroscuro. The *quadrature* for this project was created by Giuseppe de Vecentini. Completing the decorative scheme of the chapel are two large paintings in oil depicting the *Presentation of the Virgin in the Temple* and the *Birth of the Virgin*. During the period that Carlone decorated this chapel, he also painted the frescoes for the Palazzo Gallio.

Giacomo Ceruti, called Il Pitochetto active 1720–1757

Biographical data concerning Ceruti are extremely scant. A Giacomo Ceruti, Brescian by birth, or at least a resident of Brescia, born toward the very end of the 17th century, had worked in Brescia and perhaps also in Venice from 1720 up to the middle of the 18th century and perhaps even a few years beyond that date. His earliest known dated work is the *Portrait of Count Giovanni Maria Fenaroli*, signed and dated 1724 on the back, preserved in the Collection of Count F. Fenaroli, Corneto (Brescia). In 1729 he was commissioned by Andrea Memmo, magistrate and vice-captain of Brescia, to paint fifteen historical portraits of great personalities and Venetian patricians, presumably lost; Roberto Longhi proposes that two large portraits in La Pietra, Florence, are from this group. In 1734 he contracted for two large canvases, the *Nativity* and the *Death of the Virgin*, for the Basilica of Gandino. An extremely rare painting bearing the signature of the artist is one representing a *Beggar* dated 1737, in the Bassi-Rathgeb Collection, Bergamo. In the year 1738 he signed a contract to paint, in place of Angelo Trevisani, the *Baptism of Santa Giustina* for the Church of the Santo in Padua, where he remained active until 1740. He and his family are listed as residents of Padua in the year 1739. The *Portrait of a Man in Armor* in a private collection in Cremona bears an inscription on the back with the signature, the date 1743, and the name of the city Piacenza. In 1757 he received payment for the *Portrait of the Noble Attilio Lampugnani Visconti*, from the Ospedale Maggiore in Milan.

4

Portrait of a Young Man
Canvas: 213.5 x 142 cm.; 84 x 55⅞ inches
Galleria Nazionale d'Arte Antica, Rome
Not signed

DATE: C. 1734–1738

EX COLL.: Casa Martinengo, Brescia; Forghieri

REF.: A. Santangelo, "Nuovi Acquisti per i Musei de Stato," *L'Arti*, Jan, 1940, pp. 68–69; Milan, *I Pittori della Realtà in Lombardia*, 1953, cat. no. 122, related painting in the Longhi Collection, cat. no. 123; Torino, *Giacomo Geruti e la ritrattistica del suo tempo nell'Italia Settentrionale*, 1967, cat. no. 30.

A major work of Ceruti, this portrait portrays a young man wearing a bright red coat and a fur hat, standing in a very relaxed pose with his left foot resting on a stone while smoking his pipe. When compared with one of his paintings of crippled, broken outcasts, it can certainly be considered one of his gentler works. This type of straight and unsentimental portraiture which re-created nature's image finds a parallel outside Italy—a line which leads from Ribera to Velázquez and certain paintings of Murillo on to Goya. Ceruti's portraits, such as the present one, as well as many others representing beggars, laborers, dwarfs, and children, palpitate with that special breath of life which we have come to expect from those great Spanish painters.

Since this painting comes from the Casa Martinengo, Brescia, it is believed to be the portrait of some unidentified personality of that family. Santangelo, who published it shortly after it was acquired for the Galleria Nazionale d'Arte Antica, has proposed a date between 1734 and 1738, which would place it in the years preceding Ceruti's sojourn in Padua. Cipriani and Testori have pointed out the close relationship of this painting to one of approximately the same dimensions (212 x 140 cm.) representing a *Sleeping Pilgrim* in the collection of Roberto Longhi, Florence.

Ceruti the painter of the poor, the new Caravaggio, was entirely forgotten soon after his lifetime. Who had been the patrons of "Il Pitochetto," this outrageously realistic painter of peasants, hunters, cripples, beggars, idiots, vagabonds, washerwomen—in short, of the poorest segment of the population? Not until the year 1922, when there was shown in Florence on the occasion of the large exhibition of 17th- and 18th-century paintings, Ceruti's *Lavandaia* from the depots of the Pinacotheca in Brescia, had there been the slightest interest in his works, which had been relegated to store-rooms and worse. The new interest in Caravaggio had begun, and works of Ceruti found new appreciation and interpretation, especially by the young Roberto Longhi who defined Ceruti's naturalism as stupendously indigenous and antique; he noted in Ceruti's art the assertation of his extremely high moral point of view in comparison to some earlier attempts at popular genre painting usually marred by mawkish sentimentality, inevitably bringing to mind reminiscences of the works of Caravaggio, and the Le Nains. From that moment on, the popularity, if we may say so, of Ceruti has remained uncontestedly high, a popularity attested to by numerous scholarly studies and major exhibitions.

REF.: Milan, *I Pittori della Realtà in Lombardia*, 1953, Introduction by Roberto Longhi, Catalogue by Renata Cipriani and Giovanni Testori; Roberto Longhi, "Due ritratti di parata del Ceruti," *Paragone*, 1960, no. 125; Torino, *Giacomo Ceruti e la ritrattistica del suo tempo nell'Italia Settentrionale*, 1967, Catalogue by Luigi Malle and Giovanni Testori.

5

Country Girl with a Wine Flask
Canvas: 49 x 39.5 cm.; 19¼ x 15½ inches
Suida-Manning Collection, New York, New York
Not signed

DATE: c. 1738–1739

EX COLL.: William E. Suida

REF.: G. Fiocco, "Giacomo Ceruti a Padova," *Bolletino D'Arte*, Sept. 1935, p. 152; Vienna, *Italienische Barockmalerei*, Galerie Sanct Lucas, 1937, cat. no. 23, fig. 12; G. Delogu, "Pitture italiano del '600 e del '700 a Vienna," *L'Arte*, 1937, XL, pp. 222–241; Milan, *I Pittore Italiano della Realtà in Lombardia*, 1953, p. 73, cat. no. 145; Torino, *Giacomo Ceruti e la rittrattistica del suo tempo nell' Italia Settentrionale*, p. 49, cat. no. 17, 1967.

This portrait of a country girl with a flask, according to Fiocco, represents Ceruti's style at a moment which is very Venetian, close to the altarpiece in the Church of the Santo in Padua, the date of the aforementioned altarpiece being known, 1738. The mood, the style, the technique are identical to the *Portrait of a Young Man*, sometimes thought to be Ceruti's self-portrait, in the Pinacotheca Tosio Martinengo, Brescia. The iridescence of the material, so admired by Fiocco, is the product of Venetian-type glazing, a technique which recalls such painters as Piazzetta and his circle, and which is not often employed by Ceruti. Another painting in the Suida-Manning Collection represents the same model seated in a landscape, tending a cow—she is represented in the almost identical costume, down to the very ribbon around her neck; however, the technique of painting is different, closer to the one used by Ceruti in the *Portrait of a Young Girl* in a private collection, Milan (cat. no. 27 in the Turin exhibition, 1967).

Of German, or possibly Tyrolean origin, Cipper was probably born around 1670. His name is known only from signed and dated canvases between the years 1705 to 1736, at times spelled *Cipper* or *Zipper* and again in the Italianized form *Cipri*—usually followed by the descriptive name *tedesco* (German), from which his nickname Todeschini derives. His style of painting indicates that he probably settled in the area of Brescia and Bergamo as a contemporary of Ceruti, whose works have many times been attributed to Todeschini.

REF.: Bergamo, *Mostra di Fra Galgario e del Settecento in Bergamo*, 1955, p. 41; Oldrich J. Blazicek, "Ancora del Todeschini-Cipper," *Arte in Europa—Scritti di Storia dell'Arte in onore di Edoardo Arslan*, Milan, 1966.

6

The Artist in His Studio
Canvas: 127 x 165.2 cm.; 50 x 65 inches
Hampton Court Palace. Lent by gracious permission of H. M. Queen Elizabeth II

SIGNED: *Gia.mo Francesco Cipper/1736* (lower center)

EX COLL.: Collection of George III

REF.: Ernest Law, *The Royal Gallery of Hampton Court*, London, 1898, pp. 176–177; C. H. Collins Baker, *Catalogue of Pictures at Hampton Court*, 1929, pp. 23–24; W. Arslan, "Del Todeschine e di qualche pittore affine," *L'Arte* XXXVI, 1933, p. 257; M. Moijzer, "Giacomo Francesco Cipper," *Acta Historiae Artium Scientarum Hungarciae*, Budapest, 1956, p. 77 and 89, notes 3 and 6; Julius S. Held, *Paintings of the European and American Schools*, Museo de Arte de Ponce, Puerto Rico, 1965, p. 38 and p. 230, Fig. 38 (another self-portrait); Oldrich J. Blazicek, "Ancora del Todeschini-Cipper," *Arte in Europa—*

Scritti di Storia dell'Arte in onore di Edoardo Arslan, Milan, 1966, pp. 778–779.

The *Artist in his Studio*, one of four signed and dated paintings in Hampton Court, bearing the date 1736, characterizes the late style of Todeschini. It is the latest so-called "self-portrait" representing a painter wearing a turban and a housecoat, seated by the easel, painting an old woman with a crutch. There is a still-life of the instruments of painting and a small dog in front of him; within a family setting two children are drawing, one slightly older child is grinding colors, or operating a printing press, while the wife, holding the distaff, is looking over the easel. The manner of composition reminds Blazicek of similar works by other central European portrait painters, especially those of Kupecky. Blazicek, however notes also that in this as in other late works by Cipper, there appears a decided reduction in the plasticity and expressiveness of drawing with an accompanying superficial quality in the forms: the heads, which had always been rather "typed" in this artist's works, now become further reduced to variations of one single head, intentionally made crude and ugly, with a thick flattened nose, and dim eyes under a prominent forehead. In the works of some of Cipper's followers and imitators this type ends up by assuming the characteristics of a psychological idiot, very far removed from any classical concept.

Another so-called *Self-portrait* of Todeschini in the Museo de Arte in Ponce, Puerto Rico, certainly of an earlier period than the Hampton Court picture, showing a much firmer manner of draughtsmanship and plasticity, lends emphasis to the doubt concerning the application of the term "self-portrait" to such representations; the types could not be more dissimilar, even taking into consideration the different dates of origin.

Born in Bergamo, Ghislandi was the son of Domenico Ghislandi, a decorator and landscape painter. His early study was with Giacomo Cotta; and later with Bartolomeo Bianchini, a Florentine who resided in Bergamo. From his early biographer, Count Tassi, who was his friend and student, we learn that in 1675 he went to Venice where he began a study of the Venetian masters which lasted approximately thirty years. However, around 1688–1689, he was in Bergamo and painted two portraits of his father. On his return to Venice he entered the studio of the portrait painter Sebastiano Bombelli, where he worked for twelve years. By 1702 he had established himself as a lay brother of the Order of the Minims at the monastery of Galgario in Bergamo, from which derives his name Fra Galgario. Some years later he made a brief stay in Milan to perfect his work in the studio of Salmone Adler, who probably came from Danzig. In 1717 he was elected an honorary member of the Accademia Clementina in Bologna. In 1718–19 and again in 1725 he was in Milan. He died in 1743 and is buried in the church of the monastery of Galgario.

One of the finest portrait painters of the 18th century, Ghislandi's early works show influences from Bombelli; however, his most important paintings were portraits of outstanding personalities, professional men, and the nobility, executed during the last twelve or fifteen years of his life. These late works are psychological characterizations derived from G. B. Moroni (c. 1525–78) combined with brilliance of color and textural variations assimilated during his long sojourn in Venice.

REF.: Bergamo, *Mostra di Fra Galgario e del Settecento in Bergamo*, 1955, Catalogue by Franco Mazzini.

7

Portrait of a Pupil as a Gentleman
Canvas: 139.4 x 101 cm.; 55 x 39¾ inches
North Carolina Museum of Art, Raleigh, Samuel H. Kress Collection
Not signed

DATE: C. 1730

REF.: Milan, *I Pittori della Realtà in Lombardia*, 1953, with pendant cat. nos. 77 and 178; A. Riccoboni, *Emporium*, Aug. 1955, p. 55; The Samuel H. Kress Collection, North Carolina Museum of Art, Raleigh, N.C., 1960, pp. 108–111, with pendant, both reproduced, catalogue by Fern Rusk Shapley.

Poised and dignified, this portrait of a young man has been characterized by A. Morandotti as one of Ghislandi's most monumental paintings. F. R. Shapley has pointed out that Ghislandi, like Rembrandt, had great respect for nobility and was attracted to the use of very elaborate costumes, which may have been part of his studio props. It is interesting to note that the young man of the present portrait also posed for the *Portrait of a Young Slav*, wearing a turban and holding a glass of wine, which forms the companion piece to the present portrait. In this context it is very revealing to note that the swagger pose of the young man as well as his decorative costume are identical to those of Count Suardo in the famous double portrait representing *Count Suardo Accompanied by his Servant* in the Accademia Carrara in Bergamo. Ghislandi frequently returned to the use of this pose, among others in the *Portrait of Filippo Marenzi*, also in the Accademia Carrara, and the very elegant full-length *Portrait of Count G. B. Vailetti* in the Galleria dell'Accademia, Venice. Ghislandi's portraiture, like Goya's, and for that matter Rembrandt's, reveals an intense psychological knowledge and appraisal of his sitters which reaches far beyond the outward finery of dress and pose. The present portrait and its companion have been dated about 1730 by Shapley.

31

Of Lombard ancestry, Bartolomeo was born in Savona, where his father, Giovanni Antonio, worked for the local ceramic factories. It was his father who became Bartolomeo's first teacher. His studies were first dedicated to literature, but he soon embraced the church and was ordained a priest. Having never lost his interest in painting he decided to dedicate himself to art and he went to Parma, where alongside many other Genoese artists he studied the art of Correggio. Following a year in Parma he went to Venice for a prolonged sojourn. On his return to Savona he worked as a decorator of majolica of which several examples are preserved in the museum of that city as well as in the Ospedali Civili of Genoa. Later he turned to both easel and fresco paintings. His activity in Genoa included not only work for churches but also for many noble families such as Grillo, Centurione, Durazzo, and Brignole. According to Ratti, in about 1680 he was called by Victor Amadeus of Savoy to the court of Turin, where he worked until his death in 1709. His manner of painting was continued by his brother Domenico, but on a lesser level of achievement.

Guidobono must be ranked among the finest artists of the Italian Baroque. His painting has a certain pastel-like quality, the lights appear as though filtered through nebulous clouds, extremely soft and sweet, in which the forms appear almost to swim and the shadows are softened. He achieves extremely refined light effects and the details of still-life in his major works must be ranked among the highest accomplishments of this type of painting.

REF.: Genoa, *Mostra della Pittura del Seicento e Settecento in Liguria*, 1947, catalogue by A. Morassi; G. V. Castelnovi, "Richerche per Il Guidobono," *Emporium*, June 1956, pp. 242–258; Genoa, *Pittori Genovesi nel '600 e nel '700*, 1969, catalogue by I. M. Botto, P. Costa, G. Frabetti, and L. Tagliaferro.

8

The Holy Family with the Infant St. John in a Landscape
Canvas: 71.2 x 57.6 cm.; 28 x 22 inches (oval)
Suida-Manning Collection, New York
Not signed

EX COLL.: Julius Weitzner, N.Y.; Walter P. Chrysler, Jr., N.Y.

For many years this painting passed as a work of Jean-Baptiste Le Prince, a pupil of Boucher. It was recently identified as a work of Guidobono's late period, near in style to the *Holy Family with Augustinian Saints* in the Church of S. Nicola, Genoa, as well as the *Judgement of Solomon* in the collection of Conte Gambaro-Ottone, Genoa, in which the bearded man at the left, near the old man with a turban, appears almost identical with the St. Joseph in the present composition. Delicately painted and exquisite in color, it is closely related in subject as well as in style to another painting by Guidobono representing the *Rest on the Flight into Egypt* in the Bob Jones University Collection, Greenville, South Carolina.

33

Magnasco was born in Genoa where he first studied with his father Stefano, who had been a pupil of Valerio Castello (1624–29). Following his father's death, he moved to Milan where he studied with Filippo Abbiati (1640–1715). During that period, according to Ratti, Magnasco painted many portraits of excellent quality, but soon abandoned portraiture in favor of landscapes with small *staffage* figures, the type of painting for which be became very famous. His earliest signed and dated painting, 1691, is in the Gallarati Scotti collection, Milan. With the exception of several visits to his native city and a longer sojourn in Florence, he spent the major part of his life in Milan, where his friendship with Sebastiano Ricci began, and at which time he executed a number of paintings in collaboration with both Clemente Spera and Peruzzini. He also worked with other painters on the decoration of the machines and triumphal arches for the visit of Charles VI in Milan in 1711. In 1735 he returned to Genoa to be near his daughter and to spend the remaining years of his life. It was during this last phase of activity that he collaborated with the rather eclectic painter Carlo Antonio Tavella.

9

Saint Ambrose Refusing Theodosius Admittance into the Church
Canvas: 155.3 x 213 cm.; 61⅛ x 83⅞ inches
The Art Institute of Chicago, Clyde M. Carr Fund
Not signed

DATE: C. 1690–1700

EX COLL.: Julius Weitzner, New York

REF.: Roberto Longhi, "Una tema Ambrosiano del Magnasco," *Paragone*, 101, pp. 70–71, Figs. 47–48, May 1958; John Maxon, "A New Painting by Magnasco," The Art Institute of Chicago Quarterly, Sept. 1961, Vol. 55, no. 3, p. 50, ill. pp. 50–51; Renato Roli, *Magnasco*, Milan, 1964.

The painting, according to Roberto Longhi, represents one of the masterpieces of Magnasco's earliest activity, about which very little is known. Longhi ascertains that this work, entirely Genoese in character, showing Magnasco's heritage and indebtedness to such Genoese painters as Valerio Castello, Orazio de Ferrari, Castiglione, Merano, and even Piola, might conceivably have been painted on commission for a Milanese church or confraternity—a hypothesis which is advanced with great caution, since it is not supportable by documented facts. The subject thought of in connection with the city of Milan, though rare in Genoese painting, is by no means unique for that city—one painting representing this very scene by Giovanni Andrea Ferrari is in the church of S. Ambrogio, Genoa; another representation by Andrea Ansaldo is preserved in the church of S. Ambrogio, Voltri. Longhi sees great precocity in the rendition of this subject for Magnasco, in which the youthful artist even before the time of his collaboration with Clemente Spera, uses a sacred theme and interprets it in his own picaresque characterization.

During his own lifetime Magnasco enjoyed great fame, but was subsequently completely forgotten. His so called rediscovery occurred only a few decades ago, when the general interest in "Expressionism" in modern painting led to a reevaluation of Magnasco's greatness. The formation of his style is rooted in the artistic heritage of Valerio Castello as well as Grechetto, from whom he inherited the dramatic tensions, the almost demoniac lightning flashes of his illumination. To these are added the Lombard elements of Morazzone and Crespi's pathos, as well as Venetian trends, by way of Abbiati, who was after all Venetian, and from Sebastiano Ricci, among the greatest Venetian painters of his time. From these various, yet basically related backgrounds, arose the artistic personality of Magnasco, breaking all connections, emerging completely individualistic and triumphant. The personality of Magnasco did not permit him to have any pupils in the real sense of the word, only isolated imitators, such as the Neapolitan Ciccio or the Milanese Coppa. In Magnasco's artistic creations we sense an extravagant fusion of qualities which run the gamut from memories of El Greco to Guardi, foreshadowing Goya and even certain aspects of Daumier.

REF.: Genoa, *Mostra della Pittura del Seicento e Settcento in Liguria*, 1947, catalogue by A. Morassi; Genoa, *Mostra del Magnasco*, 1949, catalogue by A. Morassi; Benno Geiger, *Magnasco*, Bergamo, 1949; Dayton, Sarasota, and Hartford, *Genoese Masters—Cambiaso to Magnasco 1550–1750*, 1962–63, catalogue by R. L. Manning and Bertina Suida Manning; New York, *Genoese Painters—Cambiaso to Magnasco 1550–1750*, 1964–65, catalogue by R. L. Manning; Genoa, *Pittori Genovesi nel '600 e nel '700*, 1969, catalogue by I. M. Botto, P. Costa, G. Frabetti, and L. Tagliaferro.

IO

The Castaways
Canvas: 112.4 x 172. 8 cm.; 44¼ x 68 inches
City Art Museum of St. Louis
Not signed

DATE: (c. 1735–1749)

REF.: New York, *A Loan Exhibition of Paintings by Alessandro Magnasco*, Durlacher Bros., 1940, cat no. 5, together with the pendant, cat. no. 6, presently in the Yale University Art Gallery, New Haven, Conn.; Perry Rathbone, in the *Bulletin of the City Art Museum of St. Louis*, Dec. 1941, V. 26, pp. 78–79, ill. with detail; B. Geiger, *I Desegni del Magnasco*, Padua, 1945, p. LXVIII, p. 104, related drawing; B. Geiger, *Magnasco*, Bergamo, 1949, p. 135, Fig. 479, pendant Fig. 460, Memphis, Tenn. and Ann Arbor, Mich., *Magnasco*, The J. B. Speed Museum and the Univ. of Michigan, 1967, cat. no. 43, with related drawing, cat. no. 42.

With his magic brushwork Magnasco has created one of his many examples of seascapes which illustrate man's eternal struggle against the elements. The painting seems to fit into the period after his return to Genoa, 1735–49, when he apparently devoted himself entirely to the painting of seascapes which were no doubt inspired by what was before his eyes: the Ligurian coast, particularly the Gulf of Genoa.

A sepia wash drawing (14.9 x 12.7 cm.) in the Nelson-Atkins Museum, Kansas City, Missouri, is possibly a study for two of the foreground figures; whereas, the pendant representing *The Smugglers* is presently in the Yale Univesity Art Gallery, New Haven, Connecticut.

Lorenzo (Laurent) Pecheux 1729–1821

Born in Lyons, Pecheux came to Rome at twenty-four (1753) after a brief experience of Paris. In Rome he was close to Mengs, Batoni, and Clérisseau, and acted as an intermediary between them and members of other groups. Tough and literate, he was soon prominent as a fine, serious painter, at work at the various academies (Rome, 1762; Bologna, 1764) and with the attention of the great world of Rome and the courts of Parma and Naples. In 1777 he left Rome to become court painter in Turin, where he was to have a mediocre career as head of a provincial academy in troubled times.

Pecheux's *Regulus* (commissioned 1757 through Robert Adam; known from a 1772 engraving) is earlier than Benjamin West's version of the subject (1769), less provincial, and not much less neoclassical. But Pecheux's early neoclassical style does not advance the classically correct manner of Mengs, which it necessarily imitates. The artist's portraits were also celebrated when Pecheux was in Rome, but he avoided specialization in portraiture.   A.M.C.

REF.: L. C. Bollea, *Lorenzo Pecheux*, Turin, 1936.

11

Death of Epaminondas
Canvas: 137.6 x 153.2 cm.; $54\frac{1}{8}$ x $60\frac{1}{4}$ inches
Musée des Beaux-Arts, Chambéry (Savoie)
Not signed
DATE: (1795)

EX COLL.: Exhibited by the artist at the University of Turin, 1820; heirs of the artist; Carlo Felice of Savoy; given by Victor-Emmanuel II to Chambéry, 1860.

REF.: J. Carotti, *Catalogue raisonné des Musées de Chambéry*, 1911, no. 160; L. C. Bollea, *Lorenzo Pecheux*, 1936, pp. 307, 478 (and passim).

Apparently one of the four paintings commissioned by Victor-Amédée as cartoons for tapestries and remaining (with its pendant, *Alexander in Darius' Tent*) in the artist's estate. Pecheux gives the date of the painting, 1795, in his memoirs; the tapestry may have been executed under the direction of his son and ought still to belong to the House of Savoy in its property at Racconigi. For a Piedmontese tapestry of an earlier period see Beaumont, herewith.

The classical composition follows Poussin's *Death of Germanicus* now at Minneapolis but then in the Palazzo Barberini, Rome, hanging within a few feet of the Pecheux ceiling of 1775.   A.M.C.

One of the least known and most gifted of 18th-century painters, Traballesi was born in Florence, but best recorded in his later career in Milan, where (as elsewhere), many of his frescoes were destroyed in the last world war.

In Florence, Traballesi was a pupil of a prominent academic painter, Francesco Conti (d. 1760), but also studied architecture and scenographic design with Antonio Galli Bibiena (1751–53). He won the Parma competion in 1764 (with a neoclassical *Furius Camillus Saving Rome from the Gauls);* worked in Florence in the 1760's; in Siena and Leghorn in the 1770's; and in 1775 was summoned to Milan by Count Firmian (the Imperial minister and virtual ruler of Lombardy) to decorate the viceregal palaces and to revive the Milanese Academy. After an active career as an artist and teacher, Traballesi died in Milan, already eclipsed by his famous pupil Appiani.

Early study in both Parma (Correggio) and Bologna (the Carracci and Guido) is noted by the biographers; visits to Rome are likely, but they are not necessary to explain the style of this specialist in frescoes and monumental decorations. Before his arrival in Milan, Traballesi simply is not known; the modern suggestions of influence of Pietro da Cortona, Boucher, Batoni, and (in Milan) Tiepolo, are uncritical and misleading. One must note crucial knowledge of such old masters as Preti and the 17th-century Bolognese painters (engraved by the artist by 1796). In his Tuscan work there is a moderation and ennobling of the Tuscan Cortonesque tradition (which had become empty and shrill in mid-18th-century Florence). This is done with Bolognese grace, Roman drawing, and Neapolitan bite. Without a visit to Rome and Naples, these latter advantages could have been found in the work of Guglielmi (*q.v.*), who was in Florence in the early 1750's and 1760's. The cataloguer attributes to this period and to Traballesi the fine ceilings of Palazzo Montauti Niccolini, Florence (*Venus before Jupiter for Aeneas*), so full of knowledge of Guglielmi. Appreciation of and quotations from Guglielmi still occurred later in Traballesi's life, in the destroyed Palazzo Reale frescoes, Milan, (e.g., the *Olympus*), and are basic to his style.

A signed and dated (Livorno, 1771) model is at Nysø, Denmark; a ceiling sketch was with Julius Weitzner, New York, 1959; a signed drawing (probably pre-Milan) was exhibited by Germain Seligman, New York, 1966.

REF.: I. Fumagalli, *Elogio Storico di Giuliano Traballesi*, Milan, 1839; A. O. della Chiesa, *L'Età Neoclassica in Lombardia*, Como, 1959, cat. pp. 93–94.   A.M.C.

11a

The Glorification of the Virgin
Ceiling fresco (Illustrated by photograph in the exhibition)
Santuario della Madonna, Montenero (near Leghorn)

DATE: 1771–1774

Biographical sources describe this fresco as Traballesi's masterpiece (some say it took seven years) and, although in declining condition, it is his most impressive and attractive work, as well as probably the finest 18th-century fresco in Tuscany.

As can be seen in the photograph, Traballesi was an ample, natural, and sensible painter. Born into a somewhat mannered school and the niggardly Tuscan tradition of monotonous and angular late Cortonism, Traballesi adapted the graces of such seminal 17th-century painters as Lanfranco and Mattia Preti, adding only the light nobility—airy, weightless and grandiloquent—of a Roman contemporary, Gregorio Guglielmi (*q.v*). Such is apparent at Montenero, as well as Traballesi's exceptional fertility and strength of imagination.

For an external view of the shrine of which this fresco is the cupola decoration, see cat. no. 65, p. 160.   A.M.C.

As a very young man Gregorio de Ferrari came to Genoa to study jurisprudence, but suddenly developed an interest in the art of painting and entered the studio of Domenico Fiasella. However, the decisive influence in the formation of Gregorio's style did not come from Fiasella, but rather from Valerio Castello, and from a study of Correggio, whose works he copied during a prolonged sojourn at Parma which began in 1669. Following his return to Genoa in 1673, he lived on San Leonardo Street, near the home of Domenico Piola, whose daughter Margherita he married the following year. He formed a long friendship with Piola with whom he sometimes collaborated; but Gregorio's influence prevailed upon Piola in a decisive manner. In 1676 Piola received payment for a fresco representing the *Glory of Saint Andrea Avellino* in S. Siro, Genoa, for which he had received the commission, but the fresco was executed by Gregorio. At approximately the same date, Gregorio received a commission from Padre Teatini of Sampiedarena for two altar paintings representing the *Rest on the Flight into Egypt* and the *Ecstasy of St. Francis*, now in the sacristy of San Siro. For the parochial church of Oneglia (Imperia) Gregorio executed an altar painting representing *St. Clare Putting the Saracens to Flight*, signed and dated 1681. The following year he received a commission for two canvases depicting *St. Lawrence* and *St. Stephen* for the chapel of S. Clemente all' Annunziata del Vastato in Genoa. Gregorio painted very much in fresco. Among the works in this medium are decorations in the Palazzo Balbi Senarega, Genoa (after 1680), in the Palazzo Cambiaso a Fossatello, Genoa (1684), in the Palazzo Balbi Gropallo, Genoa (1684), in the Palazzo Rosso, Genoa (1687–1692), and in the Palazzo Granello, Genoa. He also worked in Turin (c. 1685), along the Riviera and at Marseilles; some of his paintings executed in that city for the Marshal de Noailles were brought to Paris by that gentleman. From 1715 to 1720 Gregorio was active in Santa Croce (San Camillo) of Protorio in Genoa in collaboration with his son Lorenzo (1680–1744), who began as a pupil and imitator of his father, but later developed an independent, almost neoclassical style. During his last years Gregorio executed paintings for Taggia, Sturla, and Sampiedarena, for which drawings exist in the Palazzo Bianco, Genoa.

The relationship of Gregorio's paintings to works by the sculptors of the Bernini school such as Puget, Filippo Parodi, Bernardo Schiaffino and Domenico Parodi, a friend of Gregorio's, has been pointed out. Gregorio is without doubt one of the most accomplished and original among the decorators of the Genoese Baroque period. The influence from Correggio becomes tempered by that from Castiglione toward a magnificent soaring style which seems to parallel Gaulli's stylistic concepts developed in Rome. The works of Gregorio had a certain influence on the development of eighteenth century painting style in France, particularly on Boucher and Fragonard.

REF.: Genoa, *Mostra del Pittura del Seicento e Settecento in Liguria*, 1947, catalogue by A. Morassi; Dayton, Hartford, and Sarasota, *Genoese Masters—Cambiaso to Magnasco 1550–1750*, 1962–63, catalogue by R. L. Manning and Bertina Suida Manning; New York, *Genoese Painters—Cambiaso to Magnasco 1550–1750*, 1964–65, catalogue by R. L. Manning; A. Griseri, "Per un Profilo di Gregorio de Ferrari," *Paragone*, 1955, no. 67, pp. 22–46; A. Griseri, *Gregorio de Ferrari*, (I Maestri del Colori, No. 135), Milan, 1966; Genoa, *Pittori Genovesi nel '600 nel '700*, 1969, catalogue by I. M. Botto, P. Costa, G. Frabetti, and L. Tagliaferro.

11b

Amor and Psyche; Neptune and Amphitrite
(Illustrated by photograph in the exhibition)
Fresco decorations in the Palazzo Granello, Genoa
Not signed

DATE: late 1690's

The Genoese penchant and vast talent for decorative fresco-painting reached a new pinnacle of development during the course of the 17th century. One of its most gifted and precocious exponents surely is Gregorio de Ferrari, who, toward the very end of that century found pictorial solutions which anticipate and are entirely comparable to those of the most advanced genius of the French rococo. Such frescoes as those representing the stories of *Amor and Psyche* and *Neptune and Amphitrite* in the Palazzo Granello, Genoa, creations by Gregorio of the 1690's, reveal this astonishing "modernism" to the fullest extent.

Venice and the Veneto

by Barry Flannegan

Although a native of Naples, Amigoni is considered, and was considered in his own lifetime, a member of the Venetian School. In 1711, he is recorded as already a resident of Venice and the early altarpiece by him in San Stae, Venice, usually dated to 1710, shows him well versed in the suave, yet rather heavy rococo classicism of Antonio Balestra. Recent students of Amigoni have stressed the importance of his Neapolitan origins, seeing in his work persistent recollections of Luca Giordano and Solimena. This background, the almost certain familiarity with contemporary Roman work, and his stay in Venice gave Amigoni the broad knowledge of current and past styles that characterizes artists of his generation.

It was with such cultural baggage that Amigoni in 1719 traveled to Bavaria, where until 1728 he produced an extensive series of works including numerous ceiling frescoes, in the Abbey of Ottobeuren, Schloss Schleissheim, and Nymphenburg. It was at this time, probably under the stimulation of the Electoral Court, that he developed into a major decorator of international affinities and appeal. After a brief trip to Naples, Rome, and Venice, Amigoni reached England in 1729 by way of Munich and Holland. Knowing the profitable examples of Pellegrini and the two Riccis, he likely expected to be kept busy at extensive programs of mural and ceiling decoration. However, the English taste for such work had already diminished appreciably, and it was perhaps as a makeshift that he turned to portrait painting, in which he achieved considerable success. Certainly, his English portraits of this period owe something to the conventions of early Georgian portraiture, and the occasional informal portrait in a landscape setting surely derives its distinctiveness from the English tradition. The few surviving decorative programs, such as those at Moor Park and Mereworth, show Amigoni as an accomplished rococo master, the equivalent of Boucher, but colder, more precise, and employing a deeper and more varied range of color. The brief trip to Paris in 1736 would appear to have had little effect on his development, but this point, along with much else pertaining to Amigoni, requires much more study. After his return from England to Venice in 1739, Amigoni's work reveals the belated influence of Sebastiano Ricci, and the paintings of this decade, such as the canvases for Sigismund Streit and the altar in the Church of the Fava, Venice, are the most completely Venetian of his career. However, during this same period there is a sporadic but extreme lightening of value and a further reduction of movement that show clearly the persistence of his instinctive classicism. It is this placid, concise, and rather nerveless style that Amigoni carries with him to Spain in 1747.

12

Rebecca at the Well
Canvas: 76.9 x 64.8 cm.; 30¼ x 25½ inches
Collection Walter P. Chrysler, Jr., N.Y.
Not signed

DATE: (*c.* 1740)

EX COLL.: Private Collection, Germany; Julius Weitzner, New York, 1954.

VERSIONS: Graues Kloster Gymnasium, Berlin (destroyed); Fogg Art Museum, Cambridge, Massachusetts (copy); Private collection, London (pastel).

REF.. Portland, Oregon, *Paintings from the Collection of Walter P. Chrysler, Jr.* catalogue by Bertina Suida Manning, 1956, p. 35, no. 46.

Shortly after his return from England in 1739, Amigoni was commissioned by the German merchant, Sigismund Streit, to execute a series of panels showing six biblical scenes; until their destruction in the last war these were housed in the Graues Kloster, Berlin, and were among the artist's best known works. (cf. Peter Rohrlach, "La collezione di quadri Streit nel Graues Kloster a Berlino," *Arte Veneta*, 1951, pp. 198–201.) The present picture is a version on canvas of one of these and probably dates shortly after the Streit series. The composition also appears on an English enameled tea urn (*c.* 1760; I. Untermeyer Collection, New York) in reverse, indicating that it probably had been engraved.

The painting which, because of its dazzling quality must be taken as an enlarged version of the Berlin picture (two figures have been added at the left and the top extended considerably) and not a workshop copy, clearly indicates the influence of Sebastiano Ricci and suggests the changes which overtook Amigoni's style when he returned to Venice after a ten-year absence. The compositional complexity and fluid handling indicate a new, heightened degree of decorative invention and the use of cool, varied colors, already noteworthy in the English pictures, has been expanded and, perhaps, suggests a reappraisal of his early Neapolitan sources. However, a comparison with the treatment of a similar subject by Francesco de Mura, also in this exhibition, plainly shows Amigoni's gentler, less rhetorical development of rococo narrative.

Around 1687 Balestra left his native Verona to study in Venice under Antonio Bellucci, one of the most important figures of that late seicento group of artists who favored rather pale tonalities and a firm precise style of drawing. Collectively, they represent a championing of academic standards, but the more adventurous among them were important for introducing a crisp luminosity that would develop into one of the essential characteristics of the settecento. Balestra is known to have spent several years in the early 1690's in Rome in the studio of Carlo Maratti, the standard-bearer of Roman classicism, and then passed the rest of the decade in travel to Naples and through Lombardy and Emilia with a significant pause in Bologna. For most of the first twenty years of the new century, he worked in Venice but then returned to his native city for the last phase of his career.

Rather more than usual for a painter of this period is known about Balestra from published correspondence and from his autobiography. He emerges as a staunchly pro-classical, academic personality. It was not likely accident that led him first to Bellucci and then Maratti, and of the Neapolitans he seems to have been most influenced by Solimena, the creator and popularizer of a "hard-edge" Baroque that filtered through all of Italy in the years around 1700. Balestra admitted that the wish to study Raphael and Domenichino, as much as anything, took him to Rome, while the languid and polished classicism of his Bolognese contemporary Carlo Cignani appears to have appealed greatly to him. In a letter of 1730, he lamented that painting had fallen into such a great decline because young painters refused to study the revered masters of the past and the remains of antiquity, but would rather concoct fantasies thrown together with daubs and touches of paint. Thus, into the full tide of the rococo, Balestra maintained a position somewhat apart, espousing the standards of a traditional adherence to proved academic practice and to the classical succession.

13

Juno Placing the Eyes of Argus in the Peacock's Tail
Canvas: 167.7 x 104.2 cm.; 66 x 41 inches
Norfolk Museum of Arts and Sciences, Norfolk, Virginia,
Gift of a Friend of Norfolk, 1952
Not signed

DATE: (1714)

REF.: Egidio Martini, *La pittura veneziana del Settecento*, Venice, 1964, p. 149, fig. 19.

A communication with Hugh Honour refers to the mention in an unpublished travel diary of William Kent of a visit he made while in Venice in 1714 to the house of Balestra where he saw three paintings: *Sophonisba drinking poison*, the *Triumph of Coriolanus*, and *Juno putting an eye of Argus into her Peacock's tail*. The assumption has been made that the painting mentioned by Kent is the present picture. Some slight doubt is cast on this identification by the presence in the Fototeca of the Fondazione Cini, Venice, of a photograph of another version of this subject reasonably attributed to Balestra. A list of his works compiled by Balestra himself fails to mention under the year 1714 either a *Juno* or a *Coriolanus* but does include a *Sophonisba* that may be identifiable with the one cited by Kent.

In spite of the uncertainty of the possible documentation of the Norfolk painting, 1714 would be a perfectly plausible date for its creation. Balestra's S. Oswald altarpiece in S. Stae, Venice, of 1710, exhibits exactly the same stylistic traits as the *Juno*, traits which are more or less recognizable in many of his works from the second decade. For all the studied organization, there are frequent discontinuities (probably deliberate) that give his compositions of this period a charm and slight naïveté hardly matched in Venice in these years. A small, but telling, further similarity between the two paintings is the *amorino* reclining on cloud in the lower right of the Norfolk canvas which reappears as an adult angel, in exactly the same pose and position, in the composition of the S. Oswald altar.

49

A nephew of Antonio Canal, Bellotto is known to have had his training from the uncle whose name he also later adopted, creating some confusion of their personalities which has only recently been clarified in part. Bellotto's earliest views of Venice are extremely close in style to those of his uncle and are hence of a quality that fully justified his recognition as a mature master in 1738 when he was entered in the lists of the painters' guild. His trip to Rome almost certainly took place in 1742 and was followed in 1744 by visits to Florence, Turin, and Verona, journeys recorded by a considerable number of views which already reveal his own manner. Colors tend to be darker and more opaque than those of Canaletto, there is little or no indication of light-filled air intervening between us and the landscape, the view itself is broader and more inclusive, and detail is rendered more plentifully and carefully. Possibly driven from Venice by the same lack of patronage that seems to have prompted Canaletto's voyage to London, Bellotto in 1747 traveled to Dresden where until 1757 he abundantly recorded the increasing beauty of the Saxon capital. Between 1757 and 1761, he worked at Vienna for Maria Theresa and then returned by way of Munich to Dresden. In 1763 he made his final move to Warsaw. The qualities already evident in his Italian works indicate that he was instinctively suited to perceive the special qualities of North-Central European air and light; however bright the sun, the air always appears cool. Colors, even in full light, are often very dark, while shadow spreads sharply defined voids within landscapes that are no longer on the underlying perspective structure of the earliest paintings. Contrasts of light and dark and clarity of detail are heightened to almost surrealist intensity. The late works seem a definite intimation of 19th-century realism.

REF.: Georg Lippold, *Bernardo Bellotto genannt Canaletto*, Leipzig, 1936; Rodolfo Pallucchini, *Vedute del Bellotto*, Milan, 1961; *Bernardo Bellotto gennant Canaletto*, exhibition catalogue, Vienna, 1965.

14

View of the Tiber with the Castle of S. Angelo, Rome
Canvas: 87.6 x 148.7 cm.; $34\frac{1}{2}$ x $58\frac{1}{2}$ inches
The Detroit Institute of Arts (Gift of Mr. and Mrs. Edgar B. Whitcomb)
Not signed

DATE: (1742)

EX COLL.: George Folliot, Chester, England (Sale, Sotheby's, May 14, 1931, n. 58, as Canaletto)

REF.: *Apollo*, 11 (1930), p. 404; H. Tietze, *Four Centuries of Venetian Painting*, Toledo Museum of Art, 1940, n. 13; E. P. Richardson, *Bulletin of the Detroit Institute of Arts*, vol. 20, March 1941, n. 6; E. P. Richardson, *Catalogue of the Whitcomb Gifts*, 1954, p. 89; Wm. Rockhill Nelson Gallery, *The Century of Mozart*, 1956, n. 4; R. Pallucchini, *Vedute del Bellotto*, Milan, 1961, p. 9; Plate II; W. G. Constable, *Canaletto*, Oxford Press, 1962, vol. 2, p. 375, n. 407a; Allen Memorial Art Museum, "Youthful Works by Great Artists," *AMA Bulletin*, Spring, 1963, n. 17; Wolfgang Krönig, *Miscellanea Bibliotecae Hertzianae*, "Geschichte einer Rom-Vedute," 1961, p. 403.

The attribution to Canaletto which this painting once carried is understandable, since it was almost certainly painted in 1742 when Bellotto was still relying heavily on his uncle's style; and if we accept the hypothesis that Canaletto in fact took his nephew to Rome in that year, Bellotto's Roman views may well have been painted under Canaletto's eye. Characteristic of Bellotto are the relatively unvaried values and the expansive, diffuse composition. The view looks west along the Tiber, crossed here by the Ponte S. Angelo. To the right is the Castel S. Angelo, and along the horizon rise the dome of St. Peter's and various portions of the Vatican.

Virtually nothing is known of Butafogo save that he was a native of Verona and worked for most of his life in Padua. He is first recorded as a painter in 1772 and was still living in 1817. The very limited group of works by him reveal that he had based his style closely on that of Giambettino Cignaroli, and there seems every reason to suppose that Butafogo was in fact a student of the Veronese master. His documented paintings reduce to absolute essentials traditional iconographical and compositional formulae and as such reflect the great simplification evident in painting throughout the Veneto in the closing decades of the century. He seems never to have been touched by neoclassicism; the classical phases and elements of the preceding two and a half centuries proved a source sufficient to his ambitions. His style of fleshy, ideal figures, soft, undifferentiated textures, and iconic brevity of composition is saved only by his competence and lingering traces of settecento color from the gelid kitsch of 19th-century piety.

15

Virgin and Child with S. John and S. Joseph
Canvas: 290.2 x 137.8 cm.; $114\frac{1}{4}$ x $54\frac{1}{4}$ inches
The Minneapolis Institute of Arts, P. D. McMillan Fund
Signed and dated lower left: *Ant.io Butafogo Pinx An 1783*

EX COLL.: Giovanni Castano, Boston, 1960; Saint Michael's Church, New Bedford, Mass. (purchase negotiated through Rev. Herald F. McDermott as Cignaroli).

REF.: Carlo Donzelli, *I pittori veneti del Settecento*, Florence, 1957 (general bibliography).

When recent cleaning revealed the full inscription on the present painting, it was assumed that this was the same work mentioned in Thieme-Becker's *Künstlerlexikon* (Buttafogo) as having once been in the now destroyed Paduan church of S. Giuliana; that altarpiece showed a Madonna and Child with unspecified saints and carried an almost identical inscription with the date 1783. That same work was cited in Donzelli as being in the reserve collections of the Museo Civico in Padua. An inquiry there brought to light a painting, measuring 220 × 110 cm., showing the Madonna, Child, and five saints, and inscribed "Antonius Butafogo pinxit", which the museum records indicate to be the former S. Giuliana painting. The inscription, then, lacks the date which earlier sources noted to have been on that painting. This Paduan picture is substantially inferior to the present one, and although it contains figures of distinctly Butafogo-like type, it is difficult to see how it could have been painted by him. Its inscription differs somewhat from signatures on other paintings by him, and was perhaps added in the 19th century. Thus some confusion seems to exist in regard to the relationship of the Padua and Minneapolis pictures to the record of a Butafogo in S. Giuliana.

The Minneapolis painting recalls generally norms of the High Renaissance, while the standing Christ, of an apparent age of about three years, is almost unique in settecento painting. His type and pose seemed to recall Andrea del Sarto, and further investigation showed an interesting similarity between the canvas and del Sarto's *Gambassi Madonna* of about 1525 now in the Pitti Palace. Butafogo is known to have made several prints after 16th-century paintings, and the relevance of central Italian work of the High Renaissance to Butafogo and more importantly to Cignaroli should be considered.

53

Born into a Venetian family of scenographers, Canaletto is first noted in 1716 helping prepare stage sets for the Teatro S. Angelo in Venice. This background means that he would have had thorough training in perspective construction, in large-scale massing of architectural elements and value contrasts, and an accurate but rapid facility in rendering the abundant detail ubiquitous in the stage settings of the time. Thus, he had at hand much of the necessary ability when he turned to view painting. This choice may have come about through a visit, for professional reasons, to Rome in 1720 where the local *veduta* tradition and especially the example of Vanvitelli (*q.v.*) may have prompted Canaletto to try his skill at this subject-type which, moreover, had already been introduced successfully into Venice by Carlevaris. A view of the Piazza S. Marco in the Thyssen Collection, Lugano, can be dated to before 1723 and must then represent his earliest style. In common with most of the works of the 1720's, it is rather dark with dramatic effects of irregular shadow as if wisps of one of the great clouds overhead were obscuring a sun already slightly softened by a light haze. The air seems humid and agitated as before a storm. So romantic a treatment is hardly known in the *veduta* tradition and may, if it has a source at all, have been taken over by Canaletto from the violent imaginary landscapes of Marco Ricci.

By 1725, Canaletto was accepting commissions for series of views and by the end of the decade was fully launched in his career. The evident demand for his works, a demand increasingly coming from English travellers and collectors may possibly have prompted him to seek an efficient manner. During the 1730's, the virtually watercolor refinement of value and the soft, luminous description of form of the early paintings, was superseded by heavier paint surface of less varied color and value and by a much greater reliance on precise drawing. Although the gradual change from darker to lighter values can be traced in the works of many painters of these years, the same development in Canaletto is only part of a progressive simplification. There is no lessening of quality in this process; Canaletto only comes to see his subject, Venice, in the almost blinding light of full noon and catch its appearance in the most expeditious way. Canaletto's great activity in this decade was in considerable part the result of his association with Joseph Smith, English Resident and then Consul in Venice, who from at least as early as 1729 had taken an interest in Canaletto and who became friend, adviser, patron, and agent for Canaletto. Smith both introduced possible English patrons to Canaletto and also acquired for himself a very great number of Canaletto's paintings and drawings, a large

portion of which passed with Smith's collection to the British Crown. The collaboration between Smith and Canaletto lasted until the latter's death and is the chief reason for Canaletto figuring almost as large in the history of English taste as he does in the history of Venetian painting.

The outbreak of the War of the Austrian Succession in 1741 reduced severely the number of travelers reaching Venice from the north, and it appears that at this time Canaletto, probably backed by Smith, made a second trip to Rome to undertake a series of views there. In 1746, possibly still plagued by the limited number of foreign patrons reaching Venice, Canaletto traveled to London where apart from two or three brief trips back to Venice he remained until at least 1756. In 1763 he was elected to the Venetian Academy after an earlier, unsuccessful nomination.

16

View of the Piazza San Marco, Venice, and The Piazzetta Looking towards San Giorgio Maggiore
Canvas: 134.7 x 247.7 cm.; 53 x 91½ inches
The Cleveland Museum of Art, Purchase, Leonard C. Hanna, Jr., Bequest
Not signed

DATE: (early 1730's)

EX COLL.: Earl of Craven, Combe Abbey, Warwickshire; Cornelia, Lady Craven, Hamstead Marshall, Berkshire (Sale: Sotheby's, London, Nov. 29, 1961, n. 42 (repr.))

VERSIONS: A smaller repetition, probably by Canaletto, Captain Cecil Samuel, London

REF.: W. G. Constable, *Canaletto, Giovanni Antonio Canal 1697–1768*, Oxford, 1962, vol. I, pl. 20, n. 53 and vol II, n. 53, pp. 204, 445; Henry S. Francis, "Canaletto: Piazza San Marco, Venice," *C.M.A. Bulletin*, XLIX (Oct. 1962), pp. 186–190, repr. p. 186; Rodolfo Pallucchini, "A proposito della mostra bergamasca del Marieschi," *Arte Veneta: Revista di Storia dell'Arte*, XX (1966), p. 320, fig. 381, mentioned p. 319; *Handbook*, C.M.A., 1966, p. 146; "Combe Abbey. I. Warwickshire. A Seat of the Earl of Craven," *Country Life* (Dec. 4, 1909), 794–804, repr. (The painting at the extreme right is the C.M.A.'s and the first entire painting at the left is the pendant to ours, *Grand Canal: The Salute from the Campo Sta. Maria Zobenigo* when they were both owned by the Earl of Craven. The article is signed "T".); Lionello Puppi, *Canaletto*, Rizzoli Editore, Milan, 1968, cat. n. 133A.

At the left, one looks past the façade of S. Marco and along the Piazzetta, flanked left and right by the Palazzo Ducale and the Libreria di S. Marco, to the island and church of S. Giorgio. To the right of the Campanile stretches the Procuratie Nuove, and at the extreme right, the western end of the Piazza, is the only portion of the view not perhaps familiar to modern visitors. Here in Canaletto's time stood the church of S. Geminiano flanked by returned arcades of the New and Old Procuratie. This group was demolished by order of Napoleon and replaced by the present New Wing that formed the imposing entrance to his projected royal palace fitted into other parts of the existing structures. In obtaining the proper sweep of space in this panorama of the very center of Venice,

Canaletto was obliged to widen the Piazza so that it here appears almost square. It is as if the Procuratie Vecchie which closes the Piazza on the near, north side had been removed; the shadow that closes the painting in the foreground is sufficiently irregular to show that Canaletto did not mean for us to understand that it was cast by the building that should lie to the right of our vantage point. In all probability, the view is a composite of two separate sightings taken with the aid of a camera oscura or some such apparatus.

The painting has been dated by Constable to the very first years of the 1730's, a date that accords well with the cool transparency of the shadows and the prevailing sparkling translucency of air and buildings alike.

The works of the English and post-English periods have fared less well in critical estimation than have the earlier paintings. Even the splendid panoramic views of London and the Thames have been found wanting because Canaletto transferred his Venetian way of seeing to the treatment of an English subject. More broadly, the objections leveled at these later works are those of repetition induced hardness and mechanicalness. In fact, the technique of these works is extraordinary in its summary sureness; forms are reduced to knowingly plotted, precise areas of color, and drawing becomes a cursive shorthand. The finished view is still full of light and zestful observation, only the process of simplification that went on continuously in Canaletto's development has at this point reached an extreme degree.

As is true of almost all Venetian painters of this period, Canaletto was a keen draughtsman, leaving not only a testimony of highly finished album drawings, but also sketchbooks with the quickest notations, including color notes, that would serve for the elaboration of a painted view executed in the studio. These working sketches are more than adequate proof of his command over perspective schemes and architectural rendering and of his acute and embracing eye that formed the very basis of his memorialization of Venice. In the late cursive style, although at times a little prosaic, there can be an emphatic floridness that finds an echo in the drawings of Thomas Rowlandson. In the early 1740's, Canaletto was engaged in producing a series of etchings that when published in book form carried a dedication to Smith who may have conceived the project as another make-work during the difficult war years, The title, *Vedute, altre prese da i Luoghi altre ideate*, reveals that along with specific views of Venice, there are included imaginary ones ("*ideate*") that represent Canaletto's attempts, also carried out in paintings, at inventing *capricci*. His formula is usually a mixture of buildings of Venetian type with Roman ruins, or more simply, recognizable Venetian monuments placed in a fantastic setting. They betray the conventions of the scenographer and as might be expected a somewhat literal mind. Technically, the etchings are extremely fine, and Canaletto seems to have risen to the challenge of what was for him a new medium, producing works that recall the delicate tonal subtleties of his earliest paintings.

REF.: Antonio Moschini, *Canaletto*, Milan, 1954; W. G. Constable, *Canaletto*, 2 vols., Oxford, 1962; Lionello Puppi, *Canaletto*, Milan, 1968.

17

View of the Riva degli Schiavoni
Canvas: 47.1 x 63.3 cm.; 18½ x 24⅞ inches
The Toledo Museum of Art, Gift of Edward Drummond Libbey, 1951
Not signed

DATE: (late 1730's)

EX COLL.: Bought from the artist by Prince Josef Wenzel Liechtenstein about 1740. Collection of the Princes Liechtenstein until acquired by Toledo Museum.

VERSIONS: Landesmuseum, Darmstadt, n. 135; author uncertain.

REF.: *Galerie de Son Altesse François Joseph, Chef et Prince Regnant de la Maison de Liechtenstein*, 1780, n. 199; *Catalogues of the Liechtenstein Collection*, 1730, 1870, 1925, 1927 (?), 1931, 1936, 1943, 1948; Giulio Ferrari, *I Due Canaletti*, 1914, pl. 14; A. Kronfeld, *Führer durch die Fürstlich Liechtensteinische Gemäldegalerie in Wien*, 1927, n. 199; *Toledo Museum News*, October 1953, n. 148, repr.; Vittorio Moschini, *Canaletto*, Milan, 1955, repr. p. 46; Molly Ohl Godwin, "Capolavori Italiani al 'Toledo Museum of Art'," *Le Vie del Mondo*, vol. 14, 1952, p. 1156, repr. pl. 1154; W. G. Constable, *Canaletto: Giovanni Antonio Canal, 1697–1768*, 2 vols. Oxford, 1962. vol. I, repr. pl. 30, n. 118; vol. II, n. 118, p. 233; J. G. Links, "The view paintings return to Venice," *Burlington Magazine*, vol. 109, n. 773 (Aug. 1967), p. 457; Jean-Dominique Rey, "Le Tour des Expositions," *Jardin des Arts*, Numero 156, Nov. 1967, repr., 64; Lionello Puppi, *Canaletto*, Milano, 1968, cat. n. 35, pl. 26; Venice, Palazzo Ducale, *I Vedutisti Veneziani del Settecento*, June 10–October 15, 1967, n. 52, repr., p. 121.

This view of the Riva degli Schiavoni at its extreme west end shows at the left a corner of the Palazzo Ducale and the Molo, then the Ponte della Paglia, a group of small houses in which the assassin of the Doge Vitale Michiel I was supposed to have been given refuge in 1102, and toward the right, the Gothic Palazzo Dandolo, now a part of the Hotel Danieli.

The painting forms part of a series of views formerly in the Liechtenstein collection, showing various portions of the perimeter of the basin of S. Marco. The size of the series is uncertain; three other paintings in American collections and a pair in a private Milanese collection appear to belong to the same group. Other works, such as the pair in the Kunsthistorisches Museum, Vienna, also from the Liechtenstein collection, are possibly not part of the series in spite of their conforming dimensions.

The Toledo picture carries on its reverse a note that it entered the Liechtenstein collection in 1740, while its pendant, a view of the basin toward S. Giorgio in a Milanese collection, shows the campanile of S. Giorgio as it was after remodelling in 1728. Hence, the view, and the series of which it forms part, was painted between those dates, and in view of its bright, rather tempera-like quality and emphatic handling, a date in the late 1730's would seem most likely. Too, the nature of the series suggests a particular commission, in which case the paintings would immediately predate their inclusion in the Liechtenstein collection.

A native of Udine, Carlevaris probably had his taste for painting and architecture formed by the example of his father, a painter and designer of local reputation. Left fatherless at an early age, Luca will have had his earliest formal training from still unknown masters; it would appear that his education at this date was exclusively in the sciences and related fields, since in later life he referred to himself as a mathematician. Certainly neither in Udine nor in Venice, where he moved in 1679, would there have been much guidance for the type of painting with which his name is now associated, that of view, or *veduta*, paintings. It would have been only through the experience of a lengthy residence in Rome and Florence, probably during the years 1685–1690, that he would have been able to see the variety of sources that evidently formed the collective inspiration for his activity as a painter. By the late years of the 17th century, there had arisen the practice of producing small engraved views of the most important monuments of a city, a taste that had been given definite form by the Roman engraved views of G. B. Falda. To this idea Carlevaris added the topical vitality and picturesque taste of the Bamboccianti and a knowing appreciation of the compositional and tonal riches in the seaports of Claude. The immediate impetus almost surely came from the views of Rome, Florence, and Venice being painted around 1690 by the Italianized Dutchman, Gaspare van Wittel (Vanvitelli, *q.v.*); these works are the first significant group in which the pictorial possibilities of the subject are apparent. The result of this cumulative experience and of his earlier training was the series of over a hundred etchings of the monuments and views of Venice published in 1703. The title, *Le fabriche e vedute*, reveals clearly enough the dual intention of recording not only the image of the city's major structures but, and more importantly, the appearance of the city itself. The *Fabriche* and the sizeable group of paintings of similar subjects (his first recorded commission for a painting is dated 1704) established for the entire settecento the iconographical and pictorial conventions of the Venetian *veduta*. Luca should probably also receive the credit for the specifically Venetian formulation of the *Capriccio*, a witty and rather romantic type of imaginary landscape that was particularly significant for Francesco Guardi.

REF.: Aldo Rizzi, *Luca Carlevarijs*, Venice, 1967.

18

The Molo and the Doge's Palace
Canvas: 95.9 x 192.5 cm.; 37¾ x 75¾ inches
Seattle Art Museum, Gift of Floyd A. Naramore
Not signed

DATE: (c. 1720)

EX COLL.: Possibly one of a set of four commissioned from Carlevaris in Venice by a Mr. Crowe, an ancestor of Mr. Turner, for his house in Yorkshire and later owned by this Mr. Turner (C. Turner), Squire of Stoke Rockford, Grantham, England.

VERSIONS: Although there is no exact duplication of this view by Carlevaris, it does appear in more or less the same form in the following: *Entrance of the Earl of Manchester*, Birmingham City Art Gallery; *Riva degli Schiavoni*, Milan, Levi Collection; *Riva degli Schiavoni*, Milan, Fano Collection: *Riva degli Schiavoni*, New York, Lehman Collection; The *Molo and the Palazzo Ducale*, Kiplin Hall (England), Talbot Collection; *Riva degli Schiavoni*, Milan, Private Collection; *Riva degli Schiavoni*, National Museum, Poznan, Poland; *Entrance of the Count of Colleredo*, Gemäldegalerie, Dresden.

REF.: Aldo Rizzi, *Disegni incisioni e bozzetti del Carlevarijs* (1964), cat/pl. XXXI; Aldo Rizzi, *Luca Carlevarijs*, 1967, p. 94, fig. 140; Albertinum Dresden Cat., *Venezianische Malerei* (1968), p. 47.

The Seattle painting presents a view treated a number of times by the artist. In the foreground is the broad promenade of the Riva degli Schiavoni, beyond is the lower end of the Piazzetta or, properly, the Molo, with its two great granite columns, and just behind them stretches the double arcade of Sansovino's Library. To the left opens the basin of S. Mark's, and beyond rise the bubbly domes of the Salute, the pavilion of the Dogana, and, at a great distance, Palladio's Church of the Redentore on the Giudecca.

The first time Carlevaris treated this particular view was for a painting of 1707, now in Birmingham, recording the entry of the English ambassador, the Earl of Manchester, as he was about to present his credentials to the Venetian Senate. Nothing could serve to underline more clearly the indigenous tradition that Carlevaris was just then enriching with the knowledge of his recent extra-Venetian experiences. At least as far back as the time of Carpaccio and Gentile Bellini, it had been the practice to record great occasions of state which deliberately unfolded their pomp before the well known monuments of the city. Significantly for the particular character of 18th-century patronage, when Carlevaris revived this memorial tradition, he did so through foreign commission, foreshadowing the predominating importance of non-Venetian patrons for his own later career, and for Canaletto and Guardi as well.

Probably the most important artist in Verona in the 18th century, Cignaroli studied first with the obscure Sante Prunati who had, however, been a pupil of Carlo Cignani whose master, in turn, had been Francesco Albani, a student of Annibale Carracci. Thus, Cignaroli could claim an impeccable line of descent through succeeding phases of the most esteemed 17th-century classicism, and it is little wonder that he was looked on by his contemporaries as one of the finest exemplars of that heritage. Emperor Joseph II, on being asked after a visit to Verona what he had found most noteworthy, replied that there were two things that had impressed him, the Roman amphitheatre and the time spent in the studio of Cignaroli, the foremost painter in Europe. Balestra became his second teacher and can only have re-enforced the already strongly developed classicizing flavor of Cignaroli's beliefs. Again, such terms are relative, and Cignaroli's works through the 1740's are in fact a pale, cool, tautly drawn variety of rococo. In his later years, he favored increasingly stable and even architectonic compositions with decreasing numbers of figures. As was so often the case when, after 1750, artists began to seek a calmer, more solid style, Cignaroli looked back to the major figures that might be considered classical and rather unexpectedly chose Veronese who had already contributed so much to Venetian painting of this century. It was primarily only the firmness of composition, however, taken from this source, which was combined with more overtly Bolognese figure types and a structural, not decorative, conception of light. Although the late works are not in any way true innovations, they did mark a fairly full return to a rational, carefully paced, self-consciously responsible art, a *tabula rasa* achieved with immense taste and elegance upon which the later inventions of a new and aggressive classicism could be imposed. Cignaroli would appear to have been a perfect court painter—had there been any courts in the north of Italy to employ him. In addition to the decidedly official air of his work, he was a respectable theoretician, knowledgeable about art's past and concerned with its responsibilities and means. He seems never to have been tempted out of Italy, but contented himself with a number of visits to Venice in the 1730's when he produced frescoes in the Palazzo Labia and other paintings in the Cathedral of Chioggia. People rather came to him or sent representatives to discuss commissions; usually he dealt with Italian officials of the courts of Vienna and Madrid, but Venetians and Romans figure among his visitors. There was in fact a constant flow of dignitaries, and this elevated social activity was enhanced by his own grave and courteous manner and the generous practices of his household. All this in combination with his "correct" style, so remote and illusive for the 20th century, would seem to make him a perfect example of the late Baroque princely painter. Cignaroli at least once struck an altogether more modern note when he observed that, after all, when theory and discussion are done, the artist paints by himself.

REF.: Three articles by F. R. Pesenti: "Il ritrovamento di tre libri di disegni di G. B. Cignaroli," *Arte Lombarda* I, 1959, pp. 126–130; "Appunti per Giambettino Cignaroli," *Arte antica e moderna*, n. 12, Oct.–Dec. 1960, pp. 418–422; "Due Momenti dell'attività di G. B. Cignaroli," *Arte antica e moderna*, n. 33, Jan.–March 1966, pp. 82–87.

19

Madonna and Child with Saints
Canvas: 157.5 x 85.2 cm.; 62 x 33½ inches
P. & D. Colnaghi & Co. Ltd., London
Not signed

DATE: (c. 1759)

Among the few trips made by Cignaroli was one in 1759 to Parma where the court had long been anxious for his services. Once there, he was commissioned by Louise Elisabeth, daughter of Louis XV of France and wife of Philip, Duke of Parma, the second son of Philip V of Spain and Elizabeth Farnese, to undertake an altarpiece that she might send to Spain. The finished painting is known; it is a very large work, some thirteen feet high, and shows the Madonna and Child with Saints Lorenzo, Lucia, Anthony of Padua, and Barbara, with the Guardian Angel. The work originally hung in the Spanish royal church of S. Ildefonso and is now catalogued number 99 in the Prado. The present painting is just half the size of the Spanish one and duplicates exactly its composition; it is thus almost certainly the final "modello" which Cignaroli's 18th-century biographer Bevilacqua tells us was shown to the Duchess and her ladies who were unanimous in their astonished praise.

Cignaroli took as the point of departure for the composition Veronese's altarpiece of the Marogna family in S. Paolo, Verona. The figures are rather more delicate versions of Emilian types, with the Madonna, as is often the case with Cignaroli, recalling Lodovico Carracci.

REF.: Bevilacqua, *Vita di G. B. Cignaroli*, Verona, 1771.

The notebooks of Vertue are again a helpful source since it is from them that we have our limited information about Damini. It appears that our painter followed Pellegrini to England, and hence may have already studied with him in Venice. He remained in England as a history and portrait painter until 1729 or 1730 when he returned to Italy accompanied by his student Giles Hussey (1710–1784). What followed is a bit unclear, but it seems that once again in Italy, Damini made off with their remaining funds, abandoning Hussey to the benevolence of resident English who apparently supported his subsequent study in Rome and Bologna. The next notice of Damini is his signature and the date 1737 on a painting in S. Giuliano, Aquila, where he produced a number of altarpieces (on several of which he signed himself as Venetian), until 1749 when he disappears altogether from record.

That Damini had been influenced by Pellegrini could be deduced from this painting and in fact from any of his few known works. However, the technical extravagances of Pellegrini become formal extravagances for Damini, his paintings being filled with writhing masses of brittle, pleated drapery that catch odd glimmers of light and that conceal any apparent effective form. Unlike his teacher, he favors dark, rather cool colors, conforming to a tenebrous rococo represented in less flamboyant form by Francesco Polazzo and G. B. Mariotti. That he passed a part of the 1730's in Venice seems almost certain, and it seems possible that he may have spent a little time in the south of Italy before going to England since his work also recalls Solimena's most florid manner of the 1680's and 1690's.

In the context of this exhibition, Damini may be thought of as representing another extreme limit of the periphery—stylistically, chronologically, geographically, or qualitatively—of Venetian painting in rather the same manner as Butafogo.

REF.: Rodolfo Pallucchini, *La pittura veneziana del Settecento*, Venice-Rome, 1960; C. C. Cunningham, "Vincenzo Damini—'Gaius Mucius Scaevola before Lars Porsena' ", *Wadsworth Atheneum Bulletin*, Summer 1964, pp. 19–21.

20

Joseph Interpreting Pharaoh's Dream
Canvas: 125.1 x 168.3 cm.; 49¼ x 66¼ inches
Collection Mr. and Mrs. Paul H. Ganz, New York City
Not signed

DATE: (after 1730)

REF.: Unpublished

The present painting at one time had a pendant showing the Queen of Sheba before Solomon; their meeting was shown taking place in a rather intimate interior of a marked rococo style that could hardly have been devised before 1730. The *Joseph* also betrays some familiarity with Venetian painting of the 1730's, and it seems likely that it dates from that decade since both it and its former pendant are rather more loosely composed than the works of the Aquila period.

Gaspare Diziani (de Ciano) 1689–1767

Although Diziani had his first training in his native Belluno, he is known to have been already in Venice shortly after 1700, studying first with Gregorio Lazzarini (Tiepolo's master) and then with Sebastiano Ricci. This last experience proved to be the essential one for his development, and he remained a close follower of Ricci throughout his career. A rather lengthy sojourn in Germany took place late in the second decade, with periods of work in both Munich and Dresden. Around 1726, he was in Rome, perhaps engaged on some theatrical project, in the employ of Cardinal Ottoboni, probably the most discerning patron in all of Italy at that time. By 1730, Diziani had settled in Venice and would confine his activity to the Veneto for the remainder of his life.

His scant bibliography passes over in silence his entire formative period, including the German years, and records that his earliest known dated work is as late as 1727. With the exception of a few dated series in and near Venice, there are no other known fixed points about which a detailed chronology might be constructed. It would appear, however, that he began in a somewhat delicate manner, akin to the earlier phases of the international rococo but with richer color (rather like some of Ricci's mythologies of the English period), and firmer drawing. The fullest approximation to Sebastiano seems to have come in the 1730's, although the frequent assertion that this change occurs only after Sebastiano's death in 1734 is refuted by Diziani's extremely Riccesque canvases in Santo Stefano, Venice, of 1733. Later on, Diziani participated in the general lightening of value that took place in many artists' styles around 1740, while his drawing becomes slowly more emphatic and the forms more rigid. Paint surfaces which earlier had at least recalled the glimmer and vitality of Sebastiano became pastose and labored. There seems little doubt that in his later career, Diziani succumbed to the academic tendencies that seem always present just below the surface of much painting of the time.

REF.: Aldo Rizzi, "Opere inedite di G. Diziani in Friuli," *Acropoli*, 1962, pp. 111–122; Aldo Rizzi, *La Pittura Veneta del Settecento in Friuli*, (exhibition catalogue), Udine, 1966.

21

Moses Striking the Rock
Canvas: 113.4 x 165.2 cm.; 44¾ x 65 inches
Mrs. John S. Pillsbury, Sr., Crystal Bay, Minnesota
Not signed

DATE: (c. 1740)

EX COLL.: Hazlitt Gallery, London

REF.: London (Hazlitt Gallery), *Baroque Painting in Italy*, 1967, no. 15.

Using the stream as an oblique axis (a device favored by the 17th century) Diziani constructed a fairly profound space, continuous and comprehensible to the middleground from the more remote elements fall away in feasible progression. Borrowing from the example of Tintoretto, he has placed the essential action of the subject in the middleground, at some little distance, and framed it with the two massive and involved groups in the left and right foreground. The kneeling figure in the center, which also appears in the Domenico Tiepolo in this exhibition, is derived, probably, from Tintoretto's *Brazen Serpent* in the Scuola di San Rocco, while a number of the other figures exhibit twisted poses uncommonly tense for the 18th century, but a hallmark of Tintoretto. The figure of Moses is not far different in the *Brazen Serpent* but resembles even more closely the adaptation of the Tintoretto model made by Pellegrini for his early *Moses on Sinai* in San Moisè, Venice. Very likely, among the innumerable canvases of Tinoretto's following, other sources could be found. To have been able to combine so assertive a cinquecento inspiration with the more overt characteristics learned from Ricci was no mean feat and affords a fair example of the remarkable powers of assimilation that most of the painters of the period enjoyed.

Among the many versions of the various episodes of the story of Moses that Diziani produced during his career, there is no other rendering of this particular subject. However, in many ways and especially in compostion, the present painting resembles his large *Brazen Serpent* in the apse of the Carmini, Venice. This work has traditionally been dated to around 1760 on no cited evidence, and in view of its still strongly Riccesque quality, it would seem to be considerably earlier. The Pillsbury painting itself is not too dissimilar from the dated series in San Stefano, and for it and for the Carmini canvas, a date of around 1740 seems reasonable.

65

It is best to note a series of dates which in various ways are important for the reconstruction of Francesco Guardi's life. His training will have been in his brother Giannantonio's studio, although there is no indication of when or how Francesco was admitted to full collaboration. A document of 1732 refers to the Guardi brothers as copyists so they were apparently considered more or less equal members in the family business by that date. In 1747 Francesco painted the *Allegories* now in the Ringling Museum, Sarasota, and in 1750 he is involved in a correspondence over the price of some of his own paintings of, unfortunately, unspecified subject matter; these events suggest that he had become an independent painter, but was perhaps still working at times in his brother's shop. In 1761, the year after Giannantonio's death, he was admitted to the equivalent of the painters' guild, and in 1763 painted the *Miracle of Saint Dominic* now in the Kunsthistorisches Museum, Vienna. In 1764, the diary of Pietro Gradenigo records that Francesco, a good pupil of Canaletto, had exhibited two views of Venice which he had painted for a visiting Englishman. Once in 1766 and twice in 1782, he was commissioned to record important state functions and visits in the traditional Venetian manner of observing such occasions. A documented altarpiece surviving in the church at Roncegno was almost certainly finished in 1778. Finally, in 1784, he was elected to the Academy of Fine Arts as a painter of architectural perspective. The final image emerging from these and other statistics and from well-founded inference is of a painter of figure pieces who in long decades of working on his own behalf gradually attained a modest distinction as a *vedutista*.

The immense quantity of views of Venice; real and imaginary landscapes, and *capricci* of all varieties, in his paintings and drawings, collectively constitute the final phase of that type of subject within the settecento and as well are characterized by the fullest development of the quick, free, *di tocco* manner of painting that is virtually synonymous with the best of Venetian painting in that time. The technical enrichments of the Riccis, Magnasco, Pellegrini, and Giannantonio Guardi were but the most recent and adventurous manifestations of the perennial Venetian interest in a perceptual style, relying more on the painter's direct transcription of visual sensation, as contrasted with the more prevalent conceptual style in which formal norms are imposed during the transformation from the perceived sensation to the described situation in the painting. That this Venetian innovation is owing to the unique peculiarities of Venice itself seems incontestable; water, light, and air mix in infinite combinations to yield color and movement. Mass and plastic form are unknown either in the city's image or in the reality of its site. At best, there are surfaces that by nature and artifice magnify the protean ornamentation of their environment. At most, these surfaces are only denser and more explicit points within the space-color continuum that is Venetian light. That this long development should reach its end in paintings of Venice itself was beautifully fitting and perhaps inevitable.

22

The Grand Canal, Venice
Canvas: 73 x 119.4 cm.; $28\frac{3}{4}$ x 47 inches
The Art Institute of Chicago, Wirt D. Walker Collection
Signed lower left: *Fran Guardi*

DATE: (c. 1750)

EX COLL.: S. C. Weston, Esq. 1840; A. Anderson Weston, Esq. 1884; Mrs. Isabella Frances Weston, 1949; Koetser Gallery, New York.

REF.: B. Berenson, *Venetian Painters of the Renaissance*, 1894, p. 109; A. Morassi, "Conclusioni su Antonio e Francesco Guardi," *Emporium*, vol. 57, 1951, pp. 195-219 (fig. 17); "Recent Purchases and Gifts," *Art Institute of Chicago Quarterly*, vol. 46, no. 4, 1952, ill. p. 71.

This view of the lower end of the Grand Canal looking east toward the Bacino di S. Marco is closely modelled on a composition by Canaletto now in the Royal Collection at Windsor and engraved by Visentini in 1735; one can assume that it was this engraving that Guardi used as the basis for his painting. Francesco made some attempt to bring the view up to date since along the Riva degli Schiavoni in the middle distance, the façade of the Pietà seems to be shown in its unfinished state after rebuilding had begun in 1745. This *terminus post quem* conforms well to the general style of the painting which suggests a date in the 1750's and very likely early in that decade. Characteristics of this phase are, aside from the prevailing neatness and care in drawing, the water-color-like transparency of color and value which sacrifices nothing of the richness of the oil medium, and the only slightly veiled radiance of the over-all tonality.

In spite of Francesco's ever-increasing bibliography, the basic questions of the origins and development of his career as a view painter remain unanswered and, in fact, unanswerable until more extensive documentation and a fuller understanding of Francesco's working methods are available. Until fairly recently, it was generally thought that he turned to *veduta* painting only about the time of Giannantonio's death, and that the Gradenigo notice of 1764 meant that Francesco was just then a student of Canaletto's. This idea was rather awkwardly combined with the assumption that it was also Francesco who had painted most of the figure paintings from the Guardi shop. Now that it is fairly clear that Francesco acted on his own behalf well before his brother's death and that he was not extremely active as a figure painter, we must conclude that landscapes and *vedute* occupied his attention at a much earlier date. There does exist a group of landscapes and ruin *capricci* that are modelled after those of Marco Ricci; there are as well a number of Venetian views that are close in style to the Carlevaris and to the early Canaletto. Ordinarily, it might be supposed that a painter would take only the most recent works on which to model his own paintings if he were looking for guidance and inspiration to other artists; in Francesco's case this would not probably have held, and he appears perfectly capable of appropriating another canvas or print twenty or thirty or more years after the model's creation.

In all likelihood, Francesco was producing an occasional landscape or ambitious *capriccio* already in the 1730's. To this early group would seem to belong the copy (now in the National Arts Collection of the Smithsonian Institution) of a large ruin-painting by Marco Ricci, and possibly the large seashore *capriccio* in the National Gallery, Washington, D.C., which is derived from one of Carlevaris' early paintings. Among his earliest views would be included the two canvases (in the Baltimore Museum of Art) which were formerly attributed to Marieschi and which have been reasonably dated to the 1740's.

The motivation for his gradually drifting toward a career as a view painter seems obvious. If he were to be a fully independent painter, he could not continue producing only figural subjects without immediately becoming a competitor to his brother. He seems to have tried Longhi-esque genre compositions, probably just when they were becoming popular, but must have found himself outclassed by Longhi himself. This left portraits, for which he had certainly little talent, or landscapes and *vedute;* the choice forced on him was fortunately the very type of subject to which he could bring a new and valid treatment. Since there is no reason not to

accept Gradenigo's assertion that Francesco was at one time a pupil of Canaletto, it seems likely that this association would date from before Canaletto's departure for England. In favor of this earlier dating of Francesco's serious conversion to *veduta* painting are the following considerations: When, in Francesco's work, there are recollections of Canaletto, it is the Canaletto of the '30's and the early '40's. Also, by the time of Canaletto's return to Venice, Francesco would have been close to fifty, and it is unlikely that at that age he would have taken up the position of student in Canaletto's studio. Too, that Francesco did not return to serious figure painting after 1760 suggests that he was already well established as a view-painter.

23

Piazza S. Marco
Canvas: 47.4 x 77.8 cm.; $18\frac{5}{8}$ x $30\frac{5}{8}$ inches
Virginia Museum of Fine Arts, Richmond; Museum Purchase: The Williams Fund, 1953
Not signed

DATE: (c. 1770)

EX COLL.: Princess Mathilde (sold Georges Petit, Paris, 1904, no. 62; repr.); Prince Murat, Paris; Princess Murat, Paris.

VERSIONS: Among the many canvases showing more or less this same view, only two can really be called versions. These, in the Thyssen Collection, Lugano (possibly earlier than the present example) and in the Accademia Carrara, Bergamo, (surely later than the Richmond picture), are also distinguished by the broad shadow falling over the left (north) side of the Piazza. This arrangement, which could only exist in the late afternoon around the beginning of summer, is unknown in Canaletto's treatments of this subject and appears only in the three cited paintings by Francesco.

REF.: *European Art in the Virginia Museum of Fine Arts*, Richmond, 1966, p. 23, no. 30 (ill.); Venice, *Mostra dei Guardi*, 1965, p. 230, no. 118 (ill.); *Problemi guardeschi*, Venice 1967, p. 14, fig. 135

The only internal evidence within this view of the center of Venice is the appearance of the clock tower at the left which is shown with the marble revetment that was added during the remodelling of 1755-57. However, considerations of style place this painting substantially later, immediately around 1770. In support of such a dating, one could cite the rather dense quality of the medium, the summary briskness of the architectural rendering, and the considerable reliance on linear rather than coloristic means in the construction of figures.

There is a certain irony in Francesco's probable espousal of view-painting in the 1740's since that was the decade that saw the sharp reduction in the number of travellers and buyers reaching Venice. After the departure of Canaletto and Bellotto in likely search of better markets, Francesco would have been left in control of a much diminished trade. That he was able to undertake other types of painting certainly stood him in good stead, and it may be that his development as a *vedutista* was somewhat slow at first because of limited demand.

Although a very broad pattern of change in his views can be discerned, niceties of dating and a tightly coherent evolution are still lacking for Francesco; in all probability his style was never at any time consciously fixed and wavered according to the exigencies of the commission, the character of the model if he was using one, and his own apparent impulsiveness. Generally, he moves from accurate rendering and regular forms to a quick, allusive sketchiness and attenuated, unstable shapes which are placed in all defiance of scale and perspective. Reversing the tendency of the century, he favors a clear light only in his earlier works, where however the sun seems already autumnal, and in the last fifteen years or so of his career his works are often quite dark or conceived largely in terms of strong value contrasts. A vision of the city that had begun in gleaming iridescence became, through many glittering repetitions, the crepuscular dream that reminded the Goncourts of the transformed world of a solar eclipse. It was probably in these same final years that Francesco turned more and more to small *capricci*—Venetian fantasies, still reaches of silent lagoon, fragments of flooded landscape that echo Roman painting of the first century, solitary ruins—that are perhaps his most truly personal and haunting inventions. These, his final legacy, still treat of the century's favorite conceit, illusion, and achieve it through superlative sleight of hand; their mood of melancholy, their air of isolation where only a few exquisitely chosen sensations can flourish, their enchanted apartness are already the internal landscape of the Romantic sensibility.

REF.: Venice, *Mostra dei Guardi*, catalogue edited by P. Zampetti, 1965; *Problemi guardeschi*, Venice, 1967.

24

San Giorgio Maggiore, Venice
Canvas: 46.5 x 76.3 cm.; $18\frac{1}{4}$ x 30 inches
Toledo Museum of Art, Gift of Edward Drummond Libbey
Not signed

DATE: (after 1780)

EX COLL.: Maurice Kahn, Paris; Adolph Mayer, The Hague.

VERSIONS: Of those listed, only the paintings at Temple Newsam House, Leeds, and the Accademia, Venice, are properly versions. The other paintings, including an unlisted variant in the Rothschild Collection at Waddesdon Manor, are only nominally related. A related drawing appears as no. 76 in the Guardi Mostra where its location is given as the Fondazione Cini; the drawing is most closely related to the Leeds picture.

REF.: Venice, Palazzo Ducale; *I Vedutisti Veneziani del Settecento;* June 10–Oct. 15, 1965; no. 145 and 145a, repr. p. 322, 323; F. J. B. Watson, "Eighteenth-century Painting and Decorative Arts," *Apollo,* vol. 86, no. 70, Dec. 1967, p. 465, fig. 24; Ugo Ferroni, "Los 'Vedutisti' Venecianos del setecientos," *Goya,* numero 80, Sept.–Oct. 1967; repr. p. 69, p. 74; Terisio Pagnatti, "The Contemporaneity of the Eighteenth-century Venetian 'Vedutisti'," *Art International;* vol. xi, no. 10, Christmas, 1967; p. 25, repr.; William M. Milliken, *Unfamiliar Venice;* Cleveland, 1967; repr. p. 70.

Dating from after 1780, to judge on the basis of style, the present painting displays the sharp, attenuated architecture and strong value contrasts characteristic of many of Francesco's late works. Less definable but equally true of paintings of this period is the feeling that the justification of a view painting, that is, a reasonably close approximation of an actual site, has receded from his interest and he is dealing more and more with semi-abstract elements that serve the now essential concern with picture making in a remarkably pure sense. Hence, fidelity to topographical varieties, never one of Francesco's strengths, is slighted to a marked degree in various late paintings. In this view south across the Bacino di S. Marco, the island and church of S. Giorgio to the left is fairly accurate. However, on the east end of the island of the Giudecca, at the center and right, Francesco has omitted several buildings while changing the scale of others. Palladio's little church of the Zitelle, the largest building in that row, has been substantially altered.

The older brother of Francesco Guardi, Giannantonio was born in Vienna where his father Domenico, a painter of unknown calibre, had migrated from the family's native Trento. Venice was already their home by 1702, the date of the birth of the second child, Cecilia, the future wife of Giovanni Battista Tiepolo. Giannantonio's earliest surviving work, a small devotional image dated 1717, is entirely in the murky, sensual, late Baroque unique to the Alpine area between Venice and Vienna, and very likely indicates the sort of training he received from his father. It was well after the latter's death in 1716, when Giannantonio assumed direction of the family shop, that he began to look around him and to take pointers from the leading painters in Venice, first Sebastiano Ricci, and later Piazzetta and Pellegrini. The greater part of his career was clearly uneventful and conducted at a level of artistic activity that at best was modest by contemporary standards. He must early have gained something of a reputation as a copyist and is known to have worked in that capacity for the Giovanelli family and for Marshal Schulenburg from around 1730 until 1745. Even in works that were intended to be independent, Giannantonio borrowed or adapted compositions of living or earlier painters so frequently that there is hardly any painting by him for which some source has not been discovered. His commissions more often than not came from provincial centers frequently to the north of Venice, and he seems to have been close to an anonymous figure in the eyes of his fellow Venetians. Perhaps through the influence of his brother-in-law Tiepolo he became a member of the Academy of Fine Arts in 1756.

When, in the early years of this century, figure paintings clearly connected by general style with the name Guardi were discovered, the inclination was to ascribe them to the already well-known, or, better, more familiar, Francesco. Gradually, it became clear to first one and then another scholar that such works really did not fit well into Francesco's *oeuvre*, and with the equally gradual discovery of documents and an occasional signature, the personality of Giannantonio took form and gained plausibility as the author of those canvases. The advocacy of one or the other (and sometimes both) of the brothers as author(s) of a given work gave rise to a passionate and even virulent exchange of opinion that eventually involved almost all scholars interested in the Venetian settecento. The real impetus for this long and complicated argument, which came to be known simply as the "Guardi Problem," was the extraordinarily brilliant group of paintings, above all the panels of the organ parapet in the Venetian church of S. Raffaele.

25

The Holy Family
Canvas: 115.7 x 96.2 cm.; $45\frac{1}{2}$ x $37\frac{7}{8}$ inches
The Toledo Museum of Art, Gift of Edward Drummond Libbey
Not signed

DATE: (c. 1745)

EX COLL.: Di Valsugana, Parish Church of Strigno (near Trento), to unknown date during World War I; D. Barozzi & Co., Venice, by 1922; Edward Drummond Libbey, 1925.

The Toledo *Holy Family*, as is true of most of the figure paintings associated with the Guardi, has carried attributions both to Giannantonio and to Francesco. In common with virtually all of their figure paintings, the present work is known to duplicate the composition of another painting, in this instance, an altarpiece by Andrea Pozzo formerly in the church of the Carmelitani alle Laste, Trento. Usually, it is beyond question that the Guardi version is a copy of an earlier work; the assumption is likely to hold in the present case, but it is possible in view of the numerous copies of the Pozzo canvas that the Guardi may derive from one of them.

In the catalogue of the 1965 exhibition, the argument favored Francesco in opposition to the prevailing attribution to Giannantonio, and since that time, the acceptance of Francesco for this work has been wide. The present writer, in his review of the Guardi Exhibition for the *Art Bulletin*, was perfectly in agreement that the Toledo picture could not be from the hand of Giannantonio but was reluctant, partly because of the work's successful *bravura*, to see it as a work of Francesco. Most of the writers who touched on the painting in the various articles that record the sessions of the Guardi Congress of 1965 supported Francesco's authorship, and enough was written there (most notably the weighty reasoning of Denis Mahon) and elsewhere since then to remove all but the last particle of uncertainty in assigning the *Holy Family* to Francesco.

Son of Pietro Longhi and dedicated to painting from an early age, Alessandro had his first formal training in the studio of Giuseppe Nogari, probably the best portraitist working in Venice at midcentury, and whose style is frequently discernable in his famous pupil's earlier works. As was true of Domenico Tiepolo, Alessandro reached distinction at an early age, exhibiting a portrait in 1757 and becoming a member of the Academy in 1759. In 1762, he provided the fine engraved portraits of contemporary Venetian artists for the *Compendio delle vite di pittori veneziani*. From the evidence of rather sparse documentation and of numerous portraits attributed to him, one can deduce a quiet life and considerable activity carried well into the 19th century.

In the absence of a complete study of Alessandro and aided by only a limited number of signed and dated works as yet published, one can perceive some slight evolution in his essentially exceedingly realistic style. In addition to the importance of Nogari's sober and rather soft manner, it should be borne in mind that Pietro Longhi, himself the author of occasional portraits, will have exercised a considerable influence on Alessandro; and there exists a significant group of works that have been varyingly attributed to father and son at one time or another. Of the certain youthful works of the 1750's, almost always bust-length and earnest in expression and execution, it can be said that they represent a clear predilection for an impassive and simple realism. Then, from the late '50's and early '60's come a series of quite grand portraits, forceful, sometimes rather pompous, all very worldly, and painted with great strength. Later there is a tempering of this strident vitality at the expense of expression and a complete reassertion of the stolidity of the earliest canvases. Compared with French portraits of the period, these later works seem inarticulate; with English portraits, immobile. There seems to be as well at some undetermined point in the later career a decline in means, so that many of the late, attributed works, roughly datable on the basis of costume, recall, and share the special virtues of the anonymous portrait style of American Primitives of the early Republic.

REF.: Vittorio Moschini, "Per lo Studio di A. Longhi," *L'Arte*, 1932, pp. 110–147; G. M. Pilo, "Per la datazione di tre retratti di Longhi," *Paragone*, 1957, pp. 45–50; Terisio Pignatti, "Due nuovi A. Longhi al Museo Correr," *Bolletino dei Musei Civici Veneziani*, 1959, n. 2, pp. 7–16; Alberto Riccoboni, "Opere giovanili di A. Longhi," *Emporium*, 1963, pp. 9–14; Francesco Valcanover, "New Light on Alessandro Longhi's 'Balotin del Doxe'," *The Connoisseur*, 1961, pp. 227–229.

26

Portrait of a Musician
Canvas: 144.2 x 104.2 cm.; 56¾ x 41 inches
The Art Institute of Chicago, Charles H. and Mary F. S. Worcester Fund
Not signed

DATE: (early 1760's)

EX COLL.: Prince of Liechtenstein, Vienna; Wildenstein and Co., New York

REF.: Vittorio Moschini, "Per lo studio di A. Longhi," *L'Arte*, 1932, p. 119; Alberto Riccoboni, "Opere giovanili di A. Longhi", *Emporium*, 1963, p. 11.

In the limited bibliography of Alessandro Longhi, the only thoughtful mention of the Chicago portrait was made by Vittorio Moschini in his still very useful article in *L'Arte*, 1932. Here he noted that in spite of the undeniable Longhi-like composition, expression, and modelling, the portrait really was a thing apart in the Longhi oeuvre; if, indeed, it was by Alessandro, a traditional and understandable attribution without, however, any documentary basis. Most exceptional in Moschini's estimation were the very qualities that distinguish this portrait—its extreme opulence and official air; he wrote that in this work we are without question in the most luxurious reaches of 18th-century portraiture. It is worth bearing in mind Moschini's hesitation, since although the present painting can surely be retained among the accepted works of Alessandro, it does pose problems that the present level of our knowledge does not answer.

The Chicago portrait clearly falls most satisfactorily into the "wordly" period of roughly 1757–1765 in the group of three-quarter or full-length likenesses, frequently posed like our musician and, like him full of self-importance and assurance. Essential works of this period and ones which offer useful points of comparison are the full-length Antonio Renier of 1965 in the Museo Civico, Padua, and the fragmentary portrait of the young Ermolao II Pisani in the Museum at Belluno and datable to 1758. However, none of the other works of this period come so close to being a swagger portrait as does the present one. There is little precedent in Venetian painting of the period for so glorious a portrait of a private individual, and it may be that in seeking devices to enhance the station (or pretensions) of his sitter, Longhi found it necessary to look outside the local tradition, specifically to France and to the already outdated conventions of Rigaud. Probably, in view of the absence of any recollection of Nogari and of the particularly assured handling, the Chicago *Musician* dates from the early 1760's.

Pietro Longhi (Falca) 1702–1785

A native of Venice, Longhi first studied with Antonio Balestra, although nothing of this experience is visible in the few religious and historical paintings undertaken later in his career. In 1719 he journeyed to Bologna (one wonders if it could have been on the advice of Piazzetta) to become a pupil of G. M. Crespi, a master far more in keeping with Longhi's evident tastes and one who exercised a lasting influence on the younger artist. Certainly, a number of paintings by Longhi of peasant genre, placed by modern scholars in his earliest period, show in their subject matter, figure types, and color a sympathetic understanding of Crespi's illuminating realism. Returning to Venice sometime before 1730, Longhi rapidly gained great prestige and respect as the author of small canvases illustrating some episode or scene from Venetian life. The entire social structure and activity of the city, from peasant to Doge, from below-stairs duties and hunting to gaming, dalliance, and doing nothing in great style, are caught in succinct tableaux (and the association with the stage is germane—Longhi and Goldoni were evidently friends, acknowledging and respecting parallel interests). The continuing production of these works, clearly popular among Venetian collectors and hence a clear symptom of the city's persistent and disarming narcissism, was only rarely interrupted by a religious subject or portrait. Professional honors included founding membership in the Academy of Fine Arts, where he was master of the life-drawing classes, and in 1763 his appointment as Director of the private academy in Palazzo Pisani.

In addition to his indebtedness to Crespi, Longhi's paintings show a sure familiarity on his part with the distinctive aspects of genre painting in France (Lancret and de Troy) and England (Hogarth), as well as possibly the Dutch contributions of the preceding century. Yet in an age when the representation of the habits of a social class almost always carried with it a particular point of view—sympathy, reproof, praise, or ridicule—Longhi is completely without editorial comment. He recognizes social situations for their pictorial value and records them as situations; he seems to say, "This is the way it is," and leaves it at that. Hence, his figures are essentially necessary elements in a diagram of manners in which feeling has no place; Chardin by comparison is almost as sentimental and moralizing as Greuze. The objections frequently voiced to the awkwardness of his spatial construction and to the uncertainty of placing and articulation are based on irrelevant criteria, and must in the end be silenced by the ingenuous felicities of his brush and his delighted and knowing conviction of the pictorial worth of his subject.

REF.: Terisio Pignatti, *Pietro Longhi*, Venice, 1968.

27

Lady at Her Toilet
Canvas: 56.9 x 43.9 cm.; 22¾ x 17¼ inches
The Art Institute of Chicago, Flora Erskine Miles Fund
Not signed

DATE: (late 1740's)

EX COLL.: Dr. Max Emden, Switzerland; W. Feilchenfeldt, New York

REF.: Terisio Pignatti, *Pietro Longhi*, Venice, 1968, p. 187, no. 137.

In the Chicago picture, we are assembled, or so it seems, in the interior of a patrician dwelling to observe nothing more important than the selection and placing of a carnation to complete the *tenue* of a noblewoman. From this "event" and from the limited number of persons present—casually, it would appear—and the comparably sparse bits of interior furnishings, Longhi constructs a completely closed yet self-sufficient world. He needs no more to construct an intelligible and rather particular genre episode nor anything beyond his special "verism" to convert the incident to an equally self-sufficient work of art. The relationship of the two ladies, if indeed they are of the same family, is left to our imagination: mother and daughter? sisters? Longhi hardly cares. The servant girl's station is clear enough, but who is the little figure at the right? She would seem to be not a child dressed, as was invariably the fashion, as an adult but rather a mature dwarf, most likely a privileged member of the household. The room is typical of its time and place with walls hung with dark brocade or, more rarely and in the taste of the 17th century, with tooled and painted leather.

The careful and varied rendering of textures, and the fine delicacy of the technique has led Pignatti in his recent exhaustive study of our painter to characterize this style as Longhi's French manner, one which is noticeably different from the broader, softer, more opaque manner frequently noted in the peasant and lower class scenes. The relatively small proportions of the figures within their room and the tenebrous lighting mark this as a rather early work, analogous to the pair of Longhis in the Kress Collection, the National Gallery, and the *Temptation* at Hartford. The particular luminosity of the space and the glowing richness of the figures within so admirable a foil recall strongly the splendid *Presentation* in the Louvre, which Pignatti has dated to around 1744. Given the close similarities between the present example, the Louvre canvas, and other works, perhaps a date a decade earlier than the general one of the late 1750's suggested by Pignatti for the Chicago picture might be advanced.

Domenico Maggiotto (Fedeli) 1713–1793

A native of Venice, Maggiotto had his training in Piazzetta's studio. It would appear that he remained there as an assistant after finishing his apprenticeship. Hence, his earliest known works strongly recall his master but are characterized by a considerably duller handling and (owing to the excessive use of dark, hot brown modelling) by the absence of the luminosity that distinguishes even late works of Piazzetta. Large compositions involving a number of figures tend to be awkward except when they are adaptations of his teacher's ideas. Although Maggiotto has left numerous historical and religious canvases, he seems to have had a special affinity for idyllic genre subjects, at times with a modest anecdotal or moralizing content. Most often, these paintings are simple bust length or half length figures which clearly derive from the large, highly finished drawings of character heads that were one of the most typical products of the Piazzetta circle.

The over-careful and sober manner of his earlier paintings was particularly susceptible to the "correcting" impulses that were beginning to be apparent around 1750, by which date Piazzetta himself had become a more temperate painter. Already in Maggiotto's *Allegory of the Academy*, painted in 1755 as his reception piece for the newly formed Venetian Academy he has on the one hand gone back to the seriousness of some of the reform painters of around 1700, and on the other, attempted to take cognizance of more recent, non-Venetian developments, best represented by Batoni. It appears likely, however, that he thought it appropriate to retain the darker, more sentimental style he had derived from Piazzetta for his continuing production of genre subjects. As Maggiotto is the only follower of Piazzetta included in the present exhibition, it seems worth noting here that all the principal members of the studio seem to have acted as collaborators in various of the later projects and to have fulfilled the commissions in hand at the time of Piazzetta's death. In addition to Maggiotto, the group included Giulia Lama, Egidio Dall'Oglio, Giuseppe Angeli, Francesco Cappella, and Antonio Chiozzotto. Their training appears to have stressed drawing from the model, and there exists a very extensive number of such drawings, of a full figure or details, that can be assigned to the studio if not always to a specific hand. Although well versed in Piazzetta's own manner, they were capable of developing recognizable personalities, all of which tend toward a rapprochement with the paler, more elegant prevailing taste. This change has been characterized as academic, and such an orientation would not be surprising in the light of their education. Their respective styles, however, reveal a considerable range, and in the case of Capella there is some indication that he had looked closely at

Pittoni, another master with clear pedagogical interests but whose work could hardly be more unlike that of Piazzetta. The careers of his chief followers, who were extremely important figures in later 18th-century Venice, and his own role as teacher are all in need of a great deal more study.

REF.: Rodolfo Pallucchini, "Domenico Fedeli detto il Maggiotto," *Rivista di Venezia*, November 1932, pp. 485–495.

28

Pastoral Scene (The Sleeping Shepherdess)
Canvas: 198 x 146 cm.; 78 x 57½ inches
Hamburger Kunsthalle, Hamburg, Germany
Not signed

DATE: (1740's)

EX COLL.: (in Hamburg since 1924)

REF.: Rodolfo Pallucchini, *Rivista di Venezia*, 1932, fig. 3; Rodolfo Pallucchini, *La pittura veneziana del Settecento*, Venice-Rome, 1960, p. 160, fig. 416.

When the present painting entered the Hamburg museum it carried an attribution to Piazzetta, a quite natural error, given the state of settecento studies at that time. In his article on Maggiotto in Thieme-Becker's *Künstlerlexikon*, Hermann Voss identified the correct author through a reproductive engraving issued by J. Wagner, one of the most important publishers of such material in 18th-century Venice. Since Voss' identification, the Hamburg picture has been recognized in the meagre Maggiotto literature as one of the artist's most ambitious genre compositions. The derivation from Piazzetta's group of great pastoral inventions and more especially from the Chicago example (*q.v.*) is evident; a very few figures, of realistic but contrasting type, are carefully arranged in a massive, sculptural group in the foreground of an unspecified landscape setting. However, here the similarity ends. While the meaning, the internal justification of Piazzetta's groups remains opaque and disturbing, in this instance the figures are linked by a rather banal and obvious anecdote. Even the figure to the right, which by Piazzettesque standards should be at least expressing some unfathomable reservation to the little joke, merely assumes the role of an amused onlooker. She is, though, interesting since she seems to be almost a pure quotation from G. M. Crespi, Piazzetta's own teacher; and one here can only speculate about Maggiotto's intention.

A pupil of Diziani, who was apparently a family friend, Marieschi obtained through the interest of his teacher a post at Dresden, from which, however, he had already returned to Venice by 1735. That at least a considerable part of Marieschi's early training was in architecture is attested by his choice of specializing in view-painting, by his recorded designing of an elaborate catalogue at Fano in 1735 for the observance of the death of the queen of Poland, and by his description as "painter and architect" in his publication of twenty-one etched views at Venice in 1741. If he did not in fact study with Canaletto, he surely used the older painter as a source of ideas for his own Venetian views which often echo the luminous shadows and plunging perspective of the early Canaletto.

He remains an obscure and uncertain figure. For some time it has been generally but not unanimously recognized that the small figures in his views and landscapes seem often to be painted by another hand, not always the same one, and both Guardis, the elder Tiepolo, and several other artists have been suggested as collaborators on one or another of Marieschi's canvases. As a source of further uncertainty, it would appear that an otherwise unknown painter, Francesco Albotto (or Alboro?) married Michele's widow and continued painting for another fourteen years in his predecessor's style.

REF.: Bergamo, 1966 (Antonio Morassi), *Michele Marieschi.*

29

Fantasy Landscape in the Veneto: I
Oil type on fabric: 56.3 x 74.6 cm.; 22⅛ x 29⅜ inches
The Minneapolis Institute of Arts, Gift of Mr. and Mrs. Philip W. Pillsbury
Not signed

EX COLL.: (in Minneapolis since 1960)

REF.: Minneapolis, *European Paintings in The Minneapolis Institute of Arts,* 1963.

Marieschi produced a number of *capricci* which, according to style, fall into one or the other of two groups. The present work, and its pendant, also in the Minneapolis collection, represent a number of almost identical subjects, picturesque conglomerations of squalid dwellings built into and over heavy masonry ruins. Their rather bleak landscape setting is crossed by a small river and animated by peasants and soldiers. Other well-known examples of this type are the pair in the National Gallery, London, which is very close in subject to the present painting but which does not form part of the same series, being rather larger in size. The most likely inspiration for this entire group would appear to be the 17th-century landscapes of the Roman *bamboccianti* in which one finds the same type of clustered, ramshackle buildings, the same figure types, and the same derelict air. Areas of shadow are broad and often dark; the paint surface is pastose and fairly freely worked.

Giovanni Antonio Pellegrini 1675–1741

A native of Venice, Pellegrini first studied with Paolo Pagani, a painter whose brisk and rather florid style may well have been a decisive influence on his pupil. It was while still a member of the Pagani shop that Pellegrini, with his master, made the first of his many trips outside Italy, in this instance to Austria for a stay for some six years. In Italy again by 1696, Pellegrini is likely to have spent some time before the turn of the century in Rome where, it is generally agreed, he gave particular attention to the then modern, richly colored fluency of Gaulli. Returning to Venice around 1701, he has left ample record of great activity in these years, including his marriage, to the sister of the renowned pastelist Rosalba Carriera. In 1708, his travels began again, in earnest, when he journeyed to England, along with Marco Ricci, in the entourage of the Earl of Manchester, whose embassy to the Venetian Senate had been painted by Carlevaris.

Attracted to England at least in part by the possible commission of decorating the dome of St. Paul's, Pellegrini, in fact, spent his English years in the decorating of both London and country houses, work that with the exception of the Manchester seat, Kimbolton Castle, has largely disappeared. Then in 1713, probably annoyed by Sebastiano Ricci's arrival in London seeking the same great project, Pellegrini moved on to the brilliant but brief-lived court of the Elector-Palatine Johann Wilhelm van der Pfalz at Düsseldorf. Here, he produced the monumental series of allegories on the life of the Elector and on princely virtues, a hyperbolic glorification of Absolute Monarchy directly in the tradition of LeBrun's ceiling in the Galerie des Glâces and Rubens' Medici Cycle. In the last years of the second decade, he passed rapidly through Flanders, the Netherlands (where in the Mauritshuis he left a splendid group of decorative canvases), London again, Paris, and Venice. Once more in Paris in 1720, Pellegrini was given the commission for the large ceiling in the new Banque Royale, the ephemeral creation of the Regent's crony, John Law. The ceiling lasted hardly longer than did the Mississippi Bubble, but it is worth pointing out that enough evidence for its appearance exists to have allowed Klara Garas to call into question the always repeated assertion of Longhi that this work of Pellegrini was of fundamental importance for all of French 18th-century painting. There followed a decade of incessant travel and work including stops again in Paris, in various cities of Bavaria including Würzburg, and several visits to Dresden, Venice, and Vienna, where he left a major painting in San Carlo Borromeo.

30

Sophonisba Receiving the Cup of Poison
Canvas: 185.7 x 154.3 cm.; $73\frac{1}{8}$ x $60\frac{3}{4}$ inches
The Toledo Museum of Art, Gift of Edward Dummond Libbey
Not signed

DATE: (1710 [?])

EX COLL.: Unknown English collection, supposedly "Piccadilly House" bought at auction by unknown Italian dealer; G. Gasparini, Rome; Colnaghi, London.

REF.: "La chronique des arts," *Gazette des Beaux-Arts*, vol. 69, n. 1177, Feb. 1967 (supplement to 1176), p. 83, repr. (b & w) n. 304.

Painted in all probability during Pellegrini's English sojourn the *Sophonisba* is a remarkable demonstration of the precocious advent of the rococo in Pellegrini's work. At that date, more than any other painter, he stood at the very front of the tendency that was to give settecento painting its most distinctive characteristics: the ascendency of pure color as the chief decorative and descriptive means, the achievement of visual unity at the expense of plastic coherence, a virtuoso delight in the physical possibilities of the medium, and the elaboration of expressive gesture in place of expressive movement. The ultimate masters of the rococo—Giannantonio Guardi, Maulbertsch, Fragonard—will be able to add only little to Pellegrini's vision.

That there exist at least four other versions of this same subject points up a problem that, although present to some degree in the study of most painters of the period, is particularly troublesome in Pellegrini's case. It is not uncommon for a painter to repeat subjects but usually one can discern some change, often great, between two versions separated by some period of time. However, in the Venetian settecento, a painter's attitude to composition and content appear to have remained little altered during his career, and frequently the slight changes between versions are only those of handling or tonality. Of the various Sophonisbas by Pellegrini, two, published by G. M. Pilo in *Arte Antica e Moderna*, 1960, are unquestionably early works of about 1700, since they are still quite dark with the strong chiaroscuro and very soft rendering of flesh that are components of the artist's earliest known phase. Although in both instances, the figures are only half-length, their types and arrangement are clearly the basis of the later versions. The Toledo painting is an enlarged, monumentalized amalgamation of this early pair.

The son of a Venetian sculptor and woodcarver, Piazzetta may have himself chosen, over the objections of his father, Antonio Molinari as his first master. In Molinari's studio, he would have absorbed the most recent transformation of Venetian Baroque *tenebrismo* into a highly decorative, richly colored if dark style owing not a little to the Roman High Baroque. Some idea of Molinari's ideals can perhaps be deduced from the statement of Albrizzi in his biography of Piazzetta (1760) that the young student when he went to Bologna around 1703 did so to study the works of Guercino, and we may be fairly certain that it would have been the early works of Guercino that Piazzetta sought out. However, the essential experience in Bologna proved to be study for an unknown period of time with G. M. Crespi whose dusky, glowing amalgams of sober monumentality and wry genre are necessary predecessors to Piazzetta's later accomplishments. Then, by 1711, our painter is again in Venice working as an independent artist. Thereafter followed a career of serious, slow work which only rarely betrays any knowledge on Piazzetta's part of the immense artistic activity going on around him. He appears to have refused commissions that would take him out of Venice, and the only "foreign" honor accorded him was election to the Accademia Clementina in Bologna in 1727. His interest in teaching is touched on in the present catalogue's entry for Maggiotto, and it was probably as recognition of that interest that in 1750 he was named President of the new Venetian Academy of Painting which became in 1755 the still functioning Academy of Fine Arts.

Piazzetta stands apart from his contemporaries, and was seen to do so even in his lifetime, for many reasons, but the most obvious one is the prevailing darkness and sobriety of his palette in an age that favored light, clear color. The consequences of his coming to terms with this taste can be left for consideration in the entries following; here it seems useful to touch on other major aspects of his career that distinguish him and which, in their collective weight, make him Tiepolo's rival as the most interesting painter of settecento Venice.

31

Girl with a Basket of Apples
Canvas: 34.4 x 28.9 cm.; $13\frac{1}{2}$ x $11\frac{3}{8}$ inches
Suida-Manning Collection, New York
Not signed

DATE: (perhaps 1710–1720)

EX COLL.: Julius Weitzner, London; Walter P. Chrysler, Jr., New York

REF.: Rodolfo Pallucchini, "Opere Inedite Di Giambattista Piazzetta," *L'Arte*, 1936, Fasc. III, pp. 193–194, fig. 4; Baltimore, Maryland, Museum of Art, *Three Baroque Masters: Strozzi, Crespi, Piazzetta*, 1944, p. 53, n. 43, ill; Rodolfo Pallucchini, *Piazzetta*, Milano, 1956, p. 36, fig. 84; New York, Finch College Museum of Art, *Venetian Paintings of the Eighteenth Century*, 1961; Durham, North Carolina, 1966, n. 37, "Eighteenth Century European Paintings from the Collection of Robert L. and Bertina Suida Manning," Duke University.

When Pallucchini first published this work in 1936, he dated it to the early 1740's, not long after the group of monumental genre paintings represented here by the Chicago *Pastoral Scene*. This dating was retained in his monograph of 1956, but again there was no argument presented for such a date. The broad modelling of the face and the repeatedly broken values of the rest of the figure are certainly characteristics of works either documented or accepted as late. However, the dense, smoky chiaroscuro, the rather granular quality of the pigment, and the facial type itself all recall Crespi whose overt influence would seem hardly to have lasted beyond 1720. Too, the unequivocal smile of the girl is exceptional in a Piazzetta of any date, but could well be an early adaption of such faces that are plentiful in Crespi's genre and pseudo-genre paintings. If the conception advanced by Pallucchini of Piazzetta's late years being a period of uncertain and undirected repetition of earlier manners and subject types is in fact accurate, then one might be able to include easily so charming a small painting as this. But, rather, was not his last period one of the most ambitious and serious undertakings, including his few ventures into historical narratives such as the *Mucius Scaevola* in the Palazzo Barbaro-Curtis, the *Death of Darius* in Cà Rezzonico, and the lost *Caesar and the Pirates* commissioned by Algarotti for Dresden? Certainly, the air of works of the 40's, such as the altarpiece in S. Filippo, Cortona, or the *Decollation of St. John* in the museum of the Santo, Padua, is grand and somber, and rather tense and selfconscious compared to the absorption of earlier dated works. It seems unlikely that an uncomplicated and ingratiating image of this type could have come from such preoccupations. All things considered, and in the fitful light of Piazzetta studies, an early date of perhaps 1710–1720 seems most comfortable.

85

The local artistic accomplishments of the preceding century were largely ignored by most of our painters. Eccentric to a remarkable degree, Venetian 17th-century painting derives its riches from a number of highly individual contributors and not from the accumulated strength of a general evolution; it takes on the dignity of a true tradition, in fact, only through Piazzetta's synthesis of so many of its values. Varyingly in pictorial conception, composition, light, color, and handling, his canvases invite comparison with such earlier masters as Strozzi, Fetti, Liss, Maffei, Mazzoni, Zanchi, and Loth. Perhaps these have in common only the intensity of their styles, but it was just those elements that produced such an effect that Piazzetta seems to have adopted. The force of his own works and the successful employment of devices to draw the viewer into his pictorial world are the ends to which he puts his use of the past, ends that are themselves characteristic of the 17th century, not the 18th century. That he was felt to be linked to that past is attested by his appearing in 17th-century costume in the engraved portraits of him in Albrizzi's *Studi di pittura* of 1760 and Longhi's *Compendio* of 1762. Indeed, in his drawn self-portrait of 1735, now in the Albertina, Vienna, he wears the long peruke or natural hair of the late seicento.

32

Judith and Holophernes
Canvas: 104 x 138 cm.; $40\frac{7}{8}$ x $54\frac{1}{4}$ inches
Private Collection, Milan
Not signed

DATE: late 1730's

EX COLL.: Alvise Contarini (Venice, 18th century), Ferdinando Meazza, Milan (sale 1893), Roman private collection.

VERSIONS: Accademia di S. Luca, Rome; Scuola Grande dei Carmini, Venice (unfinished and probably late).

REF.: Morassi, Antonio, "Settecento inedito", *Arte Veneta*, 1949, pp. 70–84; Pallucchini, Rodolfo, *Piazzetta*, Milan, 1956, p. 33, figs. 72, 73; color plate XIV; Pallucchini, Rodolfo, *La pittura veneziana del Settecento*, Venice, 1964, p. 80, fig. 169.

This splendid painting of Piazzetta's maturity only entered his published *oeuvre* in 1949 in Morassi's article in *Arte Veneta* of that year. There he traced its provenance and also noted that it had been engraved by Pietro Monaco, thus establishing a *terminus ante quem* of 1740. Even more interesting was the revelation that this painting is virtually the same size as the *Rebecca at the Well*, now in the Brera, and that both paintings had remained together as a pair until the very end of the 19th

century. They were, in fact, as their complementary compositions attest, pendants. The *Rebecca* is one of the most complete examples of Piazzetta's pale, light-filled style, and pastoral treatment of subject, and as such is clearly very close to the *Fortune-teller* in the Accademia, Venice, of 1740. Yet the present work is in every respect just the opposite, dark, sumptuously colored, and turbulent and dramatic in composition and mood. If, as has been generally assumed, Piazzetta abandoned his earlier dark manner when he produced the large *Assunta* of 1735 in the Louvre, and continued in the daylight manner of the latter painting for at least the following decade, it would be strange to find him working in a dark, essentially Baroque style just before 1740. What the *Judith* and *Rebecca* do clearly show is that at least in the 1730's, and very probably in the 1740's, Piazzetta did not adhere to a single style, in so far as color and mood are concerned. There is evidence as well that this practice was already established in the preceding decade, since his ceiling in the chapel of the Dominicans in SS. Giovanni e Paolo, Venice, which was finished by 1727, is conspicuous for its extremely blond palette. Yet in the same several years in the middle of the decade, he painted for the church of the Fava, Venice, the *Madonna, appearing to S. Philip Neri*, the study for which is in the National Gallery, Washington; here, he retained the nocturnal tonalities of the much earlier *Martyrdom of S. Jacob* in S. Stae, Venice. In short, the character and degree of light in a Piazzetta, which have been used as the principal means of establishing a stylistic chronology, are very uncertain guides to dating. Light and composition seem rather to be dependent on the requirements of subject type, while the pictorial light itself varies according to narrative and emotion.

In the *Judith*, the devices used to stress the tenseness of the episode and its necessary violence are a rolling, turbulent composition, massive forms, strongly contrasted chiaroscuro, and rich color. These form very nearly a catalogue of generic Baroque characteristics and reveal clearly the inspiration for this painting and a number of others which all treat scenes of actual or potential blood-letting. The heritage that this canvas makes use of would be extensive, and beyond Venetian precursors, would have to recognize Guercino, Caravaggio, or at least his followers, and possibly Rembrandt. The completely knowing and intelligent use of such traditions, the admixture of a fine-drawn sensibility and a delicacy of conception and rendering with monumental intentions, and the dilution of narrative immediacy (not as great here as with, say, Tiepolo), by sheer visual appeal, all mark the *Judith* as typically settecento.

A number of the late 17th-century painters from whom Piazzetta will have derived ideas were considered realists working in styles descending from Caravaggio and entering Venetian painting through Saraceni and, more importantly, Langetti and Zanchi. This association and his training with Crespi are the more than adequate bases for the apparent naturalism of his work, and compared with the productions of the other figure painters of the period, Piazzetta's paintings do have an air of strong plausibility. That this is so is owing largely to his choice of figure types, types which probably had their sources in particular models rather than in ideal conceptions, but nevertheless types which are repeated many times and which conform to certain favorite facial and physical patterns. It does not necessarily follow that when two paintings contain the same type of about the same age, the two works are close in date. Although the chronology of Piazzetta drawings is almost completely unstudied, it would seem likely that at least many of the bust-length studies may be early and were kept for consultation and variation for inclusion whenever it seemed appropriate; it is also possible that a number of those drawings were pure inventions and not taken from a model. However, Piazzetta's figures do basically have a naturalistic conception, and the careful and extremely knowledgeable rendering of anatomy that distinguished Piazzetta from all his contemporaries heightens the illusion of realistic immediacy of his figures.

33

Pastoral Scene
Canvas: 191.8 x 143 cm.; 75½ x 56¼ inches
The Art Institute of Chicago, Charles H. and Mary F. S. Worcester Collection
Not signed

DATE: (C. 1740)

EX COLL.: Marshal Schulenburg Collection by c. 1743 and probably sold in his London sale of 1775; 17th-Century Gallery, London, 1917; G. H. Winterbottom (sale, Christie's 1935); G. Bode; M. D. Koetser, London; Jacob Haimann, Milan, 1936; Paul Drey, New York, 1937; Charles and Mary F. S. Worcester for the Art Institute, 1937.
Versions: Tonnelleri Collection, Venice (attributed to Maggiotto); National Gallery of Ireland, Dublin.
REF.: R. Pallucchini, "Opere tarde del Piazzetta", *Arte Veneta*, I (1947), p. 112; R. Pallucchini, *Piazzetta*, Venice, 1956, pp. 33, 34, 61; A. C. Sewter and D. Maxwell White, "Piazzetta's 'Pastorale'—an Essay in Interpretation", *Art Quarterly*, XXIV

(1961), pp. 15–32; Venice, *Dal Ricci al Tiepolo*, 1969, cat. n. 62; Alice Binion, "From Schulenburg's Gallery and Records," *The Burlington Magazine*, May 1970, p. 302.

Here, we are on firm ground in regard to dating. The present painting and its companion the *Idyll on the Beach* in the Wallraf-Richartz Museum, Cologne, were listed in 1743 in the inventory of the collection Marshal Schulenburg. This pair is closely connected by style and content to the so-called *Fortune-teller* in the Accademia, Venice, which has been dated to 1740 on the strength of a notation found on its reverse. The three paintings stand apart in Piazzetta's *oeuvre* and must surely be considered the result of a preoccupation within a limited period of time.

Their common ostensible subject is a small group of figures, drawn from the middle and lower social ranks of the 18th century, passing the time of day out of doors. They appear to be simple genre paintings, and it is as such that they have been treated by most writers. D. M. White and A. C. Sewter in a series of articles undertook an explanation of this group, finding a many-layered allusion in the Chicago painting to Christian ethics, largely as interpreted by Bossuet, whose works Piazzetta knew, and to contemporary social relationships. In part, these interpretations are sustained by the paintings; the distinction of social types may indeed be deliberate, while the young boy in the Chicago picture does certainly recall the Infant Christ as for example in Caravaggio's *Palafrenieri Madonna* in the Borghese Museum, Rome. However, the web of meaning advanced by Sewter and White seems both too complex and too tenuous to have gained much acceptance. It is certainly to their credit that they recognized that there may be some fairly explicit meaning in this trio and that they are not merely genre but use that type of subject as part of their meaning.

In all three examples, the size of the canvas would be almost enough evidence for one to assume that Piazzetta had intended some serious subject, and the solidity and even grandeur of the compositions suggest the same. But it is above all the range of expression, gesture, and physical relationship among the various figures that engages the attention and implies a psychological narrative, mute though it may be. There are few paintings of the Italian settecento that raise so insistently the question of the artist's intention as do the Chicago *Pastoral Scene* and its two related canvases.

He was equally attentive to the appropriateness of gesture and expression, not in the learned way fostered, for example, by Poussin and later the French Academy, but rather following the reasonable assessment of his subject in the light of his own human experience. Here again, he invites comparison with Rembrandt. His people have an internal life, a psychological weight that is possibly equalled in the 18th century only in Watteau. But there is a further important distinction in Piazzetta. Whatever the subject and its narrative requirements, he tends to reduce their particular pictorial or iconographic distinctions in order to stress, partly through expression, the mental self-absorption of persons caught for a moment in stress, most often in the presence of the Deity. Even in the ostensible genre subjects, the characters have a self-awareness and implied knowledge of not only their own relationships but almost, as well, their relationship to the viewer. It is this caught, *engagé*, quality that is the psychological end of the realistic means within his style, but an end, this still absorption, that the vigor of the naturalistic devices would seem to deny. It is in a combination of intense and often rarified mood, to which figure types, light, color, a special kind of naturalism, and actual technique all contribute, and a pronounced grandeur of form and composition that one finds the source of the quite unique tension informing Piazzetta's art.

34

The Supper at Emmaus
Canvas: 108.6 x 141.3 cm.; $42\frac{3}{4}$ x $55\frac{5}{8}$ inches
The Cleveland Museum of Art, Purchased from J. H. Wade Fund, 1931
The signature, lower left, is nearly obliterated and very open to interpretation

DATE: (c. 1745)

EX COLL.: Giovanni Paolo Baglioni, San Cassiano, Venice, 1787; the family of Castiglioni, San Cassiano, Venice; Count Castiglioni, Padua; Italico Brass, Venice.

VERSIONS: A different rendering in the Museo Civico, Padua, and the study for it in the Museum, Göteborg.

REF.: R. Pallucchini, *L'Arte di Giovanni Battista Piazzetta* (1934), pp. 41, 51, 95, figs. 48, 49; Wart Arslan, "Studi sulla pittura del primo settecento Veneziano," *La Critica d'Arte*, I (1935–36), 195; Max Goering, "An Unknown Sketch by Piazzetta," *Burlington Magazine*, XLVIII (March 1936), p. 129; Rodolfo Pallucchini, *Giovanni Battista Piazzetta* (Rome, 1943), p. 19, pl. 42 (c. 1743); R. Pallucchini, *Piazzetta*, Tumminelli,

Rome, 1940, p. 19; R. Pallucchini, *Piazzetta* (Milan, 1956), p. 26 (dates it c. 1730–32); fig. 46, color detail of asparagus; pl. VII, fig. 47; Rodolfo Pallucchini, *La Pittura Veneziana del Settecento* (Venice, 1960), p. 81, fig. 171; Roberto Longhi, *Scritti Giovanili* (Opere complete di Roberto Longhi), I Tomo I, (Florence, Sansoni, 1961), p. 507 (attributed to Federico Bencovich); I Tomo II, p. 608, pl. 255; Venice, *Dal Ricci al Tiepolo* (exhib. cat.: Pietro Zampetti, June–October 1969), p. 138, no. 58 (repr. in full and detail).

Rarely did Piazzetta allow the Caravaggesque sources of much of his art to remain as evident as it does here. The compact grouping of naturalistic types about a table on which is spread a well-considered still life and over which falls the strong light of a *present* Deity is almost a cliché of the followers of Caravaggio, taking as their model his two versions of *The Supper at Emmaus*. What the agencies were through which Piazzetta was familiar with that tradition can hardly even be guessed at: what is rather more certain is that Piazzetta's several versions of the subject are the last important reflection of that tradition.

The placing of this canvas in Piazzetta's *oeuvre* is rather difficult, but it should be said that in spite of occasional doubts expressed as to the accuracy of this attribution, there seems no reason to question Piazzetta's authorship. Although the signature at the lower left is altogether illegible, when the painting was exhibited in Venice in 1969 in the company of a number of the artist's best-known works, it held its own admirably. At the same time, Roberto Longhi's early attribution of the *Supper* to Federico Bencovich was finally and effectively refuted. The contention in the 1969 catalogue that there is some resemblance between the present painting and Magnasco's treatment of the same subject in S. Francesco d'Albaro, Genoa, must also be rejected.

As to date, the same catalogue suggested the late 1720's. Pallucchini in his three studies of the artist has advanced as many dates: late 1730's (1934), c. 1745 (1942), and the early 1730's (1956). The uncertainty is altogether justifiable in view of stylistic inconsistencies which are themselves however a possible clue. In favor of an early dating would be the general format of half length figures in a horizontal composition and the prevailing air of placid rapture, a quality usually absent in the much more strenuous late works. The light, although tenebrous in effect, lacks the robust, form-giving nature that distinguishes its rôle in works as late as 1740. Rather here is an uncertain lunar light that creates a range of intermediate values such as are found in the *Alexander and the Body of Darius* of about 1745.

Pittoni was born in Venice where it is supposed he received his earliest training from his uncle Francesco, a painter of mediocre ability. In all likelihood, Pittoni was really self-taught, at last in the important matter of the formation of his style, and in his first known paintings, already of the second decade of the 18th century, he seems to have become aware of and assimilated several of the more promising tendencies of the period represented by Balestra, Solimena, and Federico Bencovich. From this rather oddly chosen and seemingly discordant combination, he formed a strong, nervous style employing broad areas of relatively unbroken, deep color within a predominantly dark range of values. This manner persisted through the third decade and is perhaps best represented by the splendid altarpiece in Santa Corona, Vicenza. Around 1730, he seems to have looked more closely at Sebastiano Ricci, adding further refinements of color and form to his already completely elegant manner. About this time, too, he appears to have become aware of the prevailing court rococo in Turin and Naples. The possibility of some knowledge of contemporary French painting has several times been suggested, and in the 1969 exhibition of caricature drawings by A. M. Zanetti at the Fondazione Cini, Venice, there was a sheet bearing a standing figure identified by the artist's notation as Pittoni as he looked in Paris where the drawing was made. There are some problems of chronology in placing the drawing, but it provides a first, tenuous clue for a possible Parisian sojourn.

Pittoni's paintings, whatever their size, seem to have been conceived on the scale of highly ornamented, precious miniatures. He is at his most characteristic in dealing with a court audience or ritual involving sumptuously garbed figures, swaying, bowing, gesticulating with ballet-like grace and all seeming to droop a little beneath the sudden burden of an exquisite pathos. Continually, forms are more and more attentuated and softened, emotion masked by ever more polite conventions, and narrative confrontations achieve the hushed immobility of dream images. In the very late works, where an intense languor has invaded everything, including even, is seems, the color, it is possible when the execution is extremely fine for his painting to have an extraordinary poetry. Chief among these rare late canvases is the *Annunciation*, now in the Accademia, Venice, painted as his reception piece for the newly-formed Academy of Fine Arts in 1757, just a year before he assumed the Presidency of that body.

35

Memorial to James, First Earl of Stanhope
Canvas: 221 x 142.3 cm.; 87 x 56 inches
Collection Walter P. Chrysler, Jr., N.Y.
Signed lower right, *Gio. Batt. Pittoni figuravit*

DATE: (1726–27)

EX COLL.: Sir William Morice, London, 1730; Private Collection, Germany; P. Reichenbach, Paris, 1955.

VERSIONS: For a discussion of the version of this picture see 1956 catalogue of the Chrysler collection.

REF.: Portland, Oregon, *Paintings from the Collection of Walter P. Chrysler, Jr.*, catalogue by Bertina S. Manning, 1956, pp. 36–37, no. 48; W. G. Constable, *Canaletto, Giovanni Antonio Canal*, Oxford, 1962, vol. 2, p. 433.

Another of the Tombs commissioned by McSwinny, this one was dedicated to James, first Earl of Stanhope. Not being among the ten from the collection of the Duke of Richmond and engraved in 1741, the present work would originally have been in the collection of Sir William Morice. When published in the catalogue for a travelling exhibition of works from the Chrysler Collection, circulated in America in 1956–57, the painting was attributed to Pittoni for the figures (as the inscription attests), to G. B. Cimaroli for the bits of landscape and foliage, and to Canaletto for the architecture. Some such division of hands generally is true of the entire series and was particularly in this case modelled on the same trio's having collaborated on another of the group, a *Tomb of Archbishop Tillotson*. Recently, Constable has rejected the attribution of the architecture to Canaletto, finding substantial differences in the rendering between this and others of the series more soundly given to Canaletto. Constable cites a letter of McSwinny which mentions the present painting and speaks of one Francesco Monto as being the figure painter for it; since this identification is rendered most unlikely by both the inscription and the style of the figures firmly involving Pittoni, Constable suggests that Monto may have been the painter of the architecture. However, Thieme-Becker records no Francesco Monto, and McSwinny may in a thoroughly confusing way have been referring to the Bolognese Francesco Monti who did provide the figures for a number of the Tombs. It should, as well, be borne in mind that Arslan in *Rivista d'Arte*, 1932, I, pp. 128ff., doubted that the architecture in the Tillotson Tomb was painted by Canaletto even though the engraving after the painting expressly identified Canaletto in the rôle. Thus, at least for Arslan, this picture would not have provided a well-established basis of comparison.

Pittoni's activities as a teacher remain to be studied. That he supported the time honored practice of developing a composition through an elaborate series of increasingly finished drawings, including isolated figures and details, is attested by the large body of drawings now divided among various Venetian institutions. His favorite medium was red chalk, and in the most striking of his pages, very large and exquisitely finished single figures, he used together a brick red and dull madder chalks; the paper was oiled to heighten the intensity of the tones and is now with time become a warm golden brown. These single figures are the ones that appear repeated many times in his paintings and must have been used as aides in arriving more quickly at a compositional solution. The practice of constructing a painting through the assembling of a number of isolated figure studies is not unlike the method favored by Watteau. It seems likely that such leaves formed an important part of his studio equipment and would have been studied and copied by his students. Significantly, among these were Anton Kern and at least one of the members of the Unterbergher family.

A final word should be said regarding Pittoni as a colorist, for in a century noted for its lavish and studied use of color, he perhaps excels any of the Venetians. His palette is quite varied with one range of pale, bright, relatively pure tints, another of darker, rich, mixed color, and an extensive variety of both warm and cool neutral tones. At times, he will use two tints, one dark and the other light, of a single color on the costume of the principal figure in a composition. Thus, one finds side by side a pale sky-blue and delphinium blue, cold ivory with greenish shadows next to a brassy green, or greyish-mauve beside white with paler lavender shading. The reservation of such combinations to principal characters, a sort of hierarchy of color, seems unique to Pittoni, while the refinement of conception it reveals is altogether consonant with the studied delicacy of his work.

REF.: Max Goering, "Zur Kritik und Datierung der Werke des G. B. Pittoni," *Mitteilungen des kunsthistorischen Instituts in Florenz*, 1934, pp. 301 ff.; R. Pallucchini, *I disegni di G. B. Pittoni*, Padua, 1945.

36

The Healing of Antiochus
Canvas: 126.4 x 95.3 cm.; 49¾ x 37½ inches
Museum of Fine Arts, Springfield, Massachusetts, The James Philip Gray Collection
Not signed

DATE: (c. 1733)

EX COLL.: Prince of Schwarzburg—Rudolstadt (Thuringia); Marshal Schulenberg, Vienna(?).

REF.: F. B. Robinson, "The Healing of Antiochus," Springfield, Mass., *Museum of Fine Arts Bulletin*, vol. 26, n. 1, 1959, cover illus.; *The Art Quarterly*, Spring, 1960, vol. XXIII, n. 1, pp. 94, 102; Wolfgang Stechow, "Addenda to 'The Love of Antiochus with Faire Stratonica'," *Bulletin du Musées National de Varsovie* (Poland), 1964, vol. V, n. 1, pp. 7, 10; Klara Garas, "Allegorie und Geschichte in der venezianischen Malerei des 18. Jahrhundert," *Acta Historiae Artium Academiae Scientiarum Hungaricae*, 1965, p. 498; Alice Binion, "From Schulenberg's Gallery and Records," *The Burlington Magazine*, May 1970, p. 301.

The present painting has been thought by Klara Garas and Alice Binion to belong to a series of four canvases including a *Death of Artemisia*, *Continence of Scipio*, and *The Sacrifice of Polyxena* painted for Marshal Schulenburg. The subjects thus illustrate such qualities as obedience, self-control, magnanimity, and filial piety, all stoic virtues and representative of a type of subject matter extremely popular (for as yet not altogether clear reasons), in Venetian painting in the first half of the century.

In composition and particulars of figure type, costume, and setting, the Springfield painting closely resembles a *Solomon and the Queen of Sheba* in the Walker Art Gallery, Liverpool. This work formed part of a group of paintings, one of which carries the date 1733, which may be assumed to place the entire group. On analogy, then, our painting would seem to date from the years immediately around 1733. These years evidently formed a rather brief period in Pittoni's development, one marked by especially full and heavy compositions and stately, massive figures. Probably, it was about this time that he began his academic preoccupations which later, on the evidence of his studio practice and activity as a teacher, became an essential part of his personality.

Among the great number of finished drawings by Pittoni that served as models for individual figures, the same type and pose appearing again and again in different compositions, the one published by Pallucchini as n. 126 is clearly the source for the seated physician in this painting. Although more closely related to Pittoni's *Continence of Scipio* in the Louvre, the Correr drawing I. a. D.S. 238 also seems relevant to the Springfield canvas.

Sebastiano Ricci at the age of twelve left his native Belluno to study in Venice with Federico Cervelli and later with Sebastiano Mazzoni. From this earliest phase of his formation, Ricci would hardly have retained more than a general familiarity with the somewhat belated and eccentric Venetian Baroque. His real development began only in 1678 when he moved to Bologna where, under the pervasive tutelage of its Late Baroque classicism, he gradually absorbed the lessons of the local past: the Carracci and their school, the heritage of Correggio in nearby Parma, and very likely the polymorphous, Guercino. From these years are known various works in changing and experimental styles including, significantly, essays in the fresco medium and collaboration with members of the Bibiena family. Under the continuing patronage of the Farnese, Ricci travelled on to Rome to study the great monuments and figures (Cortona and Gaulli most especially in his case) of the Roman High Baroque, the most important source for any painter of the time interested in large-scale decorative work. Then, in 1694, at the death of Ranuccio II Farnese, he returned northward to Lombardy by way of Florence and Emilia, again, looking, remembering, assimilating so that on his re-entry into the Veneto at the end of the century, he carried with him the wide knowledge then expected of a serious painter.

Marco's earliest training was almost surely with his uncle Sebastiano, but his introduction to landscape painting, the subject matter in which he was to establish his reputation, remains uncertain both in means and date. As a result of killing a gondolier in a quarrel, Marco is supposed to have fled to Spalato where, according to the same unsubstantiated account, he remained four years, studying with a celebrated landscape painter. In the catalogue of the 1963 exhibition, G. M. Pilo suggested that the anonymous master was Antonio Francesco Peruzzini of Ancona who, during his long residence in Milan is known to have collaborated with Sebastiano Ricci and Magnasco. It is possible that both the Riccis may have met Magnasco through this connection; that Marco knew Magnasco is attested by at least one known collaboration of about 1705. Peruzzini would have been a knowledgeable source of the central Italian elements in Marco's style, but a trip to Rome that Marco himself writes of would possibly have supplied him with the same background, only absorbed at first hand. Certainly, Marco was familiar with all the significant developments of landscape painting of the 17th century and particularly the types best represented by Salvator Rosa and Mola. There are, as well, indications that he knew the landscape of Gaspard Dughet, and among roughly contemporary landscape painters, he invites comparison with Jan Frans van Bloemen, better known as Orizzonte. Venice's own Baroque painters offered almost nothing in the way of landscape models, but Marco borrowed extensively from the splendid traditions of the Venetian cinquecento, most frequently from the types of Domenico Campagnola.

After Marco, in the company of Pellegrini, had gone to England in 1708, another presumed part of his training was put to use when he worked as a stage designer and painter. In 1712 there was an apparently rather acrimonious break with Pellegrini, and it may have been something like revenge that prompted Marco to urge his uncle to try his fortune in London. During the English years, Marco worked closely with Sebastiano as a supplier of landscape backgrounds, a collaboration that persisted until Marco's death.

37

Allegorical Tomb of the First Duke of Devonshire
Canvas: 217.5 x 138.5 cm.; $85\frac{3}{4}$ x $54\frac{1}{2}$ inches
Barber Institute of Fine Arts, University of Birmingham

Signed bottom right: "$\frac{B.}{M.}$ *Ricci/Faciebant*"

DATE: (1725)

EX COLL.: Sir Humphrey de Trafford, Bart., sale 26 June (Sotheby's) 1957 (54); Agnew; bought from Agnew, 1958.
VERSIONS: One of about two dozen "Allegorical Tombs" commissioned from a variety of Venetian and Bolognese painters by Owen McSwinny between 1720 and 1730, ten of which were bought by the Duke of Richmond and remained at Goodwood until c. 1790 (recorded there in 1747 by Vertue V. 149). An unsigned repetition (90 x 58 inches) is in the Victoria and Albert Museum, London: and a small grisaille copy was in the Earl of Harewood sale 2 July 1965 (102).
REF.: For a discussion of the series with bibliography see Donato Creti catalogue entry, no. 49. London, Royal Academy, *Italian Art and Britain*, 1960 (434): Bassano del Grappa, *Marco Ricci*, 1963 (59).

Another of the pictures of imaginary tombs ordered by Owen McSwinny from teams of Bolognese and Venetian painters, this one is dedicated to the first Duke of Devonshire (see catalogue nos. 35 and 49). The landscape and ruins were the responsibility of Marco while Sebastiano provided the figures —mourners, soldiers, peasants, etc.—and the figural sculpture as well, as was also true for Pittoni's participation in the Stanhope painting. The present painting is documented in a letter by McSwinny as having been finished by March 1725.

In the datable works of around the turn of the century, we see a painter of great ability and much learning, perhaps still too thoughtful and lacking some final spark but moving more and more towards a controlled virtuosity in which audacities of light and color play an increasingly important role. Slowly, the final ingredient of Sebastiano's maturity becomes apparent: Veronese, who henceforth will serve as patron genius for the century. In the ceiling canvases of S. Marziale, Venice, of around 1704, the tonalities of Veronese are already present but in the soft silverness given them by Antonio Fumiani, and united to the turbulent formal conceits of Gaulli. Then, in Florence in 1706–07, in the Palazzo Marucelli, he produced an unparalleled group of frescoes of scenes from the story of Hercules which for all their debt to the Pietro da Cortona of the Camera della Stufa, reveal the language of the new century fully formed: the ceiling of the same room, open, light-filled, structured by oblique streams of cloud and sparsely peopled by nonchalant deities may well be the first true ceiling of the settecento. In 1708, he produced the altar in San Giorgio Maggiore as an homage to Veronese, and at the age of fifty, he became a figure of European importance.

The second decade of the century is characterized by the most intense journeying. Although not a new destination, Milan, visited in 1711, provided a crucial experience in the meeting of Sebastiano and Magnasco there. The impetuous manner already adopted by the Genoese master suggested the final refinement of his own bravura style to Sebastiano, and henceforth, in varying degree, he could through the use of broken strokes, sometimes pastose, sometimes fluid, create the illusion that the light itself lay within the medium. At the urging of his nephew Marco, in 1712 Sebastiano went to London in search of the commission for St. Paul's, to the complete consternation of Pellegrini. This English period must be counted one of the most felicitous phases of Sebastiano's career. It was followed in 1716 by a sojourn to Paris where he was elected to the Academy of Painting and paid the young Watteau the compliment of copying several of his drawings.

REF.: Joachim von Derschau, *Sebastiano Ricci*, Heidelberg, 1922; Lexington, Kentucky (Michael Milkovich), *Sebastiano and Marco Ricci in America*, 1965; G. M. Pilo, *Marco Ricci*, Venice, 1963.

38

St. Paul Preaching
Canvas: 186.9 x 158.8 cm.; 73½ x 62½ inches
The Toledo Museum of Art, Gift of Edward Drummond Libbey

Not signed
DATE: (1712–1716)

EX COLL.: Richard Boyle (1698–1753) 3rd Earl of Burlington, to 1753, to his daughter, Charlotte-Elizabeth, to 1754; William Cavendish (1720–1764), Marquess of Hartington and 4th Duke of Devonshire, husband of Charlotte-Elizabeth Boyle; Dukes of Devonshire, Chatsworth, Derbyshire, England, 1754 to 1958 (sold Christie's, *Important Pictures of Old Masters from the Chatsworth Collection*, June 27, 1958, p. 12, n. (1, illus.)

VERSIONS: Burlington House, London.

REF.: *Vertue Notebooks, IV*, The Walpole Society, vol. 24, 1935–1936, Oxford, 1936, p. 118; Sutton, Denys, *Christie's Since the War, 1945–1958*, London, 1959, p. 64, p. 135; Benedict, Nicolson, "Sebastiano Ricci and Lord Burlington," *Burlington Magazine*, vol. 105, March 1963, p. 122; O. Osti, "Sebastiano Ricci in Inghilterra," *Commentari, Rivista di Critica e Storia dell'Arte*, II, 1951, p. 122, illus. fig. 127, Pl. XXXV.

In the Vertue Notebooks, mention is made of this painting when it still hung in the collection of the Earl of Burlington. Of all of Sebastiano's works which are presumed to have passed from there to the collections of the Dukes of Devonshire, only this one has an unquestionable Burlington provenance, and, as such, is a valuable and reliable indication of the close interest the Earl took in Sebastiano and his work. Similar certain evidence is supplied by the remaining decorative canvases by Sebastiano in the Earl's townhouse, the present home of the Royal Academy. Yet other paintings supposedly having belonged to Burlington have lately been replaced in his recently restored neo-Palladian villa at Chiswick. That Burlington, with his immense enthusiasm for the style of Palladio and its dissemination as a curative for architectural ills (the Baroque of Vanbrugh, Hawksmoor, and others), should have taken to the overtly Veronesesque manner of Sebastiano is hardly to be wondered at, and one may well suppose that the Earl saw in the Venetian painter an ally for his intended revival of the foreign splendors of cinquecento Venice for the use of another mercantile, land-holding oligarchy.

It has always been noticed that Sebastiano's English period works are more strongly than usual influenced by Veronese, although certainly there are important exceptions as, for example the wall paintings in the stairhall at Burlington House which are far more individual inventions in which, if any source might have been in mind, it would be the late Luca Giordano.

Born in Verona, Rotari studied first with Balestra on whose possible suggestion he passed the years 1725–27 in Venice. This was followed by four years in Rome in the studio of the Venetian painter Francesco Trevisani, and then between 1731 and 1734 by further study with Solimena in Naples. On returning to Verona in 1734 to establish his own studio and school, Rotari had thus the cosmopolitan background that would have admitted him to the pronouncedly academic and rather rarified artistic life of his native city. In the ensuing fifteen years, he produced a considerable number of large, capable works including many altarpieces still to be seen *in situ* in and around Verona. His style in those years lacks the Emilian elegance of Cignaroli and tends to favor simpler and more solid compositions. His works at times suggest a paler and more delicate recasting of the hard, Giordanesque machines of the early settecento Venetian Nicolò Bambini, while a closer comparison with the earlier phases of Pompeo Batoni should prove interesting.

For reasons that are not at all clear, in 1750 Rotari abandoned an apparently established career, travelling first to Vienna and then to Dresden. In 1756, he became court painter to Elizabeth II of Russia, a post he held until his death. Although there is as yet no documentary evidence, it is evident enough in the examination of his works that at some period, and most likely around 1750, Rotari began to specialize in quasi-genre half- or quarter-length female figures at the expense of his more ambitious and academic style. The sources of this change in subject matter and actual style are obscure; in part, these young bourgeois and peasant women are related to the strong realist tendencies (virtually social realism) in the nearby Lombard painters Ghislandi, Cipper, and Ceruti. But Rotari's subjects are considerably idealized and lack the devastating intensity that distinguishes the Brescian and Bergamasque masters. Certainly, as well, this new subject type must be related to a change in patronage and taste. Although by 1750, there had not yet become serious the decline in demand for large, traditional decorative canvases and for altarpieces, there is by that date a clearly growing popularity, attested within the generally conservative nature of Venetian painting by Pietro Longhi, Nogari, and Nazari, of simple, ostensible, perhaps sentimental realism conforming to the demands for charm, elegance, and non-learned subject that were being raised by an international *haute bourgeoisie*. Such were the requirements of the still rather parvenu Russian court, and Rotari during his last years produced hundreds of real and imaginary portraits of young women.

39
Girl with a Fan
Canvas: 83.2 x 67 cm.; 32¾ x 26⅜ inches
Collection Samuel Pryor Reed, New York
Not signed

DATE: (1740's)

EX COLL.: Italian private collection (1941).

REF.: L. Nikolenko, *Connoisseur*, July, 1969, color pl. p. 193.

The present painting, coming from an Italian provenance and hence likely painted while Rotari was still in Verona, reveals the two sources he used in creating his new subject type. The girl herself, the simple pose involving the chair, the neutral, slightly luminous space and the relation of the figure to it and to the canvas area all derive from Dutch 17th-century painters of "polite" genre—de Hooch, Metsu, Ochtervelt, and Vermeer. Whether actual paintings of this sort were known to Rotari is uncertain; what can be accepted as most likely is that prints of such works were widely circulated and would have been sufficient for transmitting formal devices such as those favored by Rotari. The second source is contemporary French painting or, more accurately, pastel painting. The fine, bland, uniform texture of Rotari's genre canvases, and the distinguishing range of color—beige, tan, grey-green, ivory, white, and light red—are those most frequently and easily employed in pastel and those especially favored by Liotard with whose work a painting such as this invites careful comparison. In spite of Rosalba Carriera's major contribution to the revival of pastel in the 18th century, she left no significant following in Venice and the Veneto, and it could have only been from French sources that came this aspect of Rotari's later manner. Again, how he gained this familiarity is unknown. In the north, and particularly at Dresden, he would have seen French painting, and since he travelled to Russia with the French portraitist Tocqué, the more overt French character of some of his Russian paintings is readily accounted for. That the pressures of demand and the availability of new models can only be deduced is an accurate reflection of how little is known about Rotari: that he did in fact effect a substantial change in his work and thinking is an equally clear foreshadowing of the swift abandonment of the conventions of the late Baroque during the third quarter of the settecento.

REF.: Emilio Barbarani, *Pietro Rotari*, Verona, 1941; Lada Nikolenko, "Pietro Rotari in Russia and America," *The Connoisseur*, July 1969, pp. 191–196.

The particular experiences in his early life that prove to be of the greatest importance for an artist's formation are often deductable from a simple comparison of his paintings with those of his teachers or older contemporaries; no such analysis has yet accounted for Tiepolo's style. Although undergoing vast transformations in the half century of his activity, even in its earliest manifestations he proclaims an assertive individuality that is only one of the qualities that sets him apart from and above his fellow painters of the settecento in Venice and, one ventures to think, all the rest of Italy. His initial study with Gregorio Lazzarini taught him beyond the rudiments some facility in devising monumental compositions along correct, Late Baroque lines, and possibly something of the value of a moderately light palette. However, in his earliest surviving canvases, Tiepolo shows himself to be a partisan of the Piazzetta-Bencovich persuasion, and it would have been as an exponent of this new tenebrism that he would have become a member of the painter's guild in 1717.

40

Apelles Painting the Portrait of Campaspe
Canvas: 54 x 74 cm.; 21¼ x 29⅛ inches
The Montreal Museum of Fine Arts, Adaline Van Horne Bequest 1945
Not signed

DATE: C. 1725

EX COLL.: A. Zaeslin, Basel; Sigmaringen Museum, 1902; Eugene Schweitzer, Berlin; Colnaghi's London, 1911; Sir William Van Horne, Montreal.

REF.: Antonio Morassi, *G. B. Tiepolo, His Life and Work*, London, 1955, p. 13, pl. 2, p. 150; John Steegman, Catalogue of the Permanent Collection, MMFA, no. 929, p. 111, 1960; Rodolfo Pallucchini, *La Pittura Veneziana del Settecento*, Rome, 1960, p. 71, pl. 197; Antonio Morassi, *A Complete Catalogue of the Paintings of G. B. Tiepolo*, London, 1962, pp. 29–30; Antonio Morassi, "Un nouveau Tiepolo pour la National Gallery de Londres," *Connaissance des Arts*, August 1964, pp. 32–39; Anna Pallucchini and Guido Piovene, *L'Opera completa di Giambattista Tiepolo*, Milan, 1968, p. 90, no. 42, ill. p. 90, no. 42, color ill. pl. nos. vi and vii.

VERSIONS: National Gallery, London; Louvre, Paris.

Among the paintings of the 1720's figures a group of rather small canvases that at first sight seem only sketches for larger works but which in the light of their careful finish and the absence of larger, more developed versions are clearly independent works. They usually are still rather nocturnal in appearance, having, however, touches of bright, livid color. Painted densely with a fluid impasto, their animation of surface and value conforms well with the agitated movement and intense expression of the figures. These small canvases are, in fact, pocket melodramas, and as such are often surprising or perplexing in the apparent treatment of their subject matter. Here, Tiepolo has undertaken to show the episode mentioned by Pliny in which Apelles was called upon by Alexander of Macedon to paint a portrait of the king's mistress Campaspe.

The subject as developed by Tiepolo is in practice only a point of departure for his sense of fantasy in which a complete disregard for historical accuracy or consistency mingles with a wry humor of uncertain intention. The painter is unmistakably the saturnine young Giovanni Battista. Beside the easel stands Tiepolo's Moorish servant Ali, and if sources have not mentioned a studio pet, the small dog looking toward us is at least representative of a Venetian taste that persists from Carpaccio to our own day. Against the wall rest two canvases that although not identifiable with any known work of Tiepolo could very well have been painted by him in the mid-1720's when the *Apelles* was probably created. In short, excepting the suggestion of a monumental interior implied by the paired, fluted pilasters, and perhaps the picturesque costume, Tiepolo in the right half of the composition has drawn heavily on his own life and surroundings as a painter; the inclusion of elements derived from real life within a quite unreal context is typical of his methods.

The sharp division of the picture along a central axis between reality and illusion (or, better, imagination) tempts one to think that here Tiepolo has made a guarded statement on the function of a painter. The group at the left, then, would not exist at all, but is simply what the painter sees or what his experience and imagination suggest to him—hence, the rapt gaze of Tiepolo-Apelles who does not seem to look at his subject but above it, seeking inspiration. The image that he conceives is then offered to us directly through the medium of his work, and the "portrait" of Campaspe is in fact not foreshortened as it should be, given the placing of the easel, but shares outward almost full face. Before the day of the archeologist and, more recently, the film director, the painter was the prime image maker of the past and interpreter of its literature; Tiepolo was never altogether faithful to the letter of his sources, but his serious dedication to the illustrative and interpretive responsibilities of his profession is attested by his entire career.

A fixed allegiance to the tendency was brief, and in the flood of works that begins already before 1720, Tiepolo casts about for a suitable vehicle for what seems to have been a mania for painting. Retaining the robustness and often the strong chiaroscuro of the first paintings, he took ideas of color and handling from Sebastiano Ricci, and possibly borrowed from Pittoni compositional and figural types. The paintings of the 1720's are marked by seething animation achieved through every technical means possible, and also by a rapid succession of ideas, dropped and taken up again for further use and elaboration. This period might properly be termed his artistic adolescence for its energy, sudden shifts of mood, and occasional awkwardnesses; the works are exciting (the gigantic martial scenes from the Ca Dolfin of which several are now in the Metropolitan Museum), amusing (the Montreal picture in the present exhibition), or unsettling (the four mythologies in the Accademia, Venice). Yet it was in this decade that Tiepolo launched into his career as a painter of large-scale decorative cycles. The ceilings in the Palazzo Sandi and the chapel of Saint Theresa in the church of the Scalzi, both in Venice, and the splendid sequence of ceiling and mural compositions in the Archepiscopal Palace in Udine are the first sustained proofs of his unequalled ability in this taxing art and raise questions for the understanding of both his own personality and subsequent Venetian painting. The use of fresco for these three projects marks the re-introduction of this medium into Venice (Ricci's use of fresco was sporadic, and frescoes of the late seicento and first two decades of the settecento are extremely rare) after which it becomes the preferred vehicle for large architectural painting. Where did Tiepolo learn this craft? Can it have been from Ricci, or from observation of the work of Veronese and his school, the only significant group of *frescanti* in Venetian art before the 18th century? Both the technique and magnitude of Tiepolo's major accomplishments would argue an extensive familiarity with the Roman or possibly the Genoese Baroque, but there is no evidence for his ever having been in any of the other major artistic centers. It has often been suggested that fresco was indeed Tiepolo's preferred medium and that the innovations in the evolution of his style were first achieved in that technique and then assimilated in the works in oil. Possibly it was truly a matter of ease and expediency since separated mural compositions like those at Udine had been and continued frequently to be executed on canvases set into stucco mouldings; if the monumental series for Ca Dolfin immediately pre-date Udine, perhaps in their creation Tiepolo had discovered the incompatibility, for him, of the oil technique with such a vast area.

41

Madonna and Child with SS. Dominic and Hyacinth
Canvas: 274.4 x 137.2 cm.; 108 x 54 inches
The Art Institute of Chicago, Mr. and Mrs. Martin A. Ryerson Collection
Not signed
DATE: (c. 1740)

EX COLL.: Morselli Collection, Florence; Hugh Lane Collection, Dublin; Ladislaus Bloch Collection, Vienna, (Sale at Muller & Co., Amsterdam, Nov. 1905, no. 66, ill.); Trotti Gallery, Paris, 1913; Kleinberger Gallaries, N.Y., 1913.

REF.: E. Sack, *Giambattista und Domenico Tiepolo, Ihr Leben und ihre Werke*, Hamburg, 1910, pp. 86, (fig. 71a., ill.), 83, 89; The Art Institute of Chicago, *Paintings, Drawings and Prints by the Two Tiepolos*, 1938 (exh. cat.) no. 12; U. A. Middeldorf, "Eine Tiepolo-Ausstellung in Chicago," *Pantheon*, vol. 21, May 1938, pp. 17–18; Antonio Morassi, *A Complete Catalogue of the Paintings of G. B. Tiepolo*, London 1962, p. 8, pl. 96; Anna Pallucchini and Guido Piovene, *L'Opera completa di Giambattista Tiepolo*, Milan, 1968.

An example of Tiepolo's most austere type of altarpiece, the present painting has in both its composition and subject matter numerous points of comparison with works of the 1730's, toward the latter part of which it likely dates. The painting is especially quiet in its structure and mood, but Tiepolo achieved a maximum play of light and color through directing a strong glow of sunlight on the black and white habits of the saints and on the glistening pastel colors of the altar frontal, leaving in a slightly reduced, reflected light the Madonna and Child. The disposition of these visual, as distinguished from formal, elements is a characteristic instance of Tiepolo's instinctive care in enlivening his compositions in this not always immediately noticeable fashion.

Although the composition derives from Veronese's *San Zaccaria Altar*, now in the Accademia, Venice, Tiepolo has reduced the asymmetry of his model and presented the enthroned Madonna and Child frontally and rigidly held in the center of the canvas by the enframing architectural setting. So hieratic an arrangement recalls classicizing painters of the seicento such as Carpioni and Ruschi, but even stronger is the recollection of altarpieces of the late 15th century of the type associated with Giovanni Bellini. There is, in fact, in a number of Tiepolo's canvases of the 1730's, a distinctly Belliniesque flavor. Most often this is suggested by a static, symmetrical composition, but at times there is also a limiting of the palette to unbroken primary colors in addition to black, white, and brown.

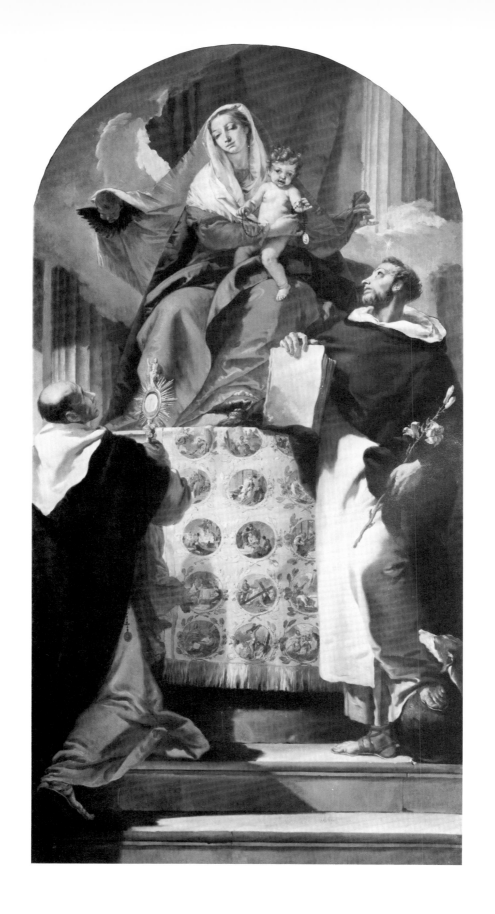

The following decade is marked by the strong influence of Veronese, principally in altarpieces but occasionally in ceilings, and by an extreme vigor and animation. Tighter and more controlled compositions allow increasingly buoyant effects, and the air of triumph, one of the most pervasive qualities of the mature Tiepolo, rapidly becomes conspicuous. After the frescoes in the Palazzo Archinto and the Palazzo Dugani, both in Milan, color lightens and becomes more transparent in the frescoes of the Cappella Colleoni in Bergamo of 1732–33, but this change is not so perceptible in the oil paintings. Figures generally retain the nimble poses of the earlier works but seem more firmly placed and do in fact appear to move less; they take on a greater massiveness, and if they still are often slender, the effect is one of elegance and grace. By the end of the decade in such works as the ceiling fresco of 1737–39 in Santa Maria dei Gesuati, Tiepolo's vision of spacious grandeur and the processes of invention necessary to it are firmly established for the incredible labors of the next quarter century.

The period 1740–60 is marked by an unvarying ease and assurance in projects of every kind and magnitude. These decades open with his first fully characteristic ceiling, in the Palazzo Clerici, Milan, have as their central monuments the frescoed salon with the story of Antony and Cleopatra in the Palazzo Labia, Venice, and the two ceilings at Würzburg, and close with the *Apotheosis of the Pisani Family* in their Villa at Stra.

Subjects tend more and more to be visions and transfigurations enacted by some pantheistic court, in whose realms of sun-washed space ambassadors of every creed and culture move in ceaseless panoply. The great figures of this universe, Christian and pagan deities alike, hardly bestir themselves at all but stand immobile supported at either hand by winged retainers or recline on foamy divans of cloud.

42

Armida Abandoned by Rinaldo
Canvas. 186.9 x 259.5 cm.; $73\frac{1}{2}$ x $102\frac{1}{8}$ inches
The Art Institute of Chicago, Gift of James Deering
Not signed

DATE: C. 1755

EX COLL.: Counts Serbelloni (of Milan) Collection, Venice; G. Cartier Collection, Genoa; Charles Sedelmeyer Gallery, Paris, 1912; James Deering Collection, 1913.

REF.: E. Sack, *Giambattista und Domenico Tiepolo, Ihr Leben und ihre Werke*, Hamburg, 1910, p. 236, no. 624, The Art Institute of Chicago, *Paintings, Drawings and Prints by the Two Tiepolos*, 1938 (exh. cat.) no. 8, p. 19 (ill. p. 68); U. A. Middeldorf, "Eine Tiepolo-Ausstellung in Chicago," *Pantheon*, vol. 21, May 1938, pp. 17–18; Rodolfo Pallucchini, *Gli Affreschi di Giambattista e Giandomenico Tiepolo, alla Villa Valmarana di Vicenza*, 1945, p. 34; G. Massariol and T. Pignatti, *Itinerario Tiepolesco*, 1951, p. 68; Antonio Morassi, *A Complete Catalogue of the Paintings of G. B. Tiepolo*, London, 1962, p. 8, pl. 274; Anna Pallucchini and Guido Piovene, *L'Opera completa di Giambattista Tiepolo*, Milan, 1968; Hylton A. Thomas, "Tasso and Tiepolo in Chicago," *Museum Studies 4*, Chicago 1969, pp. 27 ff., ill. fig. 5, details figs. 6, 9.

One of a group of four canvases illustrating the story of Rinaldo and Armida now in the collections of The Art Institute of Chicago, the present work shows Rinaldo gradually yielding to the stern remonstrances of his former colleagues in arms, Ubaldo and Carlo, while the sorceress Armida, her enchantment of Rinaldo broken, reclines at the left and gestures—half still in pleading, half in resignation at her lover's departure. The paintings of this quartet are among Tiepolo's most poetic works and are faultless evocations of Tasso's heady and yet lyrical *Gerusalemme Liberata*. The canvases are examples of his most refined manner, the transparency of light and color serving to heighten the pastoral, dreamy fragility of their subjects' conception. Unlike the mythologies and literary narratives of contemporary French painting which seem always placed in a hot house of milliners, Tiepolo's legendary world lies somewhere between the Veneto and Greece, an altogether Mediterranean setting of water, sun, and briskly moving air.

The romance of Rinaldo and Armida was used by Tiepolo on at least five occasions. The first time produced the pair of paintings from Würzburg of 1753, now at Munich, and their related sketches in Berlin and Paris. From around 1755, the same approximate date of the Chicago group, come four slender canvases in the National Gallery, London, which appear to contain allusive variations on Tasso's narrative. Then, there are the pair of paintings in the Wrightsman Collection, New York, showing Armida crowning Rinaldo with flowers and the lovers with a magical mirror. At the end of the decade come the four frescoed scenes, extremely close to the Chicago quartet, that form the decoration of one of the rooms of the Villa Valmarana, Vicenza, where Tiepolo left his most extensive and finest series of illustrations based on classical and Italian literature.

It was with almost a half century's experience behind him that Tiepolo reluctantly left Venice for Spain in 1762, summoned by Charles III to decorate the Throne Room in the new palace at Madrid. In that project and other ceilings in the palace, Tiepolo for the last time called on his familiar cast and stock of devices for what was to prove the curtain call for both himself and the long tradition of monumental fresco decoration of which he was the last great master. Those Spanish works have received mixed reviews from recent scholars, some of whom see only a tired and rather heavy repetition of ideas already developed in earlier works. Others see a continuing enrichment of formal possibilities and a serene mellowing in those rolling towers of clouds in the Throne Room ceiling which part to reveal distant clusters of spiralling figures almost lost in a light-drenched infinity. Preferring to remain at the Spanish court rather than return to Venice, Tiepolo in his very last works again took up themes central to Christian faith, and in small canvases as well as the seven altars for the church of San Pasquale at Aranjuez, he betrays for the only time a comprehension of the redeeming value of compassion, sorrow, and humility. Such thoughts are perhaps not unexpected in a man of over seventy, but the bitter circumstances of his last years may have forced him for the first time to look beyond the sustaining vitality of his own genius. Possibly even before arriving in Spain, Tiepolo may have felt that the changes in taste rapidly taking shape in all of Europe were inimical to his art, and once in Madrid, he had to contend with the hostile presence of the most dogmatic exponent of the new, incipiently neoclassical style, Anton Raphael Mengs. A significant portion of the court, including perhaps the king's confessor, appears to have supported Mengs, and Tiepolo eventually felt sufficiently threatened to have doubts as to the reception of the Aranjuez altars which were in fact removed from their site shortly after his death. Under these conditions, it is hardly surprising that in those very late, simple, silent canvases, Tiepolo, an aging expatriate and champion of a culture rapidly being discredited, could evoke pathos.

REF.. Antonio Morassi, *Tiepolo, His Life and Work*, London, 1955; Antonio Morassi, *A Complete Catalogue of the Paintings of G. B. Tiepolo*, London, 1962; Anna Pallucchini and Guido Piovene, *L'Opera completa di Giambattista Tiepolo*, Milan, 1968.

42a

Grand Stairway and the adjoining Ballroom
(Illustrated by photographs in the exhibition)

Ceiling frescoes in the Würzburg Archepiscopal Residence, Franconia

DATE: 1750–1753

REF.: Theodor Hetzer, *Die Fresken Tiepolos in der Würzburger Residenz*, Frankfurt a.M., 1943; M. H. von Freeden and C. Lamb, *Tiepolo; Die Fresken der Würzburger Residenz*, Munich, 1956; Kurt Gerstenberg, "Tiepolos Weltbild in Würzburg and Madrid," *Zeitschrift für Kunstgeschichte*, 1952. Tiepolo arrived in Würzburg in December 1750 at the invitation of the Prince-Bishop Carl Philipp von Greiffenklau to fresco the Kaisersaal (principal salon) in the new palace then being completed according to plans of Balthasar Neumann. Chosen for the program of decoration in the great oval chamber, itself one of the finest examples of South German rococo, were scenes from medieval German history alluding to the importance of Harold, first Bishop of Würzburg. In the oval summit of the ceiling vault, enframed in curling, spiky rococo gilt stuccoes, Tiepolo painted the improbable *Apollo bringing to Frederick Barbarossa his Bride, Beatrice of Burgundy*, with such zest and authority that any reservation about the coherence of the subject is dispelled. In the upper portions of the end walls, seeming to take place on the stage afforded by the cornice of the order that runs about the room and enframed in stucco draperies which function as proscenium curtains, are *The Marriage of Barbarossa and Beatrice* (performed by Bishop Harold) and *The Investiture of Harold as Bishop of Würzburg*.

Having finished, with the extensive help of his oldest son Domenico and of others, the Kaisersaal in July 1752, Tiepolo was asked to undertake the frescoing of the ceiling above the monumental stairs. Here, in an area measuring twenty by thirty meters, Tiepolo devised an exceedingly imaginative, rollicking conjunction of Allegories of the Continents (around the edge of the ceiling just above the cornice) and the Gods of Olympus, all ostensibly doing homage to the Prince-Bishop but representing through allusion and personification a virtually encyclopedic triumph of Western culture as the recipient of infinite good fortune and as itself creator of a rich and resourceful civilization. At this level of meaning, the ceiling becomes in addition to being possibly the finest architectural decoration of the century and one of the most successfully sustained artistic tasks of any period, a significant pictorial document of the Enlightenment.

Eldest son of Giovanni Battista Tiepolo, Domenico would have been preordained, in the event he showed some aptitude for painting, for training in the paternal studio in proper Venetian fashion. What could not have been predicted was his precocious development as his father's most useful assistant and even, at times, his alter ego, and later as an independent artist of a markedly different and extremely interesting personality.

His earliest works are the Stations of the Cross in S. Paolo, Venice, of 1747, which were followed by an increasing number of commissions, including several frescoes. He was his father's chief collaborator at Würzburg where in the ceiling of the Residenz Stairhall their portraits appear side by side, inconspicuous but hardly humble spectators at the marvel they created. The series of charming etchings of inventions on the theme of the Flight into Egypt date from the same period. These mark the first noteworthy appearance of Domenico's rather more intimate vision. During the 1750's, he continued working in his father's aulic manner, as in the ceiling frescoes of 1754–55 in SS. Faustino e Giovita in Brescia, while developing his own new style which had its first full exposition in his frescoes in the guest lodge of the Villa Valmarana, Vicenza, of 1757. Here, an extraordinary range of subject matter, Venetian public genre, chinoiseries, and, especially, peasant life are treated with what at first seems a special and rather pungent realism; but, in fact, Domenico's sense of fantasy is as rich and active as his father's, raising trivia to the level of the ideal.

Again the trusted assistant during the unhappy Spanish sojourn, Domenico returned to Venice in 1770 to resume his official career, becoming President of the Academy of Fine Arts in 1780, twenty-four years after acquiring membership during the presidency of his father, and undertaking one of the last great settecento ceiling frescoes in the Palazzo Ducale in Genoa in 1785. It was during the last decades that he brought to full development his "private" style, still at times gentle and ennobling, but increasingly cognizant of humanity's folly and eventually satirical in an unexpectedly humorous and at times violent way. Humans take on the full grotesqueness of their pretensions, and it is left for the tragicomic Punchinello to blunder through the inevitable banalities of life. Domenico clearly had inherited his father's wit, but the dissolution of a way of life both fed Domenico's quiet acerbity and gave him license for its expression, usually in drawings. Yet in the frescoes with which over a long period he decorated the family villa at Zianigo, and in that very notebook of Punchinello drawings evidently intended to illustrate some long story invented for the diversion of the children around him, he shows himself still capable of extracting amusement from life and still a subscriber to the 18th century's belief in the clear nature of folly and its remedies. The worst lapses are still social ones; the utter and perhaps deserved collapse of society was to be Goya's preoccupation.

REF.: Antonio Morassi, "G. B. e D. Tiepolo alla Villa Valmarana," *Le Arti*, 1941, pp. 251–262; Mercedes Precerutti Garberi, "Asterischi sull'attività di D. Tiepolo a Würzburg," *Commentari*, 1960, ill. pp. 267–283; James Byam Shaw, *The Drawings of D. Tiepolo*, London, 1962.

43

Adoration of the Shepherds
Canvas: 56 x 71 cm.; 22 x 27⅞ inches
Nationalmuseum, Stockholm
Not signed

DATE: (1754)

EX COLL.: The painting is first mentioned in 1760 (inventory of Queen Louisa Ulrica, Nr 285); her son Gustavus III; by 1804, the Royal Museum, which later became the Nationalmuseum.

REF.: Attilio Podestà, *Emporium 114*, 1951, p. 64; Rodolfo Pallucchini, *La pittura veneziana del Settecento*, Florence, 1957, fig. 668; *Cat. des peintures et sculptures des écoles étrangères du Musée de Stockholm*, 1958, p. 198.

Sack, in his early, monumental study of the Tiepolo family recorded that the *Adoration of the Shepherds* once bore the painted date 1754, a date that accords well with the style of the work and accords too with its appearance in the royal collections by 1760. Although the general style is clearly that of the elder Tiepolo, there are already present distinctive characteristics that Domenico developed, as constants of his own manner. Foremost among these is the tremulous line that in its insistent repetition becomes the scribble basic to his way of drawing. Too, the limited, enclosed space of the manger reveals a taste for interior settings quite unlike Giovanni Battista's almost claustrophobic devotion to light and air, while the placing of the heads of the group at the left along a single line of the perspective structure is a device that Domenico will carry to rather mechanical extremes.

Born in Tuscany, Zuccarelli apparently studied first with the minor landscape painter Paolo Anesi in Florence. There followed a period of study in Rome which was crucial for the formation of Zuccarelli's own landscape style; the works of Claude and the various transmutations of his manner, the rococo idylls of Locatelli, and certainly the pastoral subjects of the *bamboccianti*, especially Wouvermanns and Berchem, were all assimilated. Briefly in Florence again in 1729, Zuccarelli arrived in Venice around 1730 where he experimented with the style of Marco Ricci from which, however, he seems to have retained little save an occasional increased richness of color and slightly looser handling. His success in Venice came rapidly through the patronage of Francesco Algarotti, who included Zuccarelli among the artists to be included in the collections then being formed at Dresden, and Joseph Smith, who provided the profitable introduction to English collectors. Another of his early patrons was Francesco Maria Tassi for whom he worked in Bergamo during a number of lengthy visits between 1736 and 1751. It is some of the Bergamasque works, most likely the earlier ones of the group, that reveal a familiarity with Marco Ricci and that stylistically appear to have formed the basis for much of the production of Giuseppe Zais, an almost contemporary Venetian painter of landscapes whose exact relationship to Zuccarelli remains to be determined. It seems likely that in the course of the 1740's, Zuccarelli was influenced by Amigoni, and that it was from this source that come both the pale, cool palette and the soft, rather thin handling that characterize so much of Zuccarelli's work.

One of the most significant contacts with visiting Englishmen came in 1750 when he met Richard Wilson with whom a fairly close friendship developed. It is generally assumed that this association was essential for directing Wilson's tastes toward the kind of landscape painting for which he is noted. Equally likely is Zuccarelli's later change of style toward a broader and more serene type based on Wilson's own mature works. Zuccarelli had secured enough of a reputation in England that by the time of his journey there in late 1752, he of all the Venetian painters of the century to have made that trip was the most sure of receiving a true welcome. His dreamy, arcadian landscapes were in exact conformity with the English taste for such gentle, rustic images, touched with sentimental, moralizing allusions to a Golden Age. The discernable heritage from Claude gave his canvases an impeccable lineage, and it is hardly to be wondered that during his English years, Zuccarelli followed more and more closely his great 17th-century source.

44

Journey of Jacob
Canvas: 50.9 x 63.6 cm.; 20 x 25 inches
Suida-Manning Collection, New York, New York
Not signed

DATE: (c. 1750)

VERSIONS: Cf. *'700 Veneto: paesaggi e vedute*, Galleria Levi, Milan, 1967, pp. 48, 49. This is a large and more densely populated version. The entry records the existence of a third treatment of the subject in a Milanese private collection.

REF.: Detroit and Indianapolis, *Venice 1700–1800*, 1952, cat. n. 86; Antonio Morassi, "Documenti, pitture e disegni inediti dello Zuccarelli", *Emporium*, Jan. 1960, pp. 19–20, fig. 14; New York City, Finch College Museum of Art, *Venetian Paintings of the Eighteenth Century*, Oct. 31–Dec. 16, 1961, n. 46; Durham, North Carolina, *Eighteenth Century European Painting from the collection of Robert L. and Bertin Suida Manning*, Jan.–Mar. 6, 1966.

When Zuccarelli was called upon by inclination or commission to dignify a landscape by including some particular figural subject beyond his usual shepherds and peasants, he most often chose a simple mythological, frequently Ovidian, anecdote. However, there exists a number of paintings in which the subject is less perfunctory and secondary and the composition itself is more concerned with figures. Although the assumption has been held that most of such paintings were produced in England, the present instance seems on the basis of its style to predate 1752. The type of landscape is present in Marco Ricci while the figures appear to owe something to Tiepolo; the subject and its treatment probably descend, possibly not directly, from the many Old Testament migrations painted by Castiglione, himself one of Tiepolo's principal sources. The artificial disposition of light in the foreground and the still dense character of the paint surface argue as well that this is not a late work. On the other hand, there is present a fineness of handling and drawing that is not evident in the presumed works of the '30's. Although this painting may have some connection with the large *Jacob and Laban's Flock* painted in 1743 for Joseph Smith and now in the English Royal collections, a date of around 1750 seems the most satisfactory.

REF.: Wart Arslan, "Considerazioni su F. Zuccarelli", *Bolletino d'Arte*, 1934, pp. 209–220; Gilda Rosa, *Zuccarelli*, Milan, 1952; Antonio Morassi, "Documenti, pitture e disegni inediti dello Zuccarelli", *Emporium*, 1959, pp. 7–22; Michael Levey, "Francesco Zuccarelli in England", *Italian Studies*, 1959, pp. 1–20; Michael Levey, "Wilson and Zuccarelli at Venice", *Burlington Magazine*, 1959, pp. 139–143.

Bologna and Emilia

by Dwight C. Miller

Giuseppe Maria Crespi is the only Bolognese painter of the 18th century to have attracted the wide interest of modern scholars. He is, for example, the only Bolognese painter of this period to have had an exhibition dedicated to his career (Bologna, 1948). The reason is not difficult to discover. The appeal of his art rises above the level of local considerations. There is a human concern in his work, a directness of response to the conditions of life about him, a pungent sense of irony to whatever he characterizes, be it in a narrative, genre or portrait situation, which bring his art closer to modern sensibilities than qualities of cultivation, gentility and elegance of style. His art was free of rigid preconcepts of style. This is not to say, however, that he had not steeped himself in what he found to be the most viable aspects of his artistic patrimony. Indeed, quite the contrary, he was among the most intelligently eclectic artists of his period and his sources range widely, from the most vigorous artists of his local school (especially Ludovico Carracci, Guercino, Lorenzo Pasinelli and his own teacher, Domenico Maria Canuti), to the great 16th-century Venetians, Correggio in Parma and, perhaps even more crucially, the art of the great Umbrian painter of the later cinquecento, Federico Barocci. But Crespi's mind was powerfully independent and capable of recreating what it absorbed in a strongly personal synthesis. Furthermore, Crespi learned as much from nature as he learned from art. His son Luigi Crespi, in his biography of his father, relates that one day in the church of San Benedetto, Giuseppe Maria observed a confessional scene in which sunlight, entering through a broken window above, fell with a warm radiance on the confessor and confessional booth. (Luigi Crespi, *Vite de'Pittori Bolognesi...*, Rome, 1769, p. 212. cf. also G. P. Zanotti, *Storia dell'Accademia Clementina*, Bologna, 1739, II, 52–53). Crespi was so intrigued by the visual suggestiveness of what he saw ("*Invaghitosi di quegli accidenti, che dal sole provenivano ...*"), that he returned to his studio and began a picture involving this situation. The episode is both symptomatic of Crespi's artistic mentality and indicative of the relative modernity of his approach.

45

The Lute Player
Canvas: 121.3 x 153 cm.; 47¾ x 60¼ inches
Museum of Fine Arts, Boston, Charles Potter Kling Fund
Not signed

DATE: (c. 1700–1705)

EX COLL.: Private collection, Lombardy; Vitale Bloch, The Hague

REF.: *Pittura del '600 Emiliano*, Bologna, Palazzo dell'Archiginnasio, April 26–July 5, 1959, cat. n. 103; *Centennial Acquisitions; Art Treasures for Tomorrow*. Museum of Fine Arts, Boston, February 4, 1970, cat. n. 49; D. Miller, "Seventeenth Century Painting at Bologna," *The Burlington Magazine*, vol. 101 (June, 1959), p. 212.

Neither of Crespi's early biographers, Giampietro Zanotti and Luigi Crespi, specifically described a painting corresponding to the one here. It has been suggested that the figure of the lutenist may represent a personification of music, in which case it would be one of a pair of pictures noted by Zanotti (*op. cit.* II, 64) to have been painted for Antonio Comastri: "*Quindi per Antonio Comastri pinse due mezze figure; la pittura, che ritrae la scoltura, e l'altra si è la musica.*" This identification, however, is problematic. Among other things, Zanotti's qualification "*mezze figure*" is not really appropriate for this figure in three-quarter length. However, several decades after Zanotti's writing, the Bolognese historian, Marcello Oretti, saw a picture by Crespi in the house of a "*Sig. Zanoli, argentiere Livornese,*" which fits the description of the picture now at Boston: "*donna che accorda il liuto*" (MS 131 c. 360, Biblioteca Comunale, Bologna, as noted by M. Calvesi in the exhibition catalogue, *Pittura del '600 Emiliano*, cat. n. 103).

The lutenist, as a subject, had already enjoyed considerable popularity in European painting during the earlier 17th century. Caravaggio's involvement with musical genre and his persuasive treatment of the subject of the lutenist was chiefly responsible for bringing it into fashion. It was especially favored by the Dutch painters working with Caravaggesque themes and employed either in the single figure or in the context of the musical group. This painting of Crespi's early maturity (1700–05), so clearly brings to mind the lutenists of the Utrecht painter, Hendrick Terbrugghen, as to pose the question of this Dutch source for Crespi's work.

Crespi's handling is of extraordinary opulence. The girl's lavish drapery, with its silken profusion of material, is exuberantly brushed in a rich display of *valeur* painting. The pose, not simply upright but tilted inward, causes the head to fade into half shadows. There is a resultant suggestive remoteness—as if the girl existed at that moment only in the plane of her own absorption. Crespi obviously found the lute suggestive as a shape and had the happy idea of repeating it in transposition in the bulky form of the lute case to the right. The tension set up by this formal counterpoint does much to enliven the picture. It is a delightfully idiosyncratic interpretation of the subject—a picture rich in formal and painterly subtleties and among the most handsome genre paintings of the period.

He began his training under the Bolognese fresco decorator, Domenico Maria Canuti (1620–84). After a time he was obliged to transfer to the studio of Carlo Cignani because of the jealousy of Canuti's relatives over Crespi's favor with him. Crespi, however, remained certainly more temperamentally responsive to the vehemence of Canuti's manner than to the cool refinement of Cignani's. But equally important to his formation was the study of works by his great predecessors in Bologna. He copied decorations by the Carracci in the Palazzo Magnani and paintings by Guercino as well as other Bolognese masters of the time. He further broadened his horizon by intensive sojourns of study in Venice, Parma, and a trip through Umbria and the Marches.

Crespi's independent commissions began in the late 1680's. In this initial phase of his work he fulfilled two decorative commissions. In the church of San Francesco di Paolo at Pistoia he carried out a vault decoration (1691) with the collaboration of the *quadraturista* specialist, Marcantonio Chiarini. This was followed upon his return to Bologna by two vault decorations in rooms in the Palazzo Pepoli (now Campogrande). Curiously enough, after this very successful beginning in the field of decorative painting, Crespi seems to have abandoned this category of painting. Some idea of his antipathy for the conventional Bolognese custom of collaboration between *figurista* and *quadraturista* in decorative undertakings is obtained from a letter he wrote to Prince Johann Adam of Liechtenstein, in answer to an inquiry as to his interest in a possible offer to do fresco decorations in the latter's Garten Palast at Vienna (cf. D. Miller, "An Unpublished Letter by Giuseppe Maria Crespi," *The Burlington Magazine*, vol. 102, Dec. 1960, pp. 530–531).

46

Portrait of the Artist in his Studio
Canvas: 57.3 x 42.9 cm.; 22½ x 16⅞ inches
Wadsworth Atheneum, Hartford, Connecticut. The Ella Gallup Sumner and Mary Catlin Sumner Collection
Not signed

DATE: (c. 1705)

EX COLL.: Comm. Carlo Foresti, Milan, 1935; Arnold Seligmann, Rey & Company, Inc. N.Y. 1936.

REF.: Palazzo Comunale, Bologna 1935 "Mostra del Settecento Bolognese," Sala I, no. 20, p. 10 illus. VI (Lent by Comm. Foresti); N.Y., Durlacher Brothers, *An Exhibition of Paintings by Giuseppe Maria Crespi*, 1937, no. 8; New York, N.Y., The Metropolitan Museum of Art, *Tiepolo and His Contemporaries*, 1938, No. 5; repr.; Baltimore Museum of Art, *Three Baroque Masters, Strozzi, Crespi, Piazzetta*, 1944, No. 15; repr.; Northampton, Mass., Smith College Museum of Art, *Italian Baroque Painting—17th and 18th centuries*, 1947, No. 14; Buffalo, N.Y., Albright Art Gallery, *Eighteenth Century Italian and French Paintings*, 1948, No. 14; Hartford, Conn., Wadsworth Atheneum, *Pictures within Pictures*, 1949, No. 13; repr. Pl. III; Wadsworth Atheneum, *Handbook*, 1958, page 87 (illus.).

This little picture is among the freshest and most authentic evocations of an 18th-century painter's studio which has come down to us. The casualness with which Crespi has delineated the room and the objects in it, lends a charmingly vernacular tone to the representation, but his acuteness in catching the incidents of light which materialize the forms, indicates an unusually perceptive eye and lively mind. It is simply that we see him here in a mood of good-humored relaxation and perhaps with a certain intention of intimacy. When, for example, one thinks of the impressive Roman studio scene by the French painter Pierre Subleyras (collection of the Academy in Vienna) in comparison to this, the realization is clear that Crespi, native son of Bologna and speaking the flinty Bolognese dialect, has consciously embodied in his characterization a certain air of rustic domesticity, as if determined not to assume the airs of a cosmopolite (cf. also his characterization of his family life in his *Family of the Painter*, Uffizi Gallery). Crespi has shown himself in his high-ceilinged, rather modest but uncluttered chamber, seated before his easel, palette and mahlstick in hand, intent on the brushstroke he applies to the canvas. Behind him is a bookcase with a few vellum-bound books (somewhat reminiscent of Crespi's stupendous bookcase still-lifes in the collection of the Conservatorio G. B. Martini, Bologna). Above, is Crespi's own copy of the *Ecstasy of Saint Francis* by Guercino (Louvre). The copy, still extant, is found today in the collection of Gaetano Maccaferri, Bologna. The casts of antique heads, fragments of arm and feet, seem more curiosities collecting dust than accoutrements in any way important to the artists' preparation. Nearby a cat dozes comfortably on a wicker chair with characteristic feline contentment (this detail appears again in Crespi's *Woman Washing Dishes (La Sguattera)* in the Contini-Bonaccosi Collection, Florence.

In the production of easel painting, Crespi did an unusual variety of subjects from biblical and ancient history, mythology, rustic genre, portraiture, and even still-life. He enjoyed the patronage of Popes and Cardinals, and of secular personages of exalted rank both in Italy and abroad. Except for a period in the earlier part of his career when he served Ferdinando de'Medici, Grand Duke of Tuscany, in Florence, Crespi followed his profession in his native Bologna. From all accounts he had an abrasive personality. Apparently even in his youth he rebelled against officialdom. His biographer Giampietro Zanotti tells a story of how he did a caricature of an imposing personality, the Count Malvasia, well-known historian of Bolognese painting and at the time one of the four directors of the drawing academy Crespi was attending. Crespi's drawing caught Malvasia's likeness in the guise of a plucked capon. Everyone but the Count found it vastly amusing. The latter, infuriated by what he took to be the young artist's insolence, had him expelled from the academy. Later on, Zanotti himself was roughly, even cruelly, handled by Crespi in a series of vitriolic, bantering conversations (reported by Luigi Crespi) in which Crespi enlarged with cutting wit on the shortcomings of both the Accademia Clementina and its secretary, Zanotti.

47

The Continence of Scipio
Canvas: 220.7 x 167.7 cm.; $86\frac{7}{8}$ x 66 inches
Collection Walter P. Chrysler, Jr., New York
Not signed

DATE: (late 1720's)

EX COLL.: Count Antonio Colato, Bologna; Bertolini, San Remo; Acquavella Galleries, New York

REF.: G. P. Zanotti, *ip. cit.*, II, 63; L. Crespi, *op. cit.*, p. 216; B. S. Manning, *Paintings from the Collection of W. P. Chrysler Jr.* (1956), n. 44; Metropolitan Museum of Art, *Paintings from Private Collections*, 1958; R. L. Manning, *Baroque Painters of Bologna . . .* Finch College Museum of Art, N.Y., 1962, cat. no. 30; Brunswick, Maine, Bowdoin College, *Baroque Paintings from the Collection of Walter P. Chrysler Jr.*, 1963, cat. no. 3; The Detroit Institute of Arts, *Art in Italy, 1600–1700*, 1965, pp. 110–111; *Gods & Heroes, Baroque Images of Antiquity*, Wildenstein Gallery, N.Y., Oct. 29, 1968–Jan. 4, 1969, cat. no. 13.

The Continence of Scipio is cited by Zanotti (II, 63), along with its companion piece, *Brutus Kissing the Ground*, as having been painted for Count Antonio di Colato (also noted by Luigi Crespi, p. 216 but without specifying titles). The finer gradations of Crespi's chronology are in need of clarification but it is clear that the *Continence of Scipio* belongs to the artist's full maturity. To the present writer it seems most closely related in style to the two pictures presently in the collection of the Palazzo Venezia, Rome: *David and Abigail* and *Finding of Moses*. These paintings were ordered by the then Papal Legate to Bologna, Tommaso Cardinal Ruffo, and thus must have been commissioned during this appointment: 1721–27. It is significant that Zanotti cited the *Continence of Scipio* after mention of these two pictures; a date for it some time in the late 1720's, is indicated.

As I have written of this picture on another occasion (cf. literature, *Art in Italy 1600–1700*, Detroit, 1965), this masterpiece by Crespi offers particularly eloquent testimony as to his powers as a colorist. Typical of his work, the general tonality is somber with the figures receiving rather strong illumination in the twilight dimness of the setting. Shadows lend a nuance of mystery as they mute the faces; forms emerge suggestively out of darkness. The sumptuous local colors in the draperies, which glow forth heatedly from darkness, are richly modulated by value transitions. Plastic density and depth of color interact to give the forms extraordinary ponderability. Crespi has given an intensely personal inflection to this subject.

Donato Creti was born at Cremona in 1671 but brought by his family to Bologna at the age of two (cf. G. P. Zanotti, *op cit.* II, pp. 99 ff.). His exceptional native gift was manifested early. Count Alessandro Fava offered the young Creti the hospitality of his palace, celebrated for its several rooms decorated by the Carracci and their pupils. For nearly a decade, he sponsored Creti's training. After preliminary study with several minor masters, Creti entered the studio of one of the principal Bolognese masters of the time, Lorenzo Pasinelli. Thus he was brought into direct contact with an artistic line of descent which could be traced back through Pasinelli's teacher, Simone Cantarini, to the celebrated Guido Reni. This was among the most subtle, delicately nuanced strains in Bolognese art and from this basis mainly, Creti formulated his manner. Unlike his colleagues in the Accademia Clementina, Marcantonio Franceschini or Giuseppe Maria Crespi, both of whom were widely traveled and had extensive contacts outside Bologna, Creti's career was fairly uneventful. The impression one has, reading Giampietro Zanotti's annotations to his own official biography of Creti (*Storia dell'Accademia Clementina*, 1739, II; copy Biblioteca Comunale, Bologna, MS B. 11–12), is that the artist had a somewhat introverted personality and was given to curiously eccentric behaviour on occasion. He was a fanatical perfectionist and extremely jealous of his reputation but at the same time obsessed by a sense of inadequacy and haunted by the accomplishments of his great predecessors in Bologna. If Zanotti does not exaggerate, Creti passed his last years in Bologna a pathetic neurasthenic—a man in severe mental distress. With his older contemporary, Marcantonio Franceschini, Creti affiliated himself with the classical-idealist strain in Bolognese art. Inspired above all by the art of Reni, the basic problem Creti set for himself was the search for the perfected form in nature. Spontaneity, with its qualities of the accidental and transitory (so essential to the aims of the Baroque style), was alien to the art of Creti—antithetical, that is, to his intense involvement with what might be termed the metaphysics of ideal form. The essence of Creti's poetic conception lies, then, in the individual figure concept and its flawless delineation. Therefore he is most effective, I think, in static and meditative subjects. He is best of all in his idyllic pastorals where his assemblages of exquisite figures taking poses of ineffable grace, seem hermetically enfolded in silence. Not a leaf stirs in the idyllic landscape setting, strangely dreamlike in its serenity and seen at the break of day or verge of nightfall. Even when the subject involved a specific action—a narrative incident—the figures seem breathlessly suspended

in a "beautiful inertia"—capsulized within an abstracted rhythmic system. Moreover, in a painting by Creti, one savors not only the poetic suggestiveness of mood and situation but also the extraordinary finesse of handling—the Ingres-like precision of the drawing, with porcelain-delicate surfaces, suave and firm of plastic consistency, the colors of mineral-like preciosity which rarefy nature.

48

Pastoral Idyll: "Il Ballo Delle Ninfe"
Canvas: 142.3 x 116.9 cm.; 56 x 46 inches.
Museo di Palazzo Venezia, Rome
Not signed
DATE: (c. 1725)
REF.: G. P. Zanotti, *Storia dell'Accademia Clementina* (Bologna, 1739), II, pp. 115–116; M. Oretti, MS B.130 c. 164, Biblioteca Comunale, Bologna; L. Crespi, *Vite de' Pittori Bolognesi non Descritte nella Felsina Pittrice* (Rome, 1769), p. 259; G. B. Zaist, *Notizie Istoriche de' Pittori . . . Cremonesi* (Cremona, 1774), II, p. 127; K. Alcsuti, *Donato Creti Bolognai Festo* (Budapest, 1932); a translation of this work in Italian was published in *Il Comune di Bologna*, Sept. 1932; J. Angnelli, *Galleria di Pittura dell'E.mo. e R.mo. Principe Signor Card. Tommaso Ruffo, Vescovo di Palestrina e di Ferrera* (Ferrara, 1734) pp. 22, 48, 90; A. Santangelo, *Museo di Palazzo Venezia Dipinti*, (Rome, 1947), p. 23; *Mostra del '700 Bolognese*, Bologna, 1935, p. 34 of exhibition cat.; R. Roli, "Donato Creti," *Arte Antica e Moderna*, n. 7 (July–Sept. 1959), pp. 335 ff.; F. Haskell, *Patrons and Painters . . .* (London, 1963), p. 223; R. Roli, *Donato Creti* (Milan, 1967), cat. n. 82; pls 63–64 and p. 37, 41.

Creti's earliest biographer, Giampietro Zanotti, has recounted the circumstances relating to the commission of this picture by the Legate, Tommaso Cardinal Ruffo. The Cardinal, then residing at Ferrara as Archbishop of that city, had amassed an excellent collection of paintings by contemporary masters. One knows of it from Agnelli's commemorative verses to pictures in the collection (cf. literature above). Apparently Ruffo was so impressed by Creti's work that he commissioned three pictures of him: *Queen of Sheba before Solomon* and a companion-piece, *Solomon Adoring Idols* (these two paintings now preserved in the Musée des Beaux Arts at Clermont-Ferrand). The third picture is the one presently under discussion. Ruffo visited Creti in his studio while these paintings were being executed; he formed such a high regard for Creti that he arranged that he be knighted as Cavaliere dello Speron d'Oro. This, as Renato Roli has pointed out, occurred

during the presidency of Antonio Burrini (cf. Zanotti, I, p. 70: "*Sotto questo principato . . . Donato Creti ebbe l'ordine di Cavaliere.*"). That is the years 1724–25, which accordingly must be the time of the painting under discussion. The subject, described by Zanotti as a "*Pastorale Capriccioso*" is purely imaginary—an intensely lyrical evocation of some unspecified pastoral festival. It is a kind of classical variation of the Fête Champetre theme, well known in the art of Creti's French contemporary, Antoine Watteau. Indeed, the delicacy of formal inflection and poetic timbre of this picture makes especially understandable Longhi's characterization of the artist as a "Bolognese Watteau." In the extraordinarily fine lutenist Creti rephrased an analogous figure in Ludovico Carracci's *Dream of Jacob* (Pinacoteca, Bologna), while the lovely chorus of dancing nymphs in the middle distance was clearly inspired by Guido Reni's memorable retinue of Hours who, in his celebrated *Aurora* at Rome, accompany Apollo's chariot in its course through the sky. The use of the authoritative quote or rephrased motif, partly an act of homage, partly a display of erudition and cultivated taste, is generally characteristic of Bolognese painting of Creti's period. But it is nowhere more frequently encountered, nor handled with greater finesse and ingenuity, than in Creti's work. For him the seemingly unattainable level set by the accomplishments of his great predecessors in Bologna was a deep and abiding concern.

49

An Allegorical Tomb of the Duke of Marlborough
Canvas: 220 x 138 cm.; 86⅝ x 54¼ inches
Pinacoteca Nazionale di Bologna
Not signed

DATE: (1729)

REF.: Giampietro Zanotti, *op. cit.* II, p. 114; F. Malaguzzi Valeri, "Quadri Bolognesi Recuperati a Londra," *Cronache d'Arte* IV (March–April, 1927), pp. 340–344; E. Arslan, "Alcuni Dipinti per il McSwiny," *Rivista d'Arte* 1–2, 1932, pp. 128–132 Alcsuti, *op. cit.*, pp. 16, 18, 21; G. Zucchini, "Quadri Inediti di Donato Creti," *Il Comune di Bologna*, Oct. 1933, pp. 26–27; E. Mauceri, *La Regia Pinacoteca di Bologna* (Rome, 1935), p. 157; G. Zucchini, "Paesaggi e Rovine nella Pittura Bolognese del Settecento," (Bologna, 1947), pp. 19–20; E. Arslan, "Altri due Dipinti per il McSwiny," *Commentari*, 1955 (n. 3), p. 139; R. Roli, "Donato Creti," *Arte Antica e Moderna*, n. 7 (July–Sept. 1959), p. 336; F. Haskell, *op. cit.* pp. 288 ff.; R. Roli, *Donato Creti* (Milan, 1967), cat. n. 38 and pp. 44 ff.; A. Emiliani, *La Pinacoteca Nazionale di Bologna*, Bologna, 1967, p. 389.

The name of the Irish art entrepreneur Owen McSwiny has an important place in the annals of Italian art of the Settecento. His most imaginative promotional scheme was for a cycle of paintings depicting allegorical tombs to "perpetuate the remembrance of a set of British worthies who were bright and shining ornaments of their country." The plan called for these paintings to be executed by the foremost Italian painters of the day. Three artists, as a rule, were to collaborate on each painting; one responsible for the figures, another for the architecture, and the third for the landscape setting. McSwiny's intention was the subscription for a volume of prints after these paintings and then the subsequent sale of the paintings themselves to English collectors. (Although the projected volume of engravings reproducing twenty-four of the sepulchral monuments was never realized in its original scope, and abbreviated version reproducing nine of the paintings was published in 1741 under the title, *Tombeaux des Princes grands capitaines et autres hommes illustres qui ont fleuri dans le Grande-Bretagne vers la fin du XVII et le commencement du XVIII siècle*.)

Venetian painters were mainly engaged, most notably the two Ricci, Pittoni, Piazzetta, and Canaletto. Thus, for example, in the commemorative tomb dedicated to Lord Somers, Canaletto painted the architectural elements, Piazzetta the figures, and Cimaroli the landscape setting. Bolognese painters were also approached for the project. Donato Creti and Francesco Monti were engaged to collaborate with an assortment of architectural and landscape specialists, Nunzio Ferraioli, Carlo Besoli, and Antonio Paltronieri (called Il Mirandolese). Creti's share was very considerable. No less than eight pictures for the McSwiny project were noted to have been painted by Creti at the time of Zanotti's writing (*op. cit.* p. 114). Of these, seven are presently known either in the originals or in studio copies by Creti's pupil, Giuseppe Gabrieli (cf. Roli, 1967, pp. 43 ff.). The painting under discussion is dedicated to the great victor at Blenheim, Sir John Churchill, Duke of Marlborough. The picture belongs to the Pinacoteca of Bologna, having come into that collection through the London art market from the collection of the Duke of Richmond (1927). It was among the paintings from Richmond's collection reproduced in a volume of engravings recording nine paintings from the series (*supra*). The legend beneath the print informs one that N. Ferraioli and Il Mirandolesi collaborated with Creti. The date 1729 has been noted by Renato Roli in connection with the companion painting by Creti, the funerary monument to Boyle, Locke and Sydenham.

Marcantonio Franceschini is the oldest of the painters who represent the Bolognese school in this exhibition. His career was divided equally between the last three decades of the 17th and the first three decades of the 18th centuries. His work represents the continuation of the classical-idealist strain in Bolognese painting into the 18th century. His teacher, Carlo Cignani, had been a pupil of Francesco Albani and Franceschini himself drew inspiration throughout his career not only from Albani but also from Guido Reni and Domenichino whose style was even more decisively classical. In this sense, Franceschini's outlook was retrospective and his work and that of his younger colleague, Donato Creti, may be considered the last significant manifestation of that imposing development of Bolognese classicism which stemmed ultimately from the Roman work of Annibale Carracci.

No other Italian painter of Franceschini's time so rigorously interpreted the ideals of the 17th-century classical style with its taste for neatness and serenity of color, clarity of form, evenness of light and planometric figural arrangement. Nor, with the exception of Donato Creti, was any other painter so intensely involved in the search for what one might term the paradigmatic pose (that is ideally graceful) and the employment of linear abstraction to define the *beau idéal* in nature. Indeed, in a most intriguing way Franceschini anticipated the ascetic purity of style of international classicism of the later 18th century, as Longhi was the first to note some decades ago. ("The Climax of Caravaggio's Influence on Guercino," *Art In America*, xiv [1926], p. 133). And it is interesting to observe that among painters contemporary with him the closest analogies to the particular kind of formal elegance of figure style characteristic of Franceschini's art, are found not in Italian but in French painting—such artists as Louis de Boullogne, Francois Verdier, or René Houasse. The chilly sobriety of his architectural settings for interior scenes, call to mind those of Eustace Le Sueur, the most strenuously classical painter in the French 17th century after Poussin.

But the make-up of Franceschini's style is still more complex, for his development was also attuned to the broader tendencies of style present in European art around the turn of the century. The svelte elegance of his figures and fragile pastel-light coloring of his fresco decorations, his particular sensibility for the arcadian ideal in nature—these and less tangible qualities in his art reveal the harmonious adjustment he was able to make between his aims as a classicist and the evolving taste of his age. Indeed, this was the synthesis he achieved which gave an essential identity to his manner.

Franceschini had a very productive career. During the first decade of his activity, the 1670's, he was largely occupied as Cignani's chief assistant. In this capacity he gained experience as fresco decorator and in his subsequent career he developed into the most adept and widely active fresco decorator of his school. He fulfilled such commissions throughout northern Italy and one on occasion (1711–12), he was called to Rome by Pope Clement XI to provide cartoons for decorations in mosaic for the Cappella del Coro in St. Peter's. Franceschini's decorations in the Cathedral of Piacenza (1688), the Corpus Domini in Bologna (1691–96), the Palazzo Ducale in Modena (1696) and above all the vast historical-allegorizing cycle based on the history of Genoa, formerly in the Sala Maggior Consiglio of the Palazzo Ducale at Genoa (destroyed by fire, 1777), belong among the most extensive decorative enterprises of the age. They also combine facility with finesse of handling and cultivation of taste with intelligent narrative formulation.

There was also a steady production of altarpieces and easel paintings from Franceschini's studio. His real forte in the latter category was for subjects in pastoral settings, either from the Bible (especially the Old Testament), or mythology. Such subjects brought out, perhaps, the richest vein of poetic sentiment in his art. In pictures such as those from the Venus and Diana cycle in the Palazzo Podestà, Genoa, or the lovely *Solomon Adoring the Statue of Venus* in the Palazzo Spinola at Genoa, one observes an exquisitely refined, distinctly personal reinterpretation of the biblical and mythological pastorals of Albani and Domenichino. The influence of Poussin is also sensed. Franceschini's *Moses and the Daughters of Jethro* in the Spinola Gallery, for example, is based on Poussin's interpretation of the subject (known today only through the preparatory drawing in the Cabinet des Dessins of the Louvre). Pictures such as those I have cited, explain Franceschini's favor with collectors and cognoscenti of the day on a European-wide scale. His connection with the Liechtenstein prince, Johann Adam, is one of the most remarkable examples of patronage of the time. His work for the prince spanned nearly two decades (1691–1709). In addition to a number of ceiling and wall paintings in oil for the decor of several rooms in the Liechtenstein Garten Palast in the environs of Vienna, Franceschini also served as the Prince's agent in negotiations for the acquisition of paintings from Bolognese dealers and collectors.

REF.: G. P. Zanotti, *Storia dell'Accademia Clementina*, Bologna, 1739, I; cf. F. Wilhelm, "Neue Quellen zu Geschichte des Furstlich Liechtenstein Kunstbesitzen," *Jahrbuch des Kunsthistorisches Institutes der K. K. Zentral Kommission*, Vienna, 1911, pp. 21 ff. and 90 ff.; D. Miller, "Franceschini and the Palazzo Podestà, Genoa," *Burlington Magazine*, vol. 99, July 1957, pp. 230–235.

50

Noli Me Tangere
Canvas: 148.7 x 85.2 cm.; 58½ x 38½ inches
Collection D. C. Miller, Palo Alto, California
Not signed
DATE: (c. 1705)

The subject, *Noli Me Tangere*, occurs several times in the artist's account book, preserved in the Biblioteca Comunale, Bologna (MS B.6). The painting under discussion, which can be assigned by style to the first decade of the 18th century would then seem to relate to the one commissioned 4 June 1704 by the Marquis of Exeter, when Franceschini was still residing at Genoa in connection with the decorations in the Palazzo Ducale. A companion-piece, *Christ and the Woman of Samaria* was also requested at the same time. These paintings remained in Franceschini's studio at the death of the Marquis that same year. The popularity of the former composition is attested by the number of copies after it. Three of these are known to the writer: a good studio replica of approximately the same dimensions as the one here, in an administrative office in the Palazzo Arcivescovile, Bologna; an excellent replica, perhaps partially finished by Franceschini himself, which appeared on the art market in Berlin in the mid-1930's (photograph on file Kunsthistorisches Institut, Florence); and, finally, a good replica of the lower part of the composition traditionally said to have been done by Francesco Ange. This hangs in the sacristy of the Bolognese church, Santa Maria di Galliera. A comparison of the *Noli Me Tangere* here with the version the artist did at least a decade earlier (Spinola Gallery, Genoa), is instructive. It demonstrates the development of the artist's interpretation toward a more sober, meditated conception (P. Rotondi, *La Galleria Nazionale di Palazzo Spinola a Genova*, Milan, 1967, p. 106). This was the product of his intensified pursuit of the aims of the classical style. The handling is smoother, the concentration on clean linear rhythms more intense, the coloring clearer, lighter, the pose of Christ more formalized. In general there is a reflection here of Albani's *Noli Me Tangere* in the Servite Church, Bologna. But it is interesting to observe how in transforming the rather wistful pose of Christ in the earlier version at Genoa to one of greater formality, Franceschini paraphrased the pose given Christ in a *Noli Me Tangere* by Lucio Massari, a gifted pupil of Annibale Carracci. Franceschini must have first studied this picture when he executed his altarpiece for the high altar of this church (1686).

Two important artists belonging to the Gandolfi family of Bologna, Ubaldo (1728–81), and his younger brother Gaetano (1734–1802), were major figures in 18th-century Bolognese painting. Their energetic compositions, their cursive grace of figure style, chromatic richness of color, and brio of handling—in short, the brilliance of their work—gave them a commanding position in Bolognese painting during the second half of the 18th century. From the solid base of their Bolognese artistic culture, their work developed strongly under the influence of 18th-century Venetian painters, especially Sebastiano Ricci and Giovanni Battista Tiepolo.

Giuseppe Antonio Gandolfi, father of the two painters, was an agent for the Bolognese patrician family, the Ranuzzi. The sons were born in a villa near San Matteo della Decima in the province of Bologna. Ubaldo studied painting in the Accademia Clementina under Felice Torelli (1667–1748) (cf. D. Miller, "Felice Torelli, Pittore Bolognese," *Bollettino d'Arte*, Jan.–Mar. 1964, pp. 54 ff.). At the latter's death he continued his studies under Ercole Graziani and the sculptor-anatomist Ercole Lelli (1702–66). Gaetano, seven years Ubaldo's junior, probably began his studies under his brother and then worked at the Accademia Clementina under Ercole Lelli. In 1760 the brothers went to Venice for a sojourn of study made possible by their patron, the Bolognese merchant Antonio Buratti. As I have noted, this first-hand contact with Venetian painting was decisive for both of them. They returned to Bologna and settled down to productive careers and an active role in the artistic life of Bologna. They were both members of the Accademia Clementina; Ubaldo served a term as its president in 1772 and Gaetano taught classes in anatomy.

51

Group Portrait
Canvas: 118.2 x 175.6 cm.; 46½ x 69⅛ inches
M. H. de Young Memorial Museum, San Francisco, Gift of the Samuel H. Kress Foundation
Not signed

EX COLL.: Samuel H. Kress Collection, New York City (1955); Christie's London, (Queenborough sale, April 28, 1950); Koester, New York.

REF.: W. E. Suida, *The Samuel H. Kress Collection, M. H. de Young Memorial Museum, San Francisco* (1955); A. Neumeyer, "The Samuel H. Kress Collection of the M. H. de Young Museum, San Francisco," *The Art Quarterly* XVIII, n. 3 (Autumn, 1955), p. 280; *European Works of Art in the M. H. de Young Museum*, San Francisco, 1966, p. 169 illus.

The style of this handsome 18th-century Bolognese painting clearly relates to that associated with members of the Gandolfi family. Evidently it was William Suida who first suggested an attribution to Ubaldo Gandolfi and tentavely identified the personages in the painting as the young painter at his easel, his parents (the two older people), and possibly in the sitter, Marchese Tanari, for whom the elder Gandolfi served as agent. All this remains highly problematic. The age of the painter, apparently between twenty-five and thirty, would date the painting to the 1750's. According to Mary Taylor, who is completing a dissertation on the artist, this dating poses difficulties relative to the artist's chronology. The painting seems to her to be too accomplished both in conception and execution for such a youthful work by Ubaldo. It is quite diverse in coloring from Ubaldo's work of that period. Thus she questions the attribution. Renato Roli of the Istituto Storia dell'Arte of the University of Bologna, on the other hand, is inclined to accept it. However he would date the painting to the 1760's—that is after Ubaldo's Venetian sojourn (1760), since he detects in the handling the evidence of the "*tocco Veneto*." The present writer prefers to leave the problem open until more material on Ubaldo is available for study. But certainly the coloring, figure style and particular freshness of handling indicate that one is confronted here with a brilliant product of the Gandolfi circle.

They painted in a similar manner—so much so that the problem of distinguishing between their hands sometimes arises. In general, however, Gaetano demonstrates a somewhat greater verve of execution and richer imagination than his older brother. For the most part the two painters worked for secular and ecclesiastical patrons in the area of Emilia-Romagna. But as one learns from their biographer, Marcello Oretti (MS B 134, vol. XII, p. 185, Biblioteca Comunale, Bologna), on occasion they received commissions from as far away as Vienna, St. Petersburg and Moscow. Ubaldo died in 1781 in the midst of painting the cupola decoration in the celebrated church of San Vitale at Ravenna. Gaetano, who visited London during the years 1787–88, lived on until 1802.

52

San Francesco da Paolo

Canvas: 60.8 x 44.2 cm.; $23\frac{1}{8}$ x $17\frac{3}{8}$ inches

Collection Maestro Francesco Molinari Pradelli, Bologna

Not signed

EX COLL.: Giovanni Ceschi, Bologna

This painting is a sketch for the large *San Francesco da Paolo* in the collection of the Pinacoteca of Bologna (cf. Bianchi, *op. cit.* cat. n. 8, pl. X). This latter painting, signed *U. G.*, is mentioned by Oretti (*Notizie de' professori del disegno* . . . MS B. 134, p. 182, Biblioteca Comunale, Bologna) as at that time in the "refettorio" of the "Capitolo della Certosa" at Bologna. E. Mauceri (*La Regia Pinacoteca di Bologna*, Rome, 1935, p. 114) has noted a replica in the Bolognese church of Santa Maria Maddalena on the Via Zamboni (listed by Ricci-Zucchini, *Guida di Bologna*, 1930, p. 101, as in an adjacent Oratory). The sketch, for which Mrs. Taylor has suggested a dating of 1770–75, is fresh and vibrant in execution and demonstrates Ubaldo Gandolfi's manner at its very best. The final version at Bologna adheres closely to the sketch; only minor changes, for the most part in the background, have been made. The Calabrian saint of the 15th century, San Francesco da Paolo, is represented here with the Archangel Michael presenting a plaque inscribed *Caritas*. The Saint's characteristic virtues were said to be Charity and Humility. He is remembered as the founder of the Minims Order at Paolo in the province of Cosenza in Calabria.

The range of the production of the Gandolfi was unusually broad. In addition to large-scale fresco decorations, altarpieces, easel paintings of a variety of religious and profane subjects, and portraiture, they also did sculpture (cf. E. Riccomini, *Scultura Bolognese del Settecento*, Bologna, Museo Civico, Dec. 1965–Jan. 1966, pp. 142 ff.), and were prolific printmakers. Both artists were virtuoso draughtsmen and accustomed to making copious studies in preparation for their compositions. The corpus of their drawings hence is large. The superb improvisatory freedom of line, and sparkling, energetic handling of the washes, characteristic of their graphic technique, makes this category of their production especially sought by modern collectors.

53

Orpheus and Eurydice
Canvas: 80.2 x 61 cm.; $31\frac{1}{2}$ x $31\frac{1}{2}$ inches
Collection David E. Rust, Washington, D.C.
Not signed
DATE: (1802)

EX COLL.: collection Giovanni Ceschi, Bologna

REF.: L. Bianchi, *I Gandolfi* (Bologna, 1936), p. 86 and n. 53 (p. 155).

A preparatory drawing also in the Rust collection is inscribed on the verso: *G.G. F [ecit], 1802*. This would date the painting to the last year of Gaetano's life. The rather crabbed poses and the harsh linearism (response to the neoclassicist idiom of Felice Giani?), is characteristic of the late manner of the artist and is seen again in a picture of the same format of the one under discussion, *Apollo and Marsyas*, in the Galleria Campori, Modena (cf. L. Bianchi, *op. cit.* pl. LII). The subject is one especially congenial to the fashionable mode for pleasurable horror peculiar to the iconography of Romanticism: Orpheus, unable to restrain his anxiety, looks back toward the fiery underworld from whence he has led his beloved Eurydice, only to lose her this time forever (Ovid *Metamorphosis*, Book X, 53–63). Gaetano has interpreted the subject with appropriate *Sturm und Drang* theatrics: a strong emotional urgency in the attitudes of his figures and a lot made of the flashing horror of the underworld and the fearsome serpents which inhabit the place. A curiously naïve touch in the context of what pretends to be a high epic mode, is the transformation of Orpheus' lute into a guitar of modern design.

A word should be added here about Gaetano's son, Mauro Gandolfi (1764–1834). As one can see from the span of his career, this artist belonged as much to the earlier 19th as to the later 18th century. He was a pupil of his father and as a lad of fifteen, left the parental home to embark on five years of wandering all over Europe. He returned to Bologna in 1785. In 1794 he became a professor at the Accademia Clementina, but then one again hears of his traveling about—this time in Tuscany, the Marches, and as far south as Rome. In 1801 he is recorded as living in Paris and in 1816 he visited America and is said to have been friendly with the painter John Trumbull. Mauro Gandolfi's work is little known today. Those few paintings which have been identified as his, above all the genial self-portrait which represents him in the present exhibition, demonstrate that he was a worthy continuator of the artistic lineage of the Gandolfi family.

54

Self-Portrait
Canvas: 96 x 78 cm.; $37\frac{3}{4}$ x $30\frac{3}{4}$ inches
Pinacoteca Nazionale di Bologna
Signed lower right: *M.G.*
DATE: (c. 1795)

REF.: L. Bianchi, *op. cit.* p. 100–101; pl. LIX; E. Mauceri, *La Regia Pinacoteca di Bologna* (Rome, 1935), p. 115; A. Emiliani, *La Pinacoteca Nazionale di Bologna* (Bologna, 1967), n. 344 (reproduced).

Born in 1765, Mauro Gandolfi seems around thirty years of age in this spirited self-portrait. It must have been done, then, sometime around the mid-1790's in Bologna where the artist had settled after his years of wandering about Europe. Mauro Gandolfi's work is little known today but the evidence here of a lively engaging talent is an incentive for further study of his career.

Ercole Graziani began the study of painting under Lodovico Mattioli. He came to the attention of Count Alessandro Fava, who, as he had with Donato Creti, also came to Graziani's assistance. He offered the young man the hospitality of his palace and arranged for him to study with his other protegé, Creti. The latter, according to Zanotti, was still living in the same palace ("*Stava in casa del Conte, come gia s'è detto, Donato Creti, che si prese per ordine del Fava ad ammaestrare il Graziani . . .*"). Graziani was put to work studying and copying the paintings of his Bolognese predecessors: the Carracci, Guido Reni, Simone Cantarini. He also worked with the paintings and drawings of Creti himself. By 1727, he was advanced enough in his career to be elected to the Accademia Clementina, and in 1730, he served a term of office as its president. During the 1730's, Graziani received commissions for altarpieces for a number of metropolitan churches in Bologna as well as churches in other cities in the Lombard-Emilian area. As far as one knows, he did not undertake decorative commissions.

Graziani's manner has been known chiefly from his altarpieces in Bolognese churches. In these he appears very competent but rather pedestrian. But in the easel paintings of biblical narratives or mythologies, he is considerably more interesting. The two pictures (companion-pieces) *Lot and His Daughters* and *Susanna and the Elders*, in the Pinacoteca of Bologna, while they demonstrate the influence of both Creti and Franceschini, also show an unmistakable autonomy of style. In his essay on the artist of 1963, Renato Roli published two mythological subjects in oval format of unusual distinction. *Diana and Endymion* and its companion-piece, an as yet unidentified subject. What impresses one chiefly in these two pictures is the graciousness of the figure style (reflections of Pasinelli, Creti, and Franceschini), and the poised elegance of the figural arrangements in their woodland settings. This is somewhat analogous to the work of Creti and Franceschini but the handling is more painterly—a softer, looser brushwork and a heightened density of the colors. Since Roli's article, a lovely *Diana Discovering Callisto* has appeared on the London art market, if anything raising one's estimation of Graziani's stature even higher. The *Judith Presented to Holofernes* from Minneapolis, which represents Graziani's work in the present exhibition, maintains this quality. But it is also a picture which demonstrates a rapport of style with Graziani's exact contemporary, Francesco Monti. It is easy to tell them apart, however: Graziani's figures are more earthbound, more solidly modeled, less nervously energetic in their movements. His figural ar-rangements seem more meditated, as a rule. His artistic temperament is less febrile—less given to extravagances of style.

REF.: Zanotti, *op. cit.* II, 275 ff.; L. Crespi, *op. cit.* pp. 276–279; R. Roli, "Ercole Graziani (1688–1765)", *Arte Antica e Moderna* n. 22 (April–June, 1963), figs. 68 a-b.

55

Judith Presented to Holofernes
Canvas: 151.5 x 125.8 cm.; 67½ x 49½ inches.
The Minneapolis Institute of Arts
Not signed

DATE: (1745–1750)

EX COLL.: Bosdari, Bologna; R. Sanderson, London; J. A. Tooth, London (1961); P. & D. Colnaghi and Co. Ltd., London (1963).

REF.: *The Art Quarterly*, Winter, 1962, p. 409; *Gazette des Beaux-Arts* (La Chronique des Arts), Feb. 1963, p. 66; *The Connoisseur Year Book*, 1964, p. 102; D. C. Miller, "Viani Graziani and Monti: Contributions to the Bolognese Settecento" in *Arte Antica e Moderna*, no. 25 (Jan.–Mar. 1964), pp. 98–99.

The cataloguer first proposed this 18th-century Bolognese painting as a work by Ercole Graziani in 1964. The attribution was based on what was sensed about the picture in terms of facial and figure type, drapery style and the particular qualities of surface texture and brushwork in drapery and flesh painting. Further, there was the matter of the handling of the illumination which has a particular static, reflective character. All these elements pointed clearly to Graziani and his style of the 1740's. A relationship with paintings of this decade, most notably *San Mauro Healing the Cripple* in the Bolognese church of San Procolo (cf. Roli, "Ercole Graziani," *Arte Antica e Moderna*, n. 22, April–June, 1963, fig. 70 c), was noted. Graziani did the subject, *Judith Presented to Holofernes* in what appears to be an earlier version, one of a pair of oblong pictures in the collection of the Opera Pia dei Poveri Vergognosi at Bologna (the companion-piece, *Esther before Ahasuerus*). The composition of the picture at Minneapolis is far more dramatically concentrated and confident in execution and would seem to belong to the later 1740's. I noted in my publication that I was aware of two studio replicas of the Minneapolis painting in private Roman collections.

There is hardly a more extraordinary example of the revival of a style of painting over a century earlier, than that offered by the art of Aureliano Milani (1675-1747). As Giampietro Zanotti observed in his biography of this member of the Accademia Clementina (*Storia dell'Accademia Clementina*, Bologna, 1739, II, pp. 159 ff.), Milani deliberately set out to restore the art of the founders of the Bolognese tradition of painting, the Carracci ("*Io credo che fin d'allora gli venisse in fantasia di rinovar, se potea, la maniera de'Carracci . . .*" Zanotti, *op. cit.* II, 159). Milani's initial training in Bologna—briefly in the studios of Lorenzo Pasinelli and Cesare Gennari—apparently left him dissatisfied. He had decided rather to bypass painters of his own time and undertake an exacting study of the art of the Carracci as a basis for the formulation of his own manner. He worked first in the Palazzo Fava, copying from the celebrated mural decorations in the Sala Giasone and the Sala di Enea. His talent impressed Count Alessandro Fava and Milani was not only given free access to the palace but indeed maintained there for some time as had been the case with his colleagues, Donato Creti and Ercole Graziani. Milani also did copies of other works by the Carracci and it is evident that he was attracted above all to the art of Annibale Carracci. Zanotti has noted in this regard that he was especially influenced by his study of Annibale's *Resurrection of Christ* in the Church of the Corpus Domini in Bologna. More fully than any other painter of his time, Milani assimilated the supple organicism, weight, and plastic energy of Annibale's figure and drapery style.

Milani's first independent commissions—fresco decorations in several private houses in Bologna, and an *Annunciation* for the refectory of the Servite order in Bologna—were enthusiastically received. He was acclaimed by some of his townsmen as the new Carracci. He was commissioned by the Duke of Parma to paint nine pictures of religious subjects. Other requests came from patrician clients in Bologna and there were commissions for altarpieces for some of the more important metropolitan churches in that city. Milani became a special favorite of the influential General Luigi Ferdinando Marsili. The latter was then living in Bologna and was a vigorous promoter of the newly formed Accademia Clementina. It was Marsili who suggested that Milani take up residence in Rome. To this end he had the artist send a large drawing, *The Fall of Simon Magus*, to the Bolognese Pope, Clement XI, with the hope of being summoned to Rome. However, this did not come about and it was only in 1718 that Milani finally settled there. He was greatly assisted in establishing himself with the Roman art public by Marsili's

friend, Cardinal Paolucci, Secretary of State to Clement XI. Milani remained in Rome for the rest of his career. His pictures can be found in a number of churches there: San Marcello, SS. Giovanni e Paolo, S. Bartolomeo dei Bergamaschi, Santa Maria del Monte Esquilino, etc. But by far his most impressive Roman enterprise was the fresco cycle in the vault of the Galleria degli Specchi in the Palazzo Doria. In this extraordinary series of scenes from the Labors of Hercules, with their sumptuous *quadrature* settings animated by a variety of nudes, Milani had the proper stage for the demonstration of his power as a figure painter ("*. . . che di nudi musculosi, e fieri abbisognano estimando che qui consista la somma del suo sapere,*" as Zanotti observed). In this superb fresco cycle, the spirit of Annibale Carracci and the Galleria Farnese decorations was brought forward into the 18th century in a learned and viable recreation.

56

Episode from Roman History (?)
Canvas: 170.8 x 133.4 cm.; $67\frac{1}{4}$ x $52\frac{1}{2}$ inches
Signed and dated: *Aureliano Milani. MDCCVIII* (on entablature of temple)
Collection Walter P. Chrysler, Jr., New York

REF.: *Bolognese Baroque Painters*, Finch College Museum of Art, N.Y., Feb.–April, 1962, cat. n. 38 (catalogue by R. L. Manning)

The tentative identification of the subject of this picture as *Achilles Slaying Hector*, is not satisfactory. The goddess protector, seen in the sky, could hardly be Athena, who would be called for in the Homeric episode. She seems rather to be Venus; and the whole tone of the narrative seems more appropriate to the history of Rome than Greece. Such an episode as Aeneas slaying Mesentius from Virgil's *Aeneid* (end of Bood X), or Horatius killing the Alban Curatius (Titus Livius, *History of Rome*, Book I, 25), though not fully satisfactory as an identification of the subject, would be closer to the mark.

The painting, an early work by Aureliano Milani, is signed and dated on the entablature of the pedimented temple behind the group. Costume, figure type, and pose, more than anything else, recall the figure style employed by the Carracci in their early mural cycles in the Palazzo Fava, Bologna. It is this connection which lends the picture a certain quasi-Mannerist character, noted by a previous commentator (cf. Ref., above). However, Milani's two figures, counterpoised in their action, seem to have been adapted from two analogous figures in the *Death of Amulius* from a somewhat later fresco cycle by the Carracci in the Palazzo Magnani in Bologna.

Francesco Monti, born at Bologna in 1685, came to prominence as a painter in that city by the 1720's. He had studied initially with the Modenese painter Francesco Caula, but had subsequently been drawn into the orbit of the Bolognese school as a pupil of Giovanni Gioseffo Dal Sole. This subtle master, with his opalescent coloring, filmy elegance of drapery and intriguing repertory of facial types, was probably Monti's strongest formative influence. But the effect of the art of Monti's somewhat older contemporary, Giuseppe Maria Crespi, is also evident. This is especially true of a group of paintings correctly given to Monti by Renato Roli ("Traccia per Francesco Monti Bolognese," *Arte Antica e Moderna*, n. 17, 1962, figs. 27 a–d and 31 a). In these pictures, the tonality is unusually somber, and the figures receive a strong light. As Roli notes, there is a *"certa Crespiana fraganza degli impasti."* Monti went on to develop his own very distinctive manner— one characterized by a figure style of exotic fancifulness. The body canon is elongated, the head small, the features dainty, of an abstracted comeliness, the face suggestively veiled by shadows, the limbs gracefully tapered. There is a recherché elaboration of pose, based on twisting, turning movements. The coloring has an exotic charm, based as it is on unusual tints and admixtures. Indeed, all of this luxuriating in the more esoteric possibilities of style in which Monti indulges, has an inescapable connection with the more rarified aspects of 16th-century Mannerism. Reflections of Parmigianino are unmistakable and one senses as well a connection with the art of the late Mannerists in northern Europe such as Spranger or Hans van Achen. If Franceschini and Crespi carry the classical strain into the 18th century in Bologna, Monti's style represents a kind of neo-Mannerist development—one in which his colleagues Vittorio Bigari and Giuseppe Marchesi (called Il Sansone) were also involved to a degree. This is likewise true of the Parmigian artist (active later in Rome), Michele Rocca. Monti was an active member of Bologna's Accademia Clementina; he served a term as its president in 1727. In easel paintings his subjects ranged from biblical and ancient history to mythology. The corpus of his extant drawings is unusually large and has been the subject of a recent book by Ugo Ruggieri. Monti was among the most active fresco decorators of his school. From the later 1730's on, he worked for the most part in Lombardy, undertaking large-scale decorative projects, both secular and ecclesiastical, in Brescia, Bergamo, and Cremona. Among these enterprises, the extensive decorations of the Brescian church of Santa Maria della Pace in Brescia is most noteworthy. He died in Brescia in 1767.

57

Judith with the Head of Holofernes
Canvas: 113.1 x 151.2 cm.: $44\frac{1}{4}$ x $59\frac{1}{2}$ inches.
Collection D.C. Miller, Palo Alto, California
Not signed

DATE: (c. 1735)

REF.: D. Miller "Viani, Graziani 2nd Monti: Contributions to the Bolognese Settecento," *Arte Antica e Moderna*, n. 25 (Jan., March, 1864), p. 99, pl. 32b.

Although this *Judith with the Head of Holofernes*, is not cited in either of the biographies of Monti by Zanotti and Luigi Crespi, it is easily recognizable as his both from the facial types (that of Judith amounts to a kind of hall mark of Monti's work), and the particular handling of the drapery passages, fluidly articulated, and with Monti's characteristic touch in the coloring and brushwork. (The attribution of the painting to Monti (cf. Miller *supra*) curiously enough was rejected by Ugo Ruggieri, *Francesco Monti*, Bergamo, 1968, p. 9, but his alternative proposal, p. 18, f.n. 50, that the picture is by Donato Creti can hardly be taken seriously). The finer gradations of Monti's chronology have yet to be firmly established but it is clear that the picture belongs to the middle years of the artist's career, to the second half of the 1730's. This is the period of the fresco decorations in the Brescian church of Santa Maria della Pace (1738), the huge *Martyrdom of St. Peter Martyr* in the church of San Domenico at Modena or the *Judgement of Solomon* in the Opera Pia dei Poveri Vergognosi, Bologna, (cf. Roli, *op. cit.*, fig. 29d). There is no evidence in the *Judith with the Head of Holofernes* of the coarsening of execution which one can observe in Monti's later work in Brescia and Bergamo of the 40's and 50's. The picture well represents the neo-Mannerist aspect of Monti's style. The tenuous refinement of type here, recalls the art of Parmigianino as do certain painterly blandishments such as the evanescently soft handling of Judith's diaphanous veil or the smouldering effect of the illumination by oil lamp in this murky ambience. The lost profile of Judith's old servant woman further enhances Monti's intriguingly oblique approach to the narrative.

REF.: Zanotti, *Storia dell'Accademia Clementina*, II, pp. 217 ff.; L. Crespi, *op. cit.*, pp. 314 ff.; U. Ruggieri, *Franceschini Monti, Bolognese 1685–1768;* D. Miller, "Vittorio Bigari and Francesco Monti, Two Decorative Painters of the Bolognese Settecento," *Art Quarterly*, XXXI, n. 4 (Winter 1868), pp. 421 ff.; D. Miller, "Viani, Graziani and Monti: Contributions to the Bolognese Settecento," *Arte Antica e Moderna*, no. 25, Jan.–Mar. 1964, p. 99, pl. 32b.

57a

Frescoes for the salone of Palazzo Aldrovandi, Bologna
(Illustrated by photographs in the exhibition)

DATE: 1755

Vittorio Bigari (1692–1776), made a brilliant debut in Bologna as a decorative painter, with frescoes in the vaults of the stair and *salone* of the sumptuous new palace of the Aldrovandi, on the via Galliera (1722–23). As *figurista* he collaborated in this work with a specialist in architectural painting (*quadraturista*), Stefano Orlandi (1681–1760). Their work, as Zanotti observed, was received with "grandissime laude" by the Bolognese art public and following this success, the two painters went on to fulfill other such enterprises: a vast ceiling decoration in a gallery in the Palazzo Ranuzzi in Bologna (1724–25) and in 1728, the decoration of several rooms in the Palazzo

del Popolo in Faenza. By this time, Bigari's reputation was sufficiently widespread that he was receiving decorative commissions which took him to Verona, Milan and Turin. Later in his career (1755), he returned to the Palazzo Aldrovandi to paint episodes from Roman history in a gallery and to continue the program of decorations in the *salone* of the palace which he had initiated some twenty years earlier with the vault fresco where one sees Aurora on her course through the heavens. In the coving of this vault he now painted scenes illustrating events connected with careers of distinguished members of the Aldrovandi family. These are identified by inscriptions in Latin in cartouches beneath each fresco. Ulisse Aldrovandi (1522–1605), renowned for his vast work of classification in Natural History, is seen delivering a lecture to his students in an imposing hall in the Archiginnasio (at

the time the seat of the University of Bologna). In two other scenes, one sees episodes from the career of Pompeo Aldrovandi (1668–1752), who had a distinguished career in the Church. He is seen received by Philip V of Spain, as Papal Nuncio to the Spanish court at Madrid. Pompeo received the Cardinalate in 1734 and in a subsequent event we see him, successor to Cardinal Martini as Papal Legate to Romagna, entering the city of Ravenna to assume his office. Finally, there is an event involving Nicolò Aldrovrandi, who as representative of the Bolognese Senate, gives the keys of the city during an official visit of the Spanish Cardinal from Castile. The locus of this event is easily identified on the Strada Maggiore with the church of San Bartolomeo Porta Ravegnana to the right and behind, the two pendant towers of Bologna, the Asinelli and Garisenda.

These narrative murals are done in a delightfully colorful, theatrical manner which combines a sprightly topical realism of costume and setting and discursive richness of figural composition, with gracious figure poses and exhilaratingly airy lightness of coloring. In Bigari's hands, this elegant late Baroque idiom comes as close to the rococo style as anything in eighteenth-century Bolognese painting. Although still very little known outside Bologna, these frescoes in the Palazzo Aldrovandi represent one of the high points in large scale decorative painting in 18th-century Italy.

REF.: D. Miller, "Vittorio Bigari and Francesco Monti, Two Decorative Painters of the Bolognese Settecento," *The Art Quarterly*, XXXI, no. 4, Winter, 1968, pp. 421–432. Giampietro Zanotti, *Storia dell'Accademia Clementina*, Bologna, 1739, II, pp. 285–292.

Florence and Tuscany

by Mina Gregori

Bonechi was a pupil of Giovanni Camillo Sagrestani, who had set up a busy studio in Florence in which participated, besides Bonechi, important artists like Ranieri del Pace and Giuseppe Moriani. In 1702 he worked with Sagrestani in a chapel of San Frediano al Cestello. In the same decade he received the important commissions for San Domenico in Fiesole (1705) and San Jacopo Oltrarno in Florence (1709). Among his many works in Florentine palaces (in Palazzo Corsini, perhaps in the 1690's, and in Palazzo Giraldi), the most notable works are the grand staircase praised by Lanzi and the salon of Palazzo Capponi. In his maturity appear other frescoes for Florentine churches, and after the death of Sagrestani he designed for the Medici tapestry works. At an advanced age he executed the *Martyrdom of Saint Bartholomew* for the Cathedral of Pistoia (1753).

58

Diana and Endymion
Canvas: 82 x 103.6 cm.: $32\frac{1}{4}$ x $40\frac{3}{4}$ inches
The Hylton A. Thomas Collection, University Gallery, University of Minnesota, Minneapolis.
Not signed.
Date: after 1705

EX COLL.: Augusto Volpini, Leghorn 1914; Claudio Gallo, Milan 1932; Hazlitt Gallery, London, 1963.

REF.: *Catalogo della collezione d'Arte e d'Antichità appartenuta al pittore prof. Augusto Volpini di Livorno*, Leghorn, March-April 1914, no. 153 (as Venetian School of the Eighteenth Century); L. Coggiola Pittoni, "L'arte di G. B. Pittoni e una nuova serie di opere inedite di lui," *Rassegna d'Arte*, XIV, 1914, pp. 180–181 (as Pittoni); L. Coggiola Pittoni, *G. B. Pittoni*, Florence, 1921, fig. 36; V. Bloch, "La pittura italiana a Berlino," *Vita artistica*, 1927, pp. 179–180 (as Bonechi); G. Fiocco, *La Pittura Veneziana del Seicento e del Settecento*, Florence-Munich, 1929, p. 91 (as Bonechi); Hazlitt Gallery, London, *Seventeenth and Eighteenth Century Italian Paintings*, 1963, cat. no 3; "Londra, Dipinti italiani alla Hazlitt Gallery," *Emporium*, CXXXVIII, 1963, p. 234.

With its pendant, *Pluto and Persephone*, it has been given back to Bonechi by V. Bloch. Both have been recognized independently by L. Berti, G. Ewald, and M. Gregori as the sketches for the ceiling of the grand staircase of Palazzo Capponi in Florence. The dating can be deduced from the date 1705 in the inscription in the courtyard of the palace. The style seems only a little developed from the Boston sketch. Bologna (oral communication) has thought more likely Sagrestani.

With Sagrestani and the other artists of his studio, Bonechi introduced to Florence a new decorative style. This style, much opposed by contemporary classicists like Gaburri, appears to be the product of a more modern interpretation of directions already taken in Florentine art by Gherardini—a new interpretation allied to the work of Sebastiano Ricci and echoing somewhat French painting. Bonechi's most intense activity falls in the first two decades of the eighteenth century. With the frescoes of the chapter hall of SS.ma Annunziata (1722), one observes a softer manner, paralleling the tendencies seen in the cartoons of Sagrestani for the tapestry cycle "The Four Parts of the World."

REF.: M. Maragoni, "La pittura fiorentina nel Settecento," *Rivista d' Arte* VIII, 1912, pp. 84–85, 97; R. Wittkower, *Art and Architecture in Italy—1600 to 1750*, Pelican History of Art, 1958, pp. 309, 383.

59

The Virgin Consigns the Rosary to Saint Dominic
Canvas: 46.5 x 57.9 cm.; $18\frac{1}{4}$ x $22\frac{3}{4}$ inches.
Museum of Fine Arts, Boston, given in memory of William Crowninshield Endicott by his wife.
Not signed
Date: 1705

EX COLL.: George Peabody, Salem (acquired in Europe *c.* 1832); Ellen Peabody Endicott; William Crowninshield Endicott.

REF.: W. G. Constable, "Some unpublished Baroque Paintings," *Gazette des Beaux-Arts*, XXIII, 1943, p. 234, ill. p. 232.

The sketch, which carries an old attribution to Bonechi, relates to the fresco on the triumphal arch of San Domenico in Fiesole. Bonechi executed it in 1705 together with the decoration of the dome of the church and of the façade wall, in collaboration, with the architectural work of Lorenzo del Moro and Rinaldo Botti, as appears from the records of the convent (published in *Nuovo Osservatore Fiorentino*, edited by P. Franceschini, Florence, 1885–86, 8 Nov. 1885, p. 136). Constable has noted the similarities to two models from the Rothman collection in the Berlin exhibition of 1927, and attributed to Bonechi by Voss. They reappeared later in the New York art market in 1943. The subject and the composition of the sketch exactly correspond to the fresco of the triumphal arch. The *Glorification of Saint Dominic*, with the saint carried to heaven by angels, is represented in the dome. On the façade wall are the two figures of *Faith* and *Charity* in monochrome.

Born in Florence, he moved with his family to Imola, where he frequented the studio of Francesco Chiusuri. Returning to Florence in 1708, he followed the manner of Tommaso Redi and Sebastiano Galeotti, and later resided in Bologna for five years, in the studio of Torelli, follower of Gian Gioseffo Dal Sole. By 1714 he had returned to Florence. The frescoes discovered by this writer in the Villa Amati Cellesi at Scornio are dated 1715, and close to these must be placed a ceiling in the Palazzo Giraldi. After a short period of activity in Imola, he worked chiefly in Tuscany. His activity as portraitist is little known; better known are his humourous subjects, like the famous *Storie di Arlecchino* engraved by Bartolozzi, and his caricatures. He also designed for the Medici tapestry works in 1728.

Ferretti completed his artistic education in Bologna, along with other Florentines already linked with this center, like Sebastiano Galeotti. His first activity is connected with this painter and with Ranieri del Pace. His definitive style, which appears during his Imolese period, is inspired by the painting of Bologna to seek new goals of synthesis and of mere sculptural modelling, much as the great Venetians were also influenced by Bologna. In his late work, oriented toward the academy, he is perhaps in contact with Roman painting, presaging the beginnings of Tuscan Neoclassicism.

REF.: M. Marangoni, "La pittura fiorentina nel Settecento", *Rivista d'Arte*, VIII, 1912, pp. 87–90, 98; L. Sandrini, "Gian Domenico Ferretti," *Atti dell'Associazione per Imola storico-artistica*, I, 1944, pp. 14–18; L. Berti, "Inediti di Giovan Domenico Ferretti," *Commentari*, I, 1950, pp. 105–108; E. A. Maser, "The Disguises of Harlequin by Ferretti," *The University of Kansas, the Register of the Museum of Art*, 1956; M. Gregori, "Nuovi accertamenti in Toscana sulla pitture 'caricata e giocosa,'" *Arte antica e moderna*, 1961, pp. 400–416; M. Gregori, *70 pitture e sculture del '600 e '700 fiorentino*, Florence, 1965, pp. 35–36, 63–64; E. A. Maser, *Gian Domenico Ferretti*, Florence, 1968; G. Ewald, "Some unpublished works by Giovan Domenico Ferretti," *Apollo*, LXXXIX, 1968, pp. 278–289; G. Ewald, "Aggiunte al Ferretti," *Antichità viva*, VIII, 1969, no. 5, pp. 3–18.

60

The Glory of St. Philip Neri
Canvas: 104.2 x 76.9 cm.; 41 x 30¼ inches.
The Minneapolis Institute of Arts.
Not signed
Date: 1731–35

EX COLL.: Newhouse Gallery, New York 1961.
REF.: *The Burlington Magazine*, CII, January, 1960, illustrated p. XII; M. Gregori, *70 ditture e sculture del '600 e '700 fiorentino*, Florence, 1965, p. 63; E. A. Maser, *Gian Domenico Ferretti*, pp. 57–58, 84 (no. 120), colorplate XIII and fig. 111.

This summarily executed sketch, of which we have other examples by Ferretti, is perhaps the first thought for the main fresco in the church of SS. Prospero and Filippo in Pistoia, dedicated to the latter saint in 1715 and on that occasion restored with major transformations. The pictorial decoration begins in the nave about 1731 with the important *quadratura* by Lorenzo del Moro and successively by Pietro Anderlini after del Moro's death (1735). Ferretti's intervention in the vault can be dated about this year or immediately later. The general concept, more expansive and looser in the fresco, is similar to works executed in the 1730's, such as the frescoes in the Florentine Abbey, completed between 1733 and 1734, and the ceiling of San Niccolò del Ceppo, which can be dated 1735, as Maser has determined. Their affinities with this fresco are very close, and the attitudes of the Madonna and saint are also similar, especially if one compares it with the preparatory sketch for San Niccolo del Ceppo, in the Museum at Narbonne.

One can distinguish two periods in the decoration of the church of San Filippo: the first included the façade wall, and the vault of the nave, divided in three parts, one with *Saint Philip in Glory*. The second was devoted to the cupola, the choir and the apse, and can be dated 1746, by an inscription with the signature of the artist in one of the crests of the cupola. Stylistic features also confirm this chronological interval.

61

Jason and Medea
Canvas: 218.5 x 177.9 cm.; 86 x 70 inches
Collection Professor Caesar Pinnau, Hamburg-Blankenese.
Not signed
Date: c. 1742–1745

EX COLL.: Baron Ferdinand von Stumm, Rohlstorf, Holstein; A. Weinmüller, Munich 1964.

REF.: A. Weinmüller, Munich, 25 September 1964, Auktion 91, no. 1770 (as 18th century anonymous Austrian); E. A. Maser, *Gian Domenico Ferretti*, Florence, 1968. pp. 47–81, 107.

Dated around 1745 by Maser, it falls among the mature works of the artist. The figure of Medea presents close similarities to that of the Woman of Samaria in one of the frescoes executed by Ferretti in 1742 for the refectory of the Convent of SS. Annunziata (Maser, *op. cit.*, fig. 69). The continuity of this academic and classicist phase in the second half of the eighteenth century can be observed in the work of Giuliano Traballesi.

He was among the first pensioners of Cosimo III at Rome where he studied with Ciro Ferri, following which he lived in Venice. He returned to Florence during the years 1680–90, where he executed portraits in the manner of Bombelli and received important commissions for paintings and frescoes. He became official painter to the Gran Principe Ferdinando de' Medici, and worked in the Pitti Palace and for the principal Florentine families (Corsini, Gerini, Acciaioli, Strozzi, Ridolfi palaces). The large fresco with the *Apotheosis of Cosimo the Elder* at Poggio a Caiano is from 1698; the following year he returned again to Venice in order to please his patron and improve his color. The *Appearance of the Virgin to Saint Philip Neri* of Maratti, which Ferdinando had withdrawn from the church of San Giovanni dei Fiorentini at Rome, was the model for his painting of 1724 of the same subject in San Firenze.

A follower of Cortona at the outset, the influence of this style now become 'routine' remains in his decorative work. His travels mirror the tendencies of the Late Baroque, with its divergent Roman and Venetian tendencies. The prevalent influence of Maratti turned him towards classicism, shown also in his portraits (the Uffizi *Self-Portrait* of 1685). This is the artistic atmosphere that fostered his caricatures and also his landscapes, much praised in his time (notable examples the frescoes of the Gerini palace inspired by Albani and Mola, and many drawings in the Uffizi). His fame as the greatest representative of the classical style in Florence, upheld above all by his principal biographer and pupil Ignazio Hugford, seems debatable today. However, Gabbiani is important as a draughtsman and his memory endured into the late 18th century, when from his many drawings were gathered the engravings of the 'Cento pensieri' published in 1762.

REF.: A. Bartarelli, 'Domenico Gabbiani,' *Rivista d'Arte*, XXVII, 1953, pp. 106–130; F. Haskell, *Patrons and Painters*, London, 1963, pp. 131, 133; M. Gregori, *70 Pitture e Sculture del '600 e '700 fiorentino*, Florence, 1965, pp. 29–30.

62

The Finding of Moses
Canvas mounted on board: 116.9 x 144.9 cm.; 46 x 57 inches
The Brooklyn Museum, Gift of Mrs. Cornelia K. Hood
Not signed

DATE.: C. 1690–1700

Formerly given to a French 18th-century painter, but now referred by Erich Schleier rightly to Gabbiani, this picture can be dated prior to the 18th century, because of its echoes of Cortona interpreted with an intense Venetian manner. The Venetian influence is also visible in the fine landscape on the right, which refers to Gabbiani's activity as a landscape painter, which is still to be worked out. The most pleasing aspects of the first period of Gabbiani's, before this classicistic phase appearing between the first and second decades of the 18th century, are expressed in canvases of small size, nearly sketches, such as this painting and the *Feast in the House of Levi*, Dresden, n. 512.

Schleier bases his attribution on two drawings in the Gabinetto Disegni e Stampe of the Uffizi: 15479F (study of Pharaoh's daughter) and 7114F (study of the whole composition). 15945F, also in the very large cache of Gabbiani drawings at the Uffizi, is the study for a head similar to the one of Pharaoh's daughter. M.G. and A.M.C.

A disciple of Alessandro Rosi, he spent his youth in Pontremoli, a small town that enjoyed considerable prosperity. During that period the artist must certainly have known the principal centers of North Italy. Returning to Florence after 1690, he got important commissions on the same terms as Gabbiani, Pier Dandini and other painters connected in a more orthodox manner with the Cortona style. F. S. Baldinucci, to whom we owe the *vita* of the artist, mentions other stays at Pontremoli and Leghorn, where he died.

After an early Late Baroque period, as seen in his first work at Pontremoli, Gherardini elaborated a lighter and more animated style, a novelty that depended on Giordano, who had worked in Florence, and also on Genoese painting, especially that of Gregorio de Ferrari. In the last decade of the 17th century he is certainly among those furthest advanced in anticipating the taste of the 18th century, so much so as to appear to prefigure Sebastiano Ricci, who repeatedly frequented the Florentine scene. His preferences for the picturesque and his continuing relations with North Italy constitute an independent phenomenon in the special Tuscan artistic world of Ferdinando de' Medici.

REF.: M. Marangoni, "La pittura fiorentina nel Settecento", *Rivista d'Arte* VIII, 1912, pp. 72–78, 99; M. M. Pieracci, "La difficile poesia di un ribelle all'Accademia: Alessandro Gherardini," *Commentari* IV, 1953, pp. 299–305; R. Wittkower, *Art and Architecture in Italy, 1600–1750*, Pelican Books, 1958, pp. 309, 383, no. 18; G. Ewald, "Il pittore fiorentino Alessandro Gherardini", *Acropoli* III, 1963, pp. 81–132; M. Gregori, *70 pitture e sculture del '600 e '700 fiorentino*, Florence, 1965, pp. 33–35, 57–58.

63

Madonna and Child with Angels
Canvas: 87.5 x 73.5 cm.; $34\frac{1}{2}$ x $28\frac{7}{8}$ inches
Collection Mina Gregori, Florence
Not signed.
Date: c. 1697–1700.

EX COLL.: Sestieri, Rome.

REF.: G. Ewald, "Il pittore fiorentino Alessandro Gherardini", *Acropoli* III, 1963, p. 132, no. 20; M. Gregori, *70 pitture e sculture del '600 e '700 fiorentino*, Florence, 1965, pp. 57–58.

The painting was first attributed to Gherardini by Longhi (oral opinion). Silvia Meloni proposes that it may be identified with the "Effige di Nostra Donna col puttino in braccio, il tutto fatto con sommo studio," executed for Ferdinando Santi, President of the Ducal Chamber at Piacenza, and mentioned in the *vita* manuscript of F. S. Baldinucci (publ. by G. Ewald, *loc. cit.*, p. 92). The dating suggested by its relation to other works of the last years of the 17th century does not contradict this conjecture, since we know that the artist came to Piacenza from Pontremoli a little before the end of the century. The debt to Luca Giordano is especially evident in the head of the Madonna, while in the Child appear echoes of Giovanni da San Giovanni, a Florentine painter who was also esteemed by Sebastiano Ricci.

Anonymous Tuscan (?), 18th Century

64

View of Pisa
Canvas: 125.5 x 160.4 cm.; 49⅜ x 62⅛ inches.
Wadsworth Atheneum, Hartford, Connecticut. The Ella
Gallup Sumner and Mary Catlin Sumner Collection.
Not signed

DATE: C. 1774–1775

EX COLL.: Tower Family, Weald Hall, Brentwood, Essex;
M. de Beer, London 1947; Durlacher Bros., New York 1947.

REF.: C. C. Cunningham, "A View of Pisa—Giovanni Paolo
Panini," *Wadsworth Atheneum Bulletin*, November, 1947, p. 1;
Hartford, *Fifty Painters of Architecture*, 1947, no. 33 (as Panini);
Dayton, *The City by the River and the Sea—Five Centuries of
Skylines*, 1951, no. 16; F. Arisi, *Gian Paolo Panini*, Piacenza,
1961, pp. 206–207 (as Panini); W. G. Constable, "Vedute
Painters in the Wadsworth Atheneum," *Wadsworth Atheneum
Bulletin*, Fifth Series, no. 14, Summer 1963, pp. 17–20; Hart-
ford, *The Coast and the Sea—a Loan Exhibition assembled from
the Collections of the Wadsworth Atheneum*, 1964, no. 18; G.
Briganti, *L'Europa dei Vedutisti*, Milan, 1968, tav. 108 (by the
same anonymous painter of the Buffalo *Feast at the Sanctuary
of Montenero*.

For a long time attributed to Panini, an attribution accepted
by Arisi; other equally unacceptable names have been proposed for the painting: Guiseppe Bottani by Leandro Ozzola
and Ulrich Middeldorf; Thomas Patch, Giuseppe Tosca,
Francesco Battaglioli. It has also been supposed that it is by
the same hand as the Buffalo *Festival Outside the Church of
Montenero* (Cat. no. 65). At present the museum attributes it to
Giuseppe Zocchi. It is certainly a work closely related to the
Buffalo painting: they have the same dimensions (perhaps
they belonged to a larger series, since they cannot be considered pendants from the point of view of the composition);
both came from the Tower family. They were executed, per-

haps, as "souvenirs," by a remarkable painter, so far unidentified, working around Pisa and Leghorn, an area which during
the eighteenth century was much frequented by foreigners,
especially Anglo-Saxons. Numerous features, taken together,
permit a dating in the 1770's: the style of the costumes and the
similarities with the *veduta*-painting produced after the mid-
century by Battaglioli and Joli, with its bird's-eye perspec-
tives; even more, the immediate relationship with the art of
Thomas Patch, who was active in Florence from 1755 and
whose luminous architectural renderings derive from Panini
and Bellotto.

Even though a first glance suggests certain inconsistencies in
the respective styles of the view itself, of the *genre* personages
and of the group of female allegories (Gloria and Fame) with
putti holding laurel garlands, the picture must be regarded as
the work of a single hand. In the latter group, though represented in a solemn manner, there are close similarities in the
treatment of the draperies to the figures in contemporaneous
costume in the foreground of the Buffalo *Festival Outside the
Church of Montenero*. The view from above, seen probably
from the Guelph Tower, takes in the whole city: the Arno
flowing from the Porta a Mare and San Paolo a Ripa d'Arno,
up to Santa Maria della Spina and, to the north, the group of
the Duomo, Tower, and Baptistery. From the Arsenal of the
Galleys, which belonged to the Order of the Cavaliers of Santo
Stefano, a galley is being pulled out by ropes, and there are
many spectators on the banks, the Ponte a Mare, and boats.

65

Festival Outside the Church of Montenero with a View of Leghorn in the Distance
Canvas: 122.9 x 157.9 cm.; 48$\frac{3}{8}$ x 62$\frac{1}{8}$ inches
Albright-Knox Art Gallery, Buffalo, New York
Not signed
DATE: C. 1774–1775

EX COLL.: Tower Family, Weald Hall, Brentwood, Essex; Durlacher Bros., 1947

REF.: The Buffalo Fine Arts Academy. *Gallery Notes*, XII, no. 1, Autumn 1947, pp. 10–12 (as Panini); *Art News*, XLVII, no. 5, September 1948, p. 30; *Art News Annual*, XVIII, 1948, p. 158; The Buffalo Fine Arts Academy, Albright-Knox Art Gallery, *Catalogue of Painting and Sculpture in the Permanent Collection*, 1949, p. 198, no. 57; Houston, Texas, Museum of Fine Arts, *George Washington's World*, 1954, no. 163; Syracuse, *Exhibition*, Jan. 1956, no. 14; F. Arisi, *Gian Paolo Panini*, Piacenza, 1961, p. 293 (as Giuseppe Bottani ?); *Painting and Sculpture from the Albright-Knox Art Gallery*, New Haven, 1961, no. 55; G. Briganti, *L'Europa dei Vedutisti*, Milan, 1968, tav. 108 (as anonymous 18th century); Northampton, Mass., Smith College Museum of Art, *Italian Baroque Painting—17th and 18th Centuries*, 1947; Vassar College Art Gallery, *Problem Pictures—Paintings without Authors*, 1965.

The attribution to Panini, with which the painting entered the museum, is today no longer accepted. One must also exclude the present attribution to Zocchi, an artist who never reached such notable results in any easel painting. It is certainly one of the most unexpected paintings of "vedutismo." The humor with which the vivacious groups are represented, the natural spectacle of open-air festivity, and certain features which demonstrate a knowledge of English portraiture, mirror the Anglo-Florentine climate of the genre paintings of Ferretti, the Uffizi *Self-Portrait* of Ignazio Hugford, and the *vedute* and conversation pieces of Thomas Patch. The painter, still hidden in anonymity, has almost certainly represented himself on the right, wearing a beret and with a glass in hand.

The Church of Montenero had its moment of splendour when the work begun in 1720 for the new chapel of the miraculous Virgin was completed and the sacred image was placed on the altar in 1774. Great festivals were held between the 8th and 12th of September at Montenero and Leghorn. Perhaps the artist intended to evoke the picturesque and worldly aspects of this event.

Rome and the Papal States

by Anthony M. Clark

Famous for his paintings of children, Amorosi's work has been confused since the 18th century with that of Monsù Bernardo (Bernhard Keil; see R. Longhi, *Critica d'Arte*, 1938, pp. 121–130) who worked in an older, distinct style. Amorosi was a Marchigian, as was his teacher Giuseppe Ghezzi; he was a fellow pupil with the younger P. L. Ghezzi (*q.v.*). A seminarian in the 1680's, he was an established painter doing monumental commissions in towns of the Papal States (1690's) and in Rome itself, using his own and his teacher's important connections. From about 1700 Amorosi seems to have specialized in genre paintings and to have become very fashionable. Besides these and his few altarpieces there are also portraits, which indicate that his fashion lasted from about 1700 to 1730.

Amorosi took part in the decoration (*c.* 1720) of the frescoed ground floor rooms of Palazzo Ruspoli on the Corso, the most important commission of the first half of the century for the "minor forms," the landscape, genre, and associated types of painting. Pannini and van Bloemen were not present. Amorosi did at least one room with scenes of Roman history (the room had a ceiling by the obscure Giulio Solimena). M. A. Ceruti (the anti-academic frescoist, no relation of cat. no. 4, 5) did "*alcune stanze a guazzo.*" Alessio de Marchis (*q.v.*) did two rooms of landscapes, Andrea Locatelli (*q.v.*) did the fifth room with seascapes and other landscapes. P. P. Cenini, the floral painter, did a pergola ceiling; Cristiano Reder, the over-productive battle painter, with the problematical landscapist Monsù Francesco Borgognone (or Francesco Francesi) decorated at least the largest room. This last has since disappeared into a modern bank. Several other of the rooms still exist but are unstudied.

Amorosi's dark, rich style is very close to that of his teacher and is a conscious descent from such strong painters of the first half of the previous century as Lanfranco and Guercino. Less ornamental and grand than his master, Amorosi is also affected by the soft, beautiful handling of Trevisani (*q.v.*). Far more evocative than P. L. Ghezzi, Amorosi also produced burlesque paintings with caricatural ingredients which, unlike Ghezzi's caricatures, reworked and prettified 17th-century Dutch scenes of Roman lowlife.

REF.: Eugenio Battisti, *Commentari*, 1953, pp. 36–38 and 155-164. do., *do.*, 1954, pp. 79–80 (compare Federico Zeri, *Paragone*, 1953, 45, p. 47); C. Faldi Guglielmi, *ad voc.*, *Dizionario Biografico degli Italiani*, 3, Rome, 1961, pp. 13–14.

66

Vagabond
Canvas: 34.3 x 26.4 cm.; 13½ x 10⅜ inches
National Gallery, Prague
Signed and dated: inscribed on the back of the canvas: *originale de Antonio amorosi Romano 1710*

EX COLL.: permanently exhibited since 1948 in the National Gallery, Prague.

REF.: Sbírka Starého umění, Katalog, 1949, no. 6, p. 2; do., 1955, no. 6, p. 2.

Amorosi specialized in paintings of children—of infants dressed up and holding a medal, a dove, a necklace, grapes, or some other proud or pacifying object; these were a necessary ingredient of European painting collections of the first half of the 18th century. There are also genre incidents of children and young adults (Dorotheum, Vienna, 576, 30 May 1967, lot 5), incipient puberty (*Young Lovers with Owl*, life-size, Gasparrini collection, Rome), full-length single youngsters out-of-doors (the Chatsworth pictures; another with Galerie St. Lucas, 1964, initialled), adolescent artists (Pascoli collection, Deruta; a *Boy Drawing*, "anonymous Venetian 16th century," Dulwich College, no. 295). But the great part of his known work consists of smoldering portraits of infants, usually boys (the same models can often be noted) and usually in Renaissance costume (one wonders what Venetian pictures Amorosi was thinking of).

The present exhibit has nothing of the artist's usual pretty, infantile scene-stealing; as Erich Schleier has pointed out to the cataloguer, the Prague painting is Amorosi's masterpiece; and, though engaging, serious and Rembrandtesque. It also serves to suggest, through its date of 1710, that the common pictures of infants largely belong to the twenties of the century —in which their more obviously Roman rococo technique would feel at home. But Amorosi's chronology is still vague; the Prague *Vagabond* gathers the Gasparrini *Lovers* and a *Girl with Vegetables* (Christie's, 14 May 1965, lot 86) together as a stylistic group between the earlier church pictures and the plentiful later works.

More important than chronology is the seriousness and accomplishment. Piazzetta, with his radical sympathies, is more enigmatic and not quite as perceptive; the Prague picture rivals the finest moments of Ceruti, Piazzetta, and Crespi, and puts Amorosi among the very few interesting 18th-century Italian masters of realism.

Roman-born, Bacciarelli studied with Benefial (*q.v.*). In 1750, or more likely 1753, he was called to Dresden where he worked for Augustus III, Elector of Saxony and King of Poland (died 1763), employed principally as a draughtsman-copyist. It is worth noting that the rising Raphael Mengs was in both Dresden (end of 1749 to early 1752) and Rome during this period, and, earlier, had been himself in Benefial's classes.

Bacciarelli followed the court to Warsaw in 1756 and probably remained there to the end of 1764. In 1761 and in 1764–5 he visited Vienna where he did portraits at the court of Maria Theresa, and worked for Prince Kaunitz (the Viennese works are untraced). In 1764 the Dresden Academy offered the artist the professorship of portraiture, which he refused. In October 1766 Bacciarelli moved permanently to Warsaw to become the court painter, head of the art school, director of buildings, and general artistic counsellor of the newly elected and last king of Poland, Stanislas Augustus Poniatowski (reigned 1764–95). He left Poland only once more (1787), going to Vienna, Venice, Bologna, Florence, Rome and Naples on a collecting trip for the king, during which he himself was loaded with honors.

Bacciarelli's many decorative works for Stanislas Augustus have largely survived the recent destruction of Poland excepting, of course, his frescoes for the Warsaw Castle and suburban palace. A good part of his more interesting portraits remain, the first known in Poland dating from 1757. It is apparent that the young Roman brought a fine training to Dresden but no strong or local idea about portraiture. The portrait of Henrietta Murray (Scone Palace, possibly 1759) shows as much French taste as anything particularly Roman. From Rome Bacciarelli would have remembered portraits by Detroy, Natoire, Subleyras, and Blanchet (as well as those of such native artists as Benefial and Batoni); at Dresden, Warsaw, and Vienna he would have known the portraits of Silvestre, Mengs, Tocqué, and the van Loo family.

The 1760's saw the assimilation of the various influences and the full development of Bacciarelli's familiar and powerful style. Friendly knowledge of Guglielmi (*q.v.*), whom the portraitist would have known in Dresden and Vienna; the later portraits of Batoni, and (after 1781) of Angelica Kauffmann, both much employed by the Poles on the Grand Tour; a knowledge of British contemporary portraiture, mainly through mezzotints; even a taste for Rembrandt; these mix to produce the rich, fine portraits of Bacciarelli from the 1770's and thereafter.

67

Self-Portrait with Children
Canvas: 76.5 x 57.5 cm.; $30\frac{1}{8}$ x $22\frac{5}{8}$ inches
Muzeum Narodowe, Warsaw
Not signed
DATE: *c.* 1766–1770.

EX. COLL.: Countess Ludwika Sobańska; Mrs. D. Krzemińska (1946).

REF.: A. Chyczewska, Marceli Bacciarelli, Zycie—Twórczość—Dzieta, Wystawa zorganizowana przez Muzeum Narodowe w Poznaniu i Muzeum Narodowe w Warszawie, Poznań 1968, s. 85, nr 17, il. 1 (Marcello Bacciarelli Exhibition of his paintings organized at the 150th anniversary of his death, Poznan 1968).

The artist is showing with his chalk-holder, portfolio of drawings, and two children, the older of which holds a drawing of his nursing mother, her hand on her brow. The painting is dated by the lenders to the first years of Bacciarelli's residence in Poland. The children would probably be Federico (born 1756), Francesco and Maria; the wife, Freiderica Richter (married 1755) became in 1759 a court painter at Dresden. From the apparent age of the two sons, an earlier date (1760 or just thereafter) might be considered.

In this delicate and vigorous portrait there is a flavor of both Detroy and Natoire, who led the French Academy in Rome just before Bacciarelli left Italy. There is also the same directness that Guglielmi (*q.v.*) was expressing in his Viennese work when Bacciarelli was there. Excepting the unfinished adolescent self-portrait in a London private collection, this is the earliest of many self-portraits.

REF.: S. Kozakiewicz, *ad voc.*, *Dizionario Biografico degli Italiani*, 5, Rome, 1963, pp. 37–41 (with bibliography to 1962; see reference above for the 1968 festivities in honor of the 150th anniversary of the artist's death).

Batoni was born in Lucca, the son of a goldsmith, and came to Rome at nineteen (May 1727), to remain all his life. He lost a pension from the Republic of Lucca for a precipitate marriage and, after studying very briefly with Conca (*q.v.*) and Masucci (*q.v.*), he began to draw from famous paintings (the *Stanze* of Raphael, the Farnese Gallery of Carracci), and famous ancient statues of Rome. These drawings were good training and also saleable. At the same time, Batoni met a painter of importance, yet independent of the Roman Academy, Imperiali, who became the nearest thing to Batoni's master, although the relationship was more that of mutual help between two independents. Batoni's first public commission came about 1733; and his style is fully formed at the end of that decade. In the next decade he was the most talked-of painter in Rome and, indeed, until his death, he was *the* great painter in Rome, rivalled only by Raphael Mengs (evident in Rome in the later 1750's to 1761; 1771 to death in 1779), after whose death Batoni was the most famous (or only famous) painter in Italy.

Batoni never made any extensive decorative schemes (his only ceiling—a group of canvas inserts in Palazzo Colonna—is rather early) and his *magnum opus*, the huge 1746–55 *Fall of Simon Magus* altar for St. Peter's, was never erected. His reputation was founded first and earliest upon the superb drawings; then upon altarpieces and devotional pictures—a steady stream of these (but, as all Batonis, not really plentiful); then scenes from classical history and mythology developed with power, grace, and personal inventiveness of a high order; and, finally, the portraits, only to be produced in any numbers from 1754 but to be the source of Batoni's wealth, and—because of such subjects as the Hapsburg Emperor (1779)—greatest fame. Not every European prince and ruler could afford a Batoni subject painting; most could afford his portraits and, for almost all, it was a part of being on the Grand Tour to be painted by Pompeo. His richest customers (and those most interested in portraits) were the British, with Eastern Europeans not far behind (or any Italian able to be a patron).

68

Prospero Cardinal Colonna di Sciarra
Canvas: 100.6 x 75.3 cm.; $39\frac{5}{8}$ x $29\frac{5}{8}$ inches.
Walters Art Gallery, Baltimore
Inscribed (on the letter): *All. Emin.mo.e Rev.mo. Prin.e / il Card. Colonna de Sciarra.*

DATE: C. 1750

EX COLL.: Don Marcello Massarenti, Rome (from Palazzo Sciarra?); Henry Walters, Baltimore (1902).

VERSIONS: engraved by J. G. Wille, 1754, in various versions as after Batoni's painting; engraved by P. A. Pazzi (using the Wille; head only).

REF.: Edouard van Esbroeck, *Catalogue du Musée . . . Accoramboni* (Massarenti), Rome, 1897, no. 288 (as Batoni; until recently it was catalogued in Baltimore as "German Schoo'"); Anthony M. Clark, "Three Roman Eighteenth-Century Portraits," *The Journal of the Walters Art Gallery*, XXVII–XXVIII, 1964–65 (1968), pp. 50–54; F. Zeri, *Apollo*, December 1966, p. 450, ill. p. 451.

Cardinal Sciarra (1708–65) studied in Parma and Padua and began his rise in the papal court in 1730. In 1743 he became a Cardinal and in 1758 Protector of France. His brother Giulio Cesare was one of the grandest Roman princes, both as head of this branch of the ancient Colonna family, and as Prince of Palestrina through his marriage to the Barberini heiress (1728). He, too, was painted by Batoni (1768).

Portraits of Roman potentates from the time, at least, of Raphael through the Baroque were frank, exquisitely painted, and severe. To increase attention upon the subject, usually no background is shown, or only a characteristic element, as here. Other early Batoni portraits show Grand Tourists out-of-doors or in a gallery of antique statues. Masucci, (*q.v.*) who was Batoni's immediate predecessor as the leading Roman portraitist, would have designed his portraits as carefully, severely, and powerfully as this one, but not as delicately nor with such a fine visual sense of color and texture.

169

Batoni's position was midway between the Baroque and the neoclassical. He moderated the rococo style with not only a classical severity, but especially with an appeal to the actual grandeur of the Renaissance and of the early Baroque masters. His mature style reacts against an earlier classical style of his own and also against the pettiness and artificiality of the rococo artists of 1740. His latest period was intense, mannered, but direct, relaxed, and freshly painted. Throughout he was not very interested in his contemporaries (Luti, Masucci, Mengs), was easily himself, and was exceptionally forceful, natural, inventive, and authoritative. Awkward in intellectual matters, Batoni was a beautiful and poetic painter. He also summarizes three centuries of official Roman tradition.

REF.: Ernst Emmerling, *Pompeo Batoni sein Leben und Werk*, Darmstadt, 1932; Anthony M. Clark, "La Carriera Professionale e lo Stile de Batoni," in the catalogue, *Mostra di Pompeo Batoni*, Lucca, 1967, pp. 23–50.

69

Benedict XIV Presenting the Encyclical "Ex Omnibus" to the Count de Choiseul
Linen: 128.9 x 179.5 cm.; $50\frac{3}{4}$ x $70\frac{5}{8}$ inches
The Minneapolis Institute of Arts, The William Hood Dunwoody Fund
Signed: *P. B. P.* 1757

EX COLL.: Painted for Domenico Cardinal Orsini who gave it to Pope Benedict XIV (died 1758); Dr. Gustav Fall, Vienna (1931); the heirs of Dr. Fall, Washington, D.C. (1961).

VERSIONS: The sketch was lot 500 in the Orsini sale, Rome, 12–23 March 1896; the pendant of the Batoni is an earlier (1752) painting by Placido Costanzi now in a private collection in Leghorn. Preparatory drawings are at Besançon and in a private collection.

REF.: E. Schaffran, "Ein Unbekanntes Historienbild des Pompeo Batoni," *Belvedere*, X, 1931, pp. 94–96, ill.; E. Emmerling, *op. cit.*, 1932, no. 178, p. 130; A.M. Clark, *The Minneapolis Institute of Arts Bulletin*, LI, September, 1962, pl 90, ill. p. 91; Michael Levey, *Rococo to Revolution*, London, 1966, pp. 175–176, 242, ill. p. 175.

The canopy is embroidered with the papal arms and the date of Benedict's reign (XVII, i.e., 1757); the Encyclical is inscribed with its preliminary lines; and the Count wears the Order of the Holy Spirit which he received from his king on January 1, 1756. The Count, who was to become a Duke for arranging the marriage of Marie Antoinette and the future Louis XVI, left Rome in January 1757. His is not a true portrait, even though his costume is shown accurately. The portrait of the ailing Pope—the most sympathetic and liberal of the century—is intended as an accurate likeness and represents a man who had been a great patron of Batoni's.

The allegorical scene shows the Pope surrounded by figures of Religion and Divine Wisdom, as the Protectors of Holy Church (SS. Peter and Paul) watch from a cloud, and the Holy Ghost inspires the Pope. Choiseul's embassy to Benedict was to obtain the Encyclical, which was intended to cool French religious and parliamentary troubles. The Encyclical letter (16 October 1756) served that purpose but in retrospect it is evident that the situation was a fatal curtain raiser to the French Revolution. As one of the great actions of Benedict's papacy a record of it was an appropriate gift to the Pope from one of the most prominent Cardinals he had created.

70

Painting
Canvas: 61.7 x 49.7 cm.: 24¼ x 19½ inches
Private Collection, U.S.A.
SIGNED: *P. Batoni. Pin. 1775.*

REF.: *Calendar of the Art Institute of Chicago*, Summer, 1970, vol. 64, no. 3, ill.

There are a number of paintings from Batoni's hand showing only half-length or waist-length single figures. As a portraitist he is excellent in this format, and some of Batoni's most famous non-portrait images (*Jesus of the Sacred Heart* and the various *Madonnas*) take advantage of its intimacy.

Batoni is also a painter of women *par excellence;* his contemporaries remembered not the gangling companies of British youth in the quickly exported portraits, but rather his young goddesses, their features selected from his several wives, his numerous daughters, and the beauties of the day. The firm oval faces—with noble brows, rather long noses, small pronounced chins and perfectly formed lips—are individualized in each case, but are all about sixteen and all belong to the delightful Batoni family. Although shy, and although perfectly convincing young people, they are not girls but goddesses. In the head-and-shoulder format there are two kinds: the sacred and profane (easily interchangeable): the Madonna and the personified Art of Painting. Both always seem to appear not as virgins but as young mothers.

In a fine *Painting* sold in a Cologne auction of November 1959 the Art is shown with the same large brushes (seven instead of six) and the same miniature palette. Mantled and wearing a pearl in her ear, Painting's hair is braided and turbaned so that she can more easily work. The painting probably dates from the mid-1740's. The 1775 *Painting* is a heroine queen; not a turbaned studio worker but a crowned ruler, mistress of a public charge. In the earlier picture the Art stares directly, ravishingly and enigmatically, into the viewer's eyes and inactively holds her brushes. In the 1775 picture her travelling glance is observing just beside us, and she is painting just out of our sight. Or perhaps she has just finished the painting we see. The pose of the first picture is exactly that of the 1772 *Self-portrait;* the pose of the second is near that of the late Uffizi *Self-portrait* except that in it Batoni looks the viewer straight in the eye.

71

John Woodyeare
Canvas: 97.9 x 71.7 cm.: $38\frac{1}{2}$ x $28\frac{1}{4}$ inches
Private Collection, U.S.A.

DATE: 1750. The painting is inscribed on the back (of the relining canvas, presumably reproducing an inscription on the original canvas): *Sig. r Pompeio Pinx / Rome 1750*. There is also a 19th-century tag giving the sitter's name and dates and as "*Painted at Rome 1750 by Pompeio Bartolomeo*" [*sic*: Batoni's middle name was Girolamo].

EX COLL.:London, Christie's, Property of a Gentleman, 13 Feb. 1925, bought M. Rothschild; do. 24 June 1960, lot 81; Sotheby's 7 Dec. 1960, lot 74, as from the Blomfield of Gorleston and Lycett Green collections, bought J. H. Weitzner.

REF.: Ernst Emmerling, *Pompeo Batoni sein Leben und Werk*, Darmstadt, 1932, p. 108, no. 57 (as 1750 and with Max Rothschild, the London dealer).

Woodyeare (1728–1812) came from Crookhill near Doncaster and was in Rome during 1750–51 with his tutor, Dr. William Drake, a young antiquary and philologist. Both are shown, Drake playing a flute and Woodyeare listening stupidly, while two other country gentlemen on the Grand Tour play the cello and hold their ears, in a caricature painted by Joshua Reynolds in Rome, 1751 (Museum of Art, Rhode Island School of Design). The costume Woodyeare wears in the Batoni is that of the King's Own Third Hussars, then recently founded by George II. There is even a portrait of a Scotch general who brought his tartan uniform to Rome to be painted by Batoni, out-of-doors, before the Colosseum, waving his sword.

Early Batoni portraits of Grand Tourists from Britain and elsewhere—of which the artist produces few before 1754, almost none before 1750—usually do not yet show an interior with Roman chair, table and antiquity, or an exterior with an antiquity and something of a view—specialities for which Batoni was to be famous. The more severe earlier portraits are especially fine for their greater attention to the quality of design and detail. Few have plain backgrounds and it is quite possible that the surroundings (a pilaster; a pilaster and a curtain; a stone table and pilaster; an antiquity, chair, and table; outdoor architecture and a view; hunting landscape near Viterbo—all of which Batoni had tried by 1752) were entirely the choice of the sitter. Batoni, at least through prints, would have known exactly what was going on elsewhere in Europe, all of which—including figures out-of-doors with antiquities—had also been long known and practiced in Rome.

Imposing, and by nature violent, Benefial followed a difficult career. The son of a Frenchman and a Roman, born in Trastevere, he was the pupil of Lamberti, an artist who prided himself on the purity of his Bolognese artistic pedigree, from the mighty Carracci to his own master, Cignani. Benefial first exhibited in 1703, without success. Soon afterwards, he became a ghost painter for several academically respectable and not very proficient painters (c. 1710–52). The Academy was closed to him until artists like Batoni, half his age, entered (1741); but, in or out, Benefial was constantly fighting the Academy or its prominent members. Nevertheless, he is not excluded from the intelligent patronage of Clement XI, the first pope of the century, and received honors as one of the painters of the Lateran *Prophets* (1716–18): one, that is, of a very careful roll call of Rome's best painters. From the mid-teens, and especially from 1720, Benefial was very productive, working usually under his own name for out-of-town commissions and under another (Germisoni first; Evangelisti from c. 1725) for his public works in Rome.

72

Pyramus and Thisbe

Canvas: 218 x 135 cm.; $85\frac{7}{8}$ x $53\frac{1}{8}$ inches

Galleria Nazionale d'Arte Antica, Rome (on deposit at the Chamber of Deputies)

Not signed

DATE: (1730's or early 1740's)

EX COLL.: Count Niccola Soderini (for whom painted? noticed in his collection 1764); Torolonia Bequest 1892.

VERSIONS: One of a pair, the other a *Hercules and Omphale* (for which a drawing in the Cleveland Museum of Art, Anonymous, TR 11136/63).

REF.: Ponfredi, *op. cit.*, p. 15; *Piccola Guida Artistica del Palazzo di Montecitorio*, Rome, n.d. (ca. 1930?), ill; Giuliano Briganti, *Il Palazzo di Montecitorio*, Rome, 1967, p. 397, pl 3.

This is one of a pair of large paintings probably painted for Benefial's main patron, Count Niccola Soderini (1691–1779). The Count was a prominent government official who owned many works by Benefial, gave the artist a large pension when he was old and blind, and saw to his academic rights and the publication of his biography.

The painting strongly recalls the 17th-century Bolognese masters and, especially, Guido Reni. It is worth comparing the Benefial with Guido's famous *St. Michael* and his *Lucretia* (then the most famous part of the Spada collection in Rome) or other of his heroines.

The scene from the classical story may be remembered from Shakespeare: the *putto* in the tree extinguishes his torch as a symbol of death; Cupid looks pleasantly if ironically at the viewer; and the heroine falls on her dead lover's sword. The painting probably dates from the 1730's or early 1740's.

Benefial's paintings are full of observation, brilliant technical verve, and a toughness and strength that are most unusual—sometimes brutal and sometimes visionary. He was really too impressive for the 18th century; and the older and more doctrinaire he became, the harder he was to bear, and the bolder his work became. A born reformer and "loner," Benefial was also one of the most intensely beautiful of 18th-century painters. Only Batoni and Mengs were even to equal him in Rome, either for his power or his beauty; but neither Mengs nor Batoni were to surpass Benefial's sublime naturalness.

REF.: G. B. Ponfredi to Count Niccola Soderini, XX July 1764, in Bottari, *Raccolta di Lettere* . . . , Rome, 1766, vol. V, pp. 1–23; F. Noack, "Marco Benefial, Ein Bahnbrecker des Klassizismus," *Monat, für Kunstw.*, XII, 1919, pp. 125–9; G. Falcidia, "Nuove Proposte per Marco Benefial Ritrattista," *Paragone*, 195, May 1966, pp. 60–68; Anthony M. Clark, "Manner and Methods of Benefial," *Paragone*, 199, September 1966, pp. 21–33.

73

Adam and Eve Adoring Their Creator
Canvas: 142 x 133 cm.; 55 $\frac{7}{8}$ x 52 $\frac{3}{8}$ inches
Galleria Nazionale d'Arte Antica, Rome
Not signed

DATE: (late 1750's)

EX COLL.: Soderini collection (?); Torlonia Bequest, 1892.

VERSIONS: One of a pair, the other an *Expulsion from Eden*, for which there is a very late drawing in Berlin (20555).

REF.: Unpublished.

This is a late (1750's) Benefial, and may come, as others of the Torlonia paintings (including the above), from the collection of the artist's patron. The primitive grandeur, power, and innocence of the late Benefial is strikingly apparent.

Born in Rome of Genoese parents, Bianchi is the great pupil and continuator of Luti (*q.v.*). He is seldom less fine than his master and, at his best, he strikes a new direction which is lithe, grand and poetic. While he may never have seen Genoa, there is nevertheless a Genoese personality—with the typical nerves and fanciness—in most of his paintings, whether gouache landscapes rather slavishly imitative of Luti, or the more noble, monumental works. The exhibit is not a demonstration of this point; the most obvious painting of Bianchi's career, the St. Peter's altarpiece, certainly is, being as if by a nephew of Piola in Rome. Despite the long subservience to Luti (1710–24), Bianchi never forgot that he had studied with the most famous of Genoese painters in Rome, G. B. Gaulli (died 1709), and yet almost never gives any superficial evidence of it.

Known as an independent artistic personality in Rome from the winter of 1715 (when he sold Lord Burlington a Maratti), there are no certain public works until the death of Luti (1724), although one wonders when the decorations of Vigna Cavalieri or the *Rest on the Flight* in S. Maria delle Fornaci, opposite the equally superb Benefial painting (and under a Pietri fresco done by the end of 1716), were done. On Luti's death Bianchi was living in the Palazzo di Spagna and aiding in the shipment of Queen Christina's marbles which the Odescalchi had just sold to the king of Spain. Rather numerous Spanish commissions would now have been begun; of these the most important are lost, but recently a signed model for one of the king's mosaic *Muses* was sold at the Dorotheum, Vienna (1 Dec. 1964, lot 10). By this time the advice and designs with which Bianchi supplied the leading Roman sculptors would also have begun.

Bianchi was a man of parts, was probably the head of Luti's studio, a dealer, and something of an entrepreneur. Ratti says he was so studious that he did little in the way of painting, and he is certainly as rare as the 1771 Potsdam catalogue said he was—and as singularly beautiful. Since the 1964 *Paragone* article, few important Bianchis have emerged. The Blairquhan "Cavallucci" *Adoration* is an exquisite work of the mid-1720's; the large "Masuccis" from the Merenda collection, Forli, are Bianchis (*St. Sebastian; Woman of Samaria; Woman Taken in Adultery; Holy Family; Pietà*), some left unfinished and completed by others (see Clark, 1967). Much more will be found with use of the excellent Ratti biography.

74

Mercury and Argus
Canvas: 186.1 x 130.3 cm.; $73\frac{1}{2}$ x $51\frac{1}{4}$ inches
Museo de Arte de Ponce (Luis A. Ferré Foundation), Puerto Rico
Not signed

EX COLL.: Painted for Pietro Mancini, Complementario de'Banchi, Rome (Ratti); with the artist's heirs (d'Argenville); Paul Ganz, New York (lent to the Minneapolis Institute of Arts, 1962, the Metropolitan Museum of Art, 1965)

REF.: A. J. Dezallier d'Argenville, *Supplement à l'abrégedé de la vie des plus fameux peintures*, Paris, 1752, II, p. 80; C. G. Ratti, *Delle vite de'pittori, scultori, ed architetti Genovese*, II, Genoa, 1769, p. 298; Anthony M. Clark, "Introduction to Pietro Bianchi," *Paragone*, 169, 1964, p. 44 and plate 58; Henry Hawley, *Neo-classicism: Style and Motive*, exhibition catalogue, Cleveland Museum of Art, 1964, no. 9, ill.; *Antiques*, September 1964, p. 316, ill.

Bianchi's biographer lists two other paintings done for Head Clerk Mancini, a small pair of St. Onuphrius and St. Mary of Egypt. The author of the 1964 *Paragone* article (who identified the present picture) recently found this pair in the collection of the descendants of Bernini, Rome. The position of the pictures in his biographies imply they are late.

Bianchi was an outdoors man and a famous landscape painter. His five landscape backgrounds in the three Mancini pictures are by a pupil of Luti, certainly, but also show sympathy with nature as seen by Locatelli (*q.v.*). The shepherd Argus's hut, shown behind the cow Io, is of an architecture still to be found in the haystacks of the Campagna, and extends back to Roman prehistory. Local and ancient meanings of the hut and cow would have been known to Bianchi and are above and beyond the Greek fable he is telling.

REF.: C. G. Ratti, *Delle Vite de'Pittori, Scultori, ed Architetti Genovesi*, vol. II, Genoa, 1969, pp. 292–305; Anthony M. Clark, "Introduction to Pietro Bianchi," *Paragone*, 169, 1964, pp. 42–47; do., p. 114; *Jahrbuch der Staatlichen Kunstsammlungen in Baden-Württemberg*, IV. 1967, p. 114.

Born in Antwerp, he came to Rome (by 1688) via Paris, Lyons, and Turin with his older brother, the painter of animals, Pieter ("Stendardo"). After a trip to Sicily and Malta the brothers set up in Rome and became successful. Orizzonte remained all his life but Stendardo returned to Antwerp in 1693, by which time the younger brother could add animals to his views perfectly in the style of the departed. The leading artists of fifty years—including Maratti, Chiari, Garzi, Luti, Panini, and Batoni—were willing to contribute human figures to his highly successful and expansive landscapes; one prominent painter, Costanzi (see the picture entry), obviously had a working arrangement with the Fleming.

There is a gentle development in the artist's work, with few surprises in the voluminous production. He began as a careful imitator of Gaspard Poussin under more shining rococo (or Bacicciesque) skies and with intentions more charmingly intelligent than grand and noble. His palette is strong and rich, becoming more radiant with age; the brush emboldens each year towards a final sparkling pointillism. The aged Orizzonte is perhaps the greatest appreciator of the rich atmosphere and wet but very encouraging light of the Roman spring. His nickname says something about this.

Only country folk (his seem at the same time biblical, classical and contemporary) inhabit his landscapes, which are all of the same season of the year, and all both Arcadian and parklike. Enough shrewdly and genially observed details ("*le vedute più vaghe . . . gli aspetti più giocondi e rare*" as his biographer, Pascoli, put it) were used to see the scene convincingly. But there are few more topographically realistic landscapes than that shown here. Each of Orizzonte's landscapes were constructed and brought to life by a delicate observer who might be called the Canaletto of the *idea* of the Roman Campagna.

REF.: Andrea Busiri-Vici, in *Dizionario Biografica degli Italiani*, X. Rome 1968, pp. 793–795; do., van Bloemen (in preparation).

75

Fantasy View of Rome
Canvas: 125.8 x 175.3 cm.; 49½ x 69 inches.
Not signed
DATE: *c.* 1741–1743

Wildenstein and Company, New York

EX COLL.: Private Collection, England.

This is one of three paintings in the same ownership, all of the same size, including a pair formerly called Dughet and another called (1957) Millet, identified by the cataloguer. The exhibited picture is a fantasy with real elements (including the top of the Colosseum over the roofs of the church of Santi Quattro Coronati) and a geography accurate only in the pleasures of its parklike arrangements. The other two pictures show different sides and weathers of a mountain somewhat similar in outline to the Soracte-like peak in the present picture, but with a natural bridge.

A similar but more simple mountain is in a 1739 Orizzonte with the same city view (ex coll. Caraceni, Rome), and the fountain's mask occurs in a view towards the Colosseum (ex coll. Rospigliosi, Rome, G. F. N. photo. E. 38494). A drawing from nature in Edinburgh (D 1734) shows a similar fountain in the Roman Campagna and Orizzonte may also be recalling the fountain which dominated the Roman Forum when still the Campo Vaccino.

The figures in the painting are by Placido Costanzi (1701–59; see *Paragone*, 139, 161, pp. 50–58; do., 219, pp. 39–54) or by the landscapist himself using Costanzi's specifications. Technically the painting corresponds to the Quirinal Coffee House decorations by Orizzonte and Costanzi (1741–43).

Roman-born of a French father, and a prodigy, Cades was a pupil of Domenico Corvi (*q.v.*) and took prizes in the Roman Academy's contests of 1762 and 1766. At sixteen, Corvi expelled Cades for independence: he had already established himself as a mature artist, an established draughtsman and a copyist. At eighteen Cades sent an altarpiece to a church in Turin and at twenty had begun his first public commission in Rome. Controversial, but a virtuoso of great facility and brilliant talent, Cades was well known by 1770 and, by 1780, one of the several artists most evident to visiting foreigners as well as to Romans. Cades only entered the Roman Academy in 1786; "official" opinion was never to be entirely favorable to his work; and, this has probably more to do with the advanced nature of his work rather than the machinations of such enemies as his former master.

The earliest Cades paintings show interest in the Mannerists of the 16th century, and even the "Primitives" of the centuries before the 16th. His artistic positions are often very vehement, and at the time Sergel, Barry, Abildgaard, and Fuseli arrived in Rome, the young Cades was beginning to practice exactly their kind of romantic, neoclassical, passionate, and bombastic style. The currency of his ideas through Cades's innumerable and very successful drawings can be guessed. The chameleon virtuoso of extraordinary sensibility is not, however, best to be found within the richness and abnormal variety of the drawings but in the paintings. These were promoted by the more liberal and independent Roman princes—Senator Rezzonico (Palazzo Senatorio, Sala di Musica, 1779), Borghese (Villa Borghese, 1787), Chigi Palazzo Chigi, 1780–86); Ariccia (1789–90), etc.—and by foreigners, especially the most wealthy groups, the Russians (for example, a good burden of work for Catherine the Great, 1784, etc.) and the British (for example, the high altar of Wardour Castle, 1775–87).

76

Self-Portrait
Canvas: 65 x 50 cm.; $25\frac{5}{8}$ x $19\frac{5}{8}$ inches
Accademia Nazionale di San Luca, Rome

DATE: The painting is inscribed: *Giuseppe Cades Pitt. re Rom.o 1786*. The date is certainly that of Cades's academic election but may have nothing to do with the creation of the self-portrait. His apparent age is 30 (i.e., c. 1780)

EX COLL.: The *Decreti* of the Academy's meetings under 1800 (p. 92v.), 23 November, note that Cades's widow gave the portrait of her late husband *"per collocarlo nella nostra galleria."*

REF.: Italo Faldi, catalogue, *Mostra di Antichi Dipinti Restaurati delle Raccolte Accademiche*, Rome, 1968, noted p. 21.

Cades, in this ravishing work (unfinished and probably cut down on all sides) shows himself with his own long hair and in a Renaissance costume. Another portrait which entered the Academy's collections more recently shows Cades at sixteen or younger. There are no other sure portraits in oil by the artist now known although Bombelli's 1786 engraving of a cleric and his 1790 engraving of a famous singer (after full-dress Cades portraits) show that they existed, as do a number of portrait drawings. There are drawn caricatures, too, including a self-portrait as a dandy with the artist's in-law, Piroli the engraver (private collection).

GIVSEPPE CADES Pitt.re Rom.   1786

The quality, intelligence, and originality of the paintings is usually very high, if sometimes uneven. While Cades learnt from Corvi, Mengs, Batoni, and his rival, Cavallucci, his ability to re-create the virtues of the early Guercino, of Strozzi, and of some obvious Renaissance masters is also apparent, as is the fact that his use of all this is highly personal. Extremely Roman in his superficial grandeur and absolute elegance, Cades was nevertheless able to make and use artistic friends outside of the city; Domenico Tiepolo and the Gandolfi are known and assimilated, at least by the time of Cades's trip to their cities (1788 c.).

REF.: Hermann Voss, *Die Malerei des Barock in Rom*, Berlin 1924, pp. 432, 665–6; Anthony M. Clark, "An Introduction to the Drawings of Giuseppe Cades," *Master Drawings*, 11, 1, 1964, pp. 18–26.

77

The Virgin and Child Waited upon by Angels
Canvas: 70.6 x 91.5 cm.; $27\frac{3}{4}$ x 36 inches
Collection Dr. Franco Di Castro, Rome
Not signed

DATE: c. 1790

EX COLL.: Villa Chigi, Castelfusano, with an old Chigi inventory no. 46 on the reverse.

VERSIONS: S. Nicolò da Tolentino, Rome; left wall of third chapel left; a large vertical version signed and dated 1790 with S. Joseph and only the standing angel.

REF.: Unpublished.

The magnificent scenes from Tasso in Palazzo Chigi at Ariccia, the Pompeian mezzanine rooms (also done in association with Liborio Coccetti) which once decorated the Palazzo Chigi in Rome, and this devotional painting are the main commissions to Cades either from the eccentric and intellectual Prince Sigismondo Chigi (1736–93; exiled from Rome, 1790) or from his son don Agostino III.

The painting surely shows the effects of Cades's trip to Venice by way of Emilia, Parma, etc. (c. 1780), and an emulation of the early Titian and the early Guercino is noticeable. As many Roman artists of radical artistic and social opinions in the closing years of the 18th century, Cades was a deeply devout Christian; exaggeratedly so, if Canova's *Journal* is to be believed. As to be expected in Italy, the large part of Cades's *oeuvre* is religious. His many altarpieces are beginning to be rediscovered, and a few spectacular *Madonnas* have recently been found; besides the exhibit, a *Madonna and Child* (as sketchily painted as the *Self-portrait*) is in a Chicago private collection, and a small *Madonna and Child* in the style of Guercino is in the Manning collection, Long Island. A drawing in the vein of the exhibit, but for an *Adoration of the Shepherds*, is at Lisbon (no. 2125) and there are a number of drawings (Lisbon and Madrid) for a monumental, vertical *Holy Family* with a preaching Child.

This delicate and lovely artist was born in Sermoneta and throughout his life was closely connected to the ancient Gaetani family, the Dukes of Sermoneta. The ceilings and decorations for the principal Gaetani palaces at Rome and elsewhere (1776–1787; the sketches and most of the ceilings still exist in the Campo Marzio palaces) are among his best works.

Although taught by Stefano Pozzi and Gaetano Lapis, both distinguished and individual Roman artists, it was surely Mengs and Batoni who impressed Cavallucci, the latter by his beauty and professionalism; the former, profoundly. Cavallucci is far more childlike and more lyrical than Mengs, less severe; and, if Mengs possessed Raphael's intellectual qualities, Cavallucci may be said to have possessed in full measure Raphael's loveliness. His style is ethereal and fascinating, that of an indrawn and delicate human being, cultivated, and with very considerable intellectual stamina.

Cavallucci was thought to be the finest painter in Rome after the death of Batoni (1787); his only serious rivals were Angelica Kauffmann and Cades (*q.v.*). The last decade of the artist's life was not the happiest moment for foreign patronage in Italy but it must be apparent that Cavallucci had a direct effect upon European painting: Girodet, Prud'hon, and others found him sympathetic and obviously took him very seriously when they saw his work in Rome.

REF.: G. B. Vinci, *Elogio Storico del Celebre Pittore Antonio Cavallucci da Sermonetta*, Rome, 1795; G. G. de Rossi, *Vita di Antonio Cavallucci da Sermoneta*, Venice, 1796; Hermann Voss, *Die Malerei des Barock in Rom*, Berlin, 1924, pp. 431, 664, 665; V. Golzio, "Il Pittore Antonio Cavallucci di Sermonetta," *Capitolium*, 1945, pp. 17–21; articles by S. Röttgen and A. M. Clark are promised to *Palatino* and *The Art Quarterly*.

78

St. Benedict Joseph Labre
Canvas: 58 x 46 cm.: 22¾ x 18⅛ inches
Private collection, U.S.A.
Not signed

EX COLL.: British private collection (1968)

VERSIONS: The present picture may possibly be that in the 1927 catalogue of Ballnastragh House, Ireland (29 x 24 inches). In 1870, in the saint's via de' Cerociferi rooms, a Cavallucci of the saint done from life while praying is noted; in 1894 the Massarenti collection, Rome, contained a Cavallucci of the saint (50 x 27 cm.). A. Mecenate made a lithograph of the present composition (to below waist, without beads) *Romae apud Post Causae* (i.e., 1850). Other compositions are attributed to Cavallucci; of these the Corsini picture and its reversed and varied brothers are probably replicas of a missing picture by Lapiccola (engraved by Barbazza, 1788). The source of all likenesses is a death mask or the Cunego 1783 engraving after an *ad vivum* portrait of 1771. At some later point a posthumous Cavallucci likeness of the saint was in a prominent enough circumstance to give its name to rival likenesses. An anonymous period likeness of the saint (rather like the Cavallucci but with the hair brushed back on the forehead) is at Frederiksborg Castle, Denmark, as a portrait of Zoega the archaeologist. Most portraits of the saint since the 1840's show as much knowledge of the Cavallucci composition as any other. The present example is slightly unfinished and shows preparation for use as an oval, perhaps as the *sottoquadro* of an altar.

REF.: Unpublished.

Benedict Joseph Labre (1748–83) was a young Frenchman who was unable to become a Trappist monk because of ill-health and instead became a mendicant pilgrim. After several years of begging on foot to most of the religious shrines of Spain, Switzerland, Germany, France, and Italy he came to rest in Rome, a fixture of the churches by day and the gutters or flophouses by night. A starving Christ's fool, in filthy rags, entirely devoted to prayer and self-abnegation, the saint might (except for the last quality) be the hippies' patron saint, complete with hair and beads. His death from exhaustion and starvation at Easter, 1783, caused a popular outpouring of intense devotion. His exemplary love for all created things, including his own lice, terrible self-mortifications, and the immediate intensity of his cult are what one might not expect in Rome of the rich autumn of the century. Inspiring and severe questions were already being asked at the beginning of the century's last quarter; at the end of that quarter Rome was a bankrupt republic whose ruler the Pope was dying in France.

Carlo Maratti (1625–1713) is the great artist in Rome at the end of the 17th century, summarizing in himself Rome's Renaissance and Baroque tradition, able to represent classical rigor and yet also creative disorder, the most famous painter in Europe. Maratti's later paintings were painted or copied by such assistants as Giuseppe Passeri (1654–1714, the most lovely and poetic), Niccolò Berrettoni (1637–82, the most vigorous and sensual), Andrea Procaccini (1671–1734, faithful and refined) and Chiari. These artists, the leading so-called *Maratteschi*, were important painters in their own right, but were also Maratti studio executives, and a potent squadron for the promotion of Maratti's noble but rather impersonal art. Of the four named (there are others almost as important) only Chiari was to be considered a successor, in the sense of replacement, of Maratti.

In the last decades of Maratti's life the artistic position of the *Maratteschi* (and even the old master himself) had departed from Maratti's grandiloquent High Baroque style and had developed more intimate, early rococo positions. In 1700 Luti (*q.v.*) could claim to be a pupil of Maratti, and Passeri had long been a dashing artist living in an entirely new world (the one the French would soon "invent"). Chiari from his earliest pictures is what can only be called a proto-rococo painter: he miniaturized, domesticated and made more "juicy" the familiar Maratti idiom.

Chiari is first recorded as an independent painter in 1675, had German patronage in 1685, by which time his first important public work was visible. From 1685, almost yearly commissions of great distinction follow to the artist's death. The 18th century began with the Colonna *Olympus* fresco of 1700; the lost Villa Torri work (where Luti and Passeri also painted); small semiprecious pictures as those in Palazzo Spada; and the huge 1708 designs (continuing the nave of Maratti's) for the Cappella della Presentazione, St. Peter's. The masterpiece may be considered the nave ceiling of S. Clemente (1715) which puts the official Roman language in fervid 18th-century terms. This is the Roman rococo. In 1725 the nave ceiling of S. Cecilia in Trastevere was done by Conca (*q.v.*), the most advanced rococo artist in Rome. It is only slightly busier than Chiari's ceiling, not different.

REF.: Bernhard Kerber, "Giuseppe Bernardino Chiari," *The Art Bulletin*, vol. L. 1968, pp. 75–86.

79

Susannah and The Elders
Canvas. 67.4 x 81.6 cm.; 26½ x 32⅛ inches
The Walters Art Gallery, Baltimore
Not signed

DATE: (c. 1712?)

EX COLL.: Don Marcello Massarenti, Rome (1897, no. 216); Henry Walters, Baltimore (1902).

REF.: Edouard van Esbroeck, *Catalogue du Musée . . . au Palais Accoramboni* (Massarenti), Rome, 1897; Ann Gabhart, "Baroque Painting in Italy, 1600–1750," *The Bulletin of the Walters Art Gallery*, Oct. 1969, vol. 22, no. 1, ill.; *do.* "Baroque in Baltimore," *Apollo*, Oct. 1969; handlist to *Italian Baroque Painting*, *1600–1750*, Walters Art Gallery, Sept. 30–Nov. 9, 1969, no. 9 (as attributed to Chiari by F. Zeri); ill., *The Connoisseur*, Jan. 1970, p. 69, fig. 1.

Another version of this painting, vertical in format, and with landscape and fountain variations, was lot 37 (as Italian, 18th-century anonymous; 48½ x 39 inches) at Sotheby, London auction, 26 May 1965. The colorprint after Chiari by J. C. Le Blon is said to resemble the Sotheby picture, and this might yield a date of c. 1712 (the composition being related to the dated *Samaritana* at Bückeburg Castle). There is technical resemblance to the 1708 Spada pictures. The composition is traditional and appeals to Maratti (the late *Bathsheba* belonging to Prince Liechtenstein and the Chiari-like variant in the Modestini collection, New York); and to the basic composition Annibale Carracci engraved, which is a familiar property of his school, and which was known to Rubens (Alte Pinacotek, Munich, 317).

Lanzi said that few could compare with Corvi for anatomy, perspective, and design, and, one is tempted to add, draughtsmanship; here is one of the best and strongest artists of the century, whose virtues (and vices) are those of a typically sturdy Roman countryman.

The young Corvi came to Rome from Viterbo, probably in 1736; in 1744 the official *Offices* for Holy Week bore a frontispiece after his design; in 1750 he won a first prize at the Academy of St. Luke (to which he was elected, while working in Viterbo, in Nov. 1756); in 1753 he lived in the next apartment to Raphael Mengs (then a young, rising painter) with Casanova the painter and brother of the lover (known as a pupil of Mengs). Probably from this period is the careful *S. Michael* in S. Trinità dei Monti which combines the brilliance of Corvi's frescoes in the Gonfalone church at Viterbo (1756) and thorough knowledge of Batoni.

Corvi's paintings are not uncommon in Roman churches (S. Marcello, by 1765; S. Caterina in via Giulia; S. Marco, the unpublished pair of nave frescoes nearest the high altar, c. 1760; S. Maria Maggiore, replacements in Capella Paolina; S. Salvatore in Lauro); and in Roman palaces (Vatican, top loggia; Doria; Borghese and Casino Borghese; Barberini; Altieri; Conservatori, cartoons for the tapestries), are plentiful in Viterbo and thereabouts and in the papal states. Works for the Piedmont, Tuscany, Lombardy, and the Veneto are important and mostly date from the 1780's; the extraordinary group of paintings in the cathedral of Solothurn are from the 1770's. Some work for Prince Yusupov who, while Russian minister at Turin, commissioned all the leading Romans, still exists in the U.S.S.R.; the Hapsburg ambassador and virtual ruler at Milan, Count Firmian's commissions, also from the 1780's, are missing, as are some of those of the Prince Luigi Gonzaga. There are also portraits: the fine group of self-portraits; the portrait of his pupil, David Allan (Edinburgh); the Capodimonte full-length of Cardinal Ruffo (as Mengs); the Hartford *Cardinal York* (early, as Ceccarini): the Gatchina full-length of Victor Amadeus III; and a few others, mostly of foreigners.

Many Corvis are yet to be discovered (or rediscovered) and almost none of the above are published (and the above survey does not include such *caches* as are at Cantelupo). Mengs, always a fine critic, had *grandissimo stima* only for two Roman painters beside himself: Batoni and Corvi.

REF.: Anthony M. Clark, "Neo-classicism and the Roman Portrait," *Apollo*, LXXVIII, 21, November, 1963, pp. 357 and 358; Italo Faldi, *Pittori Viterbese di Cinque Secoli*, forthcoming, to contain the only useful study of Corvi.

80

Allegory of Painting
Canvas: 60.5 x 73.4 cm.; $23\frac{3}{4}$ x $28\frac{7}{8}$ inches
The Walters Art Gallery, Baltimore
Not signed

DATE: 1764

EX COLL.: Don Marcello Massarenti, Rome (1902); Henry Walters, Baltimore.

REF.: Edouard van Esbroeck, *Catalogue du Musée . . . au Palais Accoramboni* (Massarenti), Rome, 1897, no. 526 (as Mengs); *Schede Vesme*, vol. 1, Turin, 1963, p. 368.

The books of the Turinese royal household for 1764 give a payment for 180 Lira to Corvi for a "half-length representing [the Art of] Painting in the act of doing her own portrait, to serve in the royal apartments." The apparent date of the Baltimore painting—which was first identified by the cataloguer and of which no other versions are known—is correct for the document and the size and price are right for this kind of decoration. Many Turinese royal paintings were lost in Napoleonic times or sold soon after.

In pictures of the 1760's Corvi's toughness and strong surfaces are moderated by an exacting refinement and attractive elegance. One can still see the soft graces and references to the Carracci (the venerated founders of the Bolognese, Roman, and, indeed, European tradition), which Corvi's teacher Francesco Mancini had promoted. The colors are rather like Mancini too, but they ring more strongly. There is a very personal version in the Corvi of what Mengs and Batoni were doing in the 1760's; what was being done during a decade characterized in Rome by great formal elegance—ornamental, strong but artificial. After this decade Corvi's work becomes more frank, vigorous to the point of bombast, and dismissive of lingering rococo graces. In his self-portraits, not a Venus but a Hercules is the type of the subject, a tough hero also seen from below, drawing a Hercules. Similarly, the portrait of David Allan shown drawing from a cast of the *Borghese Gladiator*, his painting arm repeating the punching arm of the statue.

Ghezzi is remembered as a caricaturist who, in cursory but realistic drawings, recorded everyone worth recording in Rome, however famous or humble, from the 'teens of the century to his death. Baroque caricaturists from Bernini and Mola to Zanetti and Tiepolo were inhumanly savage and pretended to a primitive drawing style. Ghezzi was less savage and often less funny (only the early brush caricatures are regularly meant to be hilarious); his intent is that of a brilliant portraitist and recorder, and not that of a passionate satirist. He is a beautifully organized recorder of accurate facial and physical detail. These details are arranged stiffly and they may be intrinsically cruel; nevertheless Ghezzi's caricature drawings are simply unidealized, pragmatic likenesses recorded with wit; and, that may have been their full intention.

P. L. Ghezzi was Maratti's godson. His father was a prominent artist and the brains of the Roman Academy. Like Giuseppe Ghezzi, Pierleone was a member of the Roman court, holding various offices as curator of the pope's painting collections, papal decorative painter, etc. He received honors from the pope and other princes, including patents of nobility. He was an important collector (drawings); an archeologist; and an amateur musician who held one of the better of many private musical academies in Rome (as home concerts were then called); and he was a prominent painter.

The politics, meaning, and personality of this personage do not obviously depend on the familiar but rather misconstrued caricatures. Ghezzi is interesting as a painter, as the cataloguer has attempted to show (1963). At least as talented as his father (who was a fine and important Roman master who died old in 1721) Pierleone is of varied quality, or—it might be more just to say, until we know quite a lot more about his rich and complicated career—of varied intentions. And we will not understand Pierleone until the paintings of Giuseppe are known and understood.

Since 1963 a number of paintings have been found that show the younger Ghezzi to be a more exciting painter than had been thought. Beside the exhibit may be cited the portrait of Clement XI; the restored altars of S. Salvatore in Lauro; the S. Luca *Allegory;* the fabulous *Diogenes* recently on the Roman auction block; Fogg Art Museum 1968.105, a genre scene; the Bob Jones *Jacob at the Well* attributed to Burrini (for which the drawing has been found by Everett Fahy in the British Museum attributed to Mola); Glasgow 3233, an anonymous *Venus and Aeneas* which is perhaps Ghezzi's most magnificent painting. The most important "new" portrait is the *Goldoni Group* in the Rhode Island School of Design Museum, attributed to Baldrighi. Except the altarpieces, none

of these has been previously published.

REF.: Mattia Loret, "Pier Leone Ghezzi," *Capitolium*, XI, June 1935, pp. 291–307; Anthony M. Clark, "Pierleone Ghezzi's Portraits," *Paragone*, 165, 1963, pp. 11–21; Didier Bodart, "Designi Giovanile. . . . ," *Palatino*, XI, 2, 1967, pp. 141–154; Francesco Negri Arnoldi, "Il Ritratto di Clemente XI di Pierleone Ghezzi," *Paragone*, 239, 1970, pp. 67–73.

8 1

Paolo de Matteis
Canvas: 39.5 x 29.2 cm.; $15\frac{1}{2}$ x $11\frac{1}{2}$ inches
Private Collection, U.S.A.
Inscribed on the paper tacked to the wall: *Ritratto di Paolo | De Matteis, Pittore | Napoletano, fatto dà | Me, Cau Ghezzi, il di 8 | Marzo 1726, il quale | fù Scolaro di Luca | Giordano Pittore Na | poletano.*

EX COLL.: New York art market, 1969 (as Hogarth).

VERSIONS: Biblioteca Vaticana, Cod. Ottoboniana, 3115, 111 (drawing; dated 1725 and inscribed that the artist returned to Naples); London, Sir Anthony Blunt (drawing, $13\frac{3}{8}$ x $8\frac{3}{4}$ inches; autograph and uninscribed version of the last.)

Excluding such curious *genre* as Cardinal Orsini (later Benedict XIII) miraculously surviving an earthquake, a votive oil in S. Philip Neri's rooms in Rome engraved by Frezza, the *trompe l'oeil* portraiture at Frascati and Torre in Pietra, this small unpublished oil painting seems to be the only caricature that is painted, and not just drawn in ink. There are two drawings showing less developed versions of the composition; these are in Ghezzi's typical pen caricature style, and one is dated to 1725.

Paolo de Matteis (*q.v.*) is known to have been in Rome between 1724 and his death in 1728; the Vatican caricature places him in Rome in 1725, and Ghezzi's remembered or immediate inscriptions are usually trustworthy. The drawings presumably precede the oil, which bears a stated date of creation, 1726.

De Matteis is shown at his easel with a cane but without the spectacles he wears in the drawings. He is painting an allegory of a naked woman standing on a wheel while crowning a resting mule or ass. Fortune is usually shown naked with a wheel, but Ghezzi was probably also aware of Punishment, standing on her wheel in the famous *Iconologia* of Ripa. The style of the painting is that of Ghezzi's more public commissions of the period, which is the most fertile moment for Ghezzi's paintings and drawings.

A native of Rome and a pupil of Trevisani (*fide* Mariette who met the artist in Paris with his friend Vernet in 1770), the strong influences on the young artist were, obviously, Conca, Giaquinto, and Subleyras. Lanzi said his frescoes were famous and his work in oils was mostly feeble, praising his compositions, Roman design, and pleasing color. He was successful from the late 1730's in Rome with frescoes for the Hospital of S. Spirito (1742), S. Trinità in via Condotti (1746–49), the Augustinian Refectory in via Ripetta, and the Biblioteca Corsiniana (an unpublished ceiling fresco, *Time Revealing Truth*). In 1739 Guglielmi painted an altarpiece for Prague Cathedral and then enjoyed the patronage of Alessandro Cardinal Albani.

By 1753 Guglielmi became one of the most important Italian itinerant painters: 1753, Dresden; 1754, Vienna; spring, 1756, Rome; 1759, Turin; 1761–62, Vienna and Schönbrunn; 1762—January, 1763, Rome; 1763 and 1764, Berlin; 1765, Augsburg and Vienna; 1765 and 1766, Turin; 1766 and 1767, Augsburg; 1770's St. Petersburg with trips to Paris, Warsaw, and Augsburg. He died in 1773 in St. Petersburg. The work in the University of Vienna (1755) and Schönbrunn (1760–61) and for the Palazzo Reale and Chiablese (1765) are deservedly well known. The Schönbrunn frescoes, full of remarkable, brilliant observations of contemporary life, rival Tiepolo's Würzburg frescoes of a decade before. They are obviously intended to do so and a comparison is not really harmful to either artist. It is interesting that Guglielmi avoided overall Baroque compositional schemes and adopted a more natural optics. He is not full of proud muscle and manner like Tiepolo and if he bores us it is only with beautiful and lucid sights arranged genially—if monotonously—as the eye would find them. His figures splendidly illustrate Metastasio and Casanova (and contain the only interesting visual record of 18th-century warfare); Tiepolo's figures are the magnificent unreality of a wicked genius (as the cruel artist shows himself next to his son, Domenico, in the staircase fresco). Guglielmi had a good lump of reason and a clear mind, a sense of nobility, and clear affinities with the French Enlightenment.

82

Philosophy

Canvas: 35.7 x 82.6 cm.; 14 x 32½ inches.

Coll. Art Gallery of Ontario, Toronto, Purchase, Walter C. Laidlaw Endowment, 1963

Not signed

DATE: 1755

EX COLL.: Hazlitt Gallery, London, *Baroque and Rococo Painting and Oil Sketches*, May, 1962, no. 18, ill. pl. 3b (as 18th-century Piedmontese).

VERSIONS: The fresco for which this is a study is in the great hall of the Alte Universität, Vienna, and shows one of the Four Faculties (the others in the various ceilings are Theology, Medicine, and Law) on a program created by the Roman who was court poet at Vienna, Metastasio. The drawing for the composition is in the Albertina (Vitzthum, pl. 63).

REF.: W. Vitzthum, "Guglielmi e Metastasio," *Paragone*, 165, 1963, p. 655, pl. 61.

REF.: R. Longhi, "Il Goya Romano e 'la Cultura di via Condotti'," *Paragone*, 53, 1954, pp. 28–39; S. Béguin, "Esquisses et Dessins inédits de Gregorio Guglielmi," *Paragone*, 63, 1955, pp. 10–13 (pp. 14–18, "Guglielmi e Falconet"); A. Griseri, "Gregorio Guglielmi a Torino," *Paragone*, 69, 1955, pp. 29–38; do., "Due 'Ritratti' Romani: un Giaquinto e un Guglielmi," *Paragone*, 83, 1956, pp. 61–66; W. Vitzthum, "Guglielmi e Metastasio," *Paragone*, 65, 1963, pp. 65–71; Klára Garas, *Gregorio Guglielmi, 1714–73*, *Acta Historiae Artium*, Budapest, 1964, vol. lx, pp. 269–294.

By 1724 Nicola Pio reported that the work of this Roman-born landscapist was in continual demand from Romans and foreigners and that he had decorated rooms in Palazzo Ruspoli (see the entry on Amorosi) and in the Cancelleria for Cardinal Ottoboni, as well as landscapes on canvas for Alessandro Cardinal Albani. Younger than van Bloemen, he became about as celebrated but not as successful. He briefly rivalled—with his almost exclusively rural scenes—Panini's more cosmopolitan success.

Locatelli's style begins in Salvator Rosa and tends to remain rough, autumnal and dry (doubtless from the Attic salt Lanzi noticed). He is a wistful and sympathetically candid artist, and the extremely delicate but rather fatuous poetry of Filippo Lauri was another influence, transformed by Locatelli into something more rough, brawny, and male. He is said to have had two styles, knowledge of which has not been recovered. It may be that his early work was more imitative of Salvator Rosa (and the formative sources of Panini) and the mature work more deeply indebted to van Bloemen. There appears to be the presence in Locatelli's presumed *oeuvre* of some paintings by van Bloemen as well as what may be the early period of his friend Aneri and other extraneous matter. Locatelli can best be compared with the older van Bloemen, than whom he is more realistic, introspective, clear in his use of light, and rounded in his sense of form. Unlike van Bloemen he almost always does his own figures, using a woebegone type, which is unusually sympathetic and sometimes exquisite. He specialized in rustic genre scenes as well as less populated landscapes and in these scenes he was imitated by his pupil Monaldi, who had none of Locatelli's sense of tension and interplay between landscape and human figure (which van Bloemen, mechanically modernizing Gaspard Poussin, also missed).

A number of trivial but fine interior decorations remain from Locatelli (for example the doors in Palazzo Corsini, Rome). His landscapes, less easily digestible than van Bloemen's, were not in sufficient demand when he died young and poor.

REF.: A. Busiri-Vici, "La Prima maniera di Andrea Locatelli," *Palatino*, XI, 4, October–December, 1967, pp. 366–374; M. M. Mosco, "Les Trois Manières d'Andrae Locatelli," *Revue de L'Art*, 7, 1970, pp. 19–39.

83

Pastoral Scene
Canvas: 81.3 x 118.2 cm.; 32 x 46½ inches
Collection Professor Giuliano Briganti, Rome
Not signed

No chronology has been suggested for Locatelli founded on facts or convincing theories. It may be that the Pannini-like Locatellis (one of which dates from 1725) copy the early Panini or are an independent development from similar sources. It may be that the earliest genre scenes looked like Miel and only later were transformed in kind and by use of human images derived from Luti, Panini and Costanzi. It may be that an early use of Salvator and Lauri was later greatly moderated by imitation of van Bloemen. Or it may have been the smaller genre pictures of whatever kind (Soldiers and Ruins, Country Inns, and decorative Arcadian snapshots), those that *do* look like potboilers, to which Lanzi referred as one of the two styles Locatelli professed. The other style, then, would contain the present picture which joins several other large and deeply memorable Locatellis. The earliest might be a landscape with figures of Tobias and the Angel added by Corrado Giaquinto (c. 1725–30) in a private collection in London; next, the famous *Washerwoman* and then the present picture; the large landscape owned by the late Arthur Appleby, London; and finally the *Trout Fishermen at Tivoli* recently on the Boston market attributed to Jacob de Heusch. The growth of ability and grandeur and the progress of maturity are apparent in all these superb, serious pictures.

In a wild valley in mountains somewhere south of Rome rather disconsolate peasant fishermen discuss their catch. In all his best pictures Locatelli's humans are battered but real participants in nature. They do not loiter in an easy park as in van Bloemen. Even though they may be pensioners of a certain defeat they are inhabitants with accurate tasks. In most of the best pictures there is a concern with water, even though water is the rarest presence in Locatelli's pictures.

A pupil of Gabbiani (*q.v.*) in his native Florence, and thus in the academic Tuscan descent from Pietro da Cortona by way of the careful Ciro Ferri, Luti came to Rome in 1691. Ferri had died in 1689 and Luti, with Tuscan protection, set about teaching himself. Respectful of the most famous painter in Rome, Luti and his fellow pupils showed their work to Maratti and otherwise sought relations with the Academy (prized from 1691, member in 1694, president in 1720). By 1698 Luti may have had his own drawing academy (i.e., he offered a model and a little instruction). The early pictures (the 1691 *Cain* and its pendant *Banquet in the House of Simon*, both at Kedleston) are dark pictures, possibly influenced by Brandi (d. 1691) and the secretary of the Roman Academy, Giuseppe Ghezzi, but also very Tuscan and very original. There is soon a fascination with old masters such as Barocci, an appreciation of such moderns as Maratti (style) and Gaulli (color), and these sources, within Luti's personal intensity and ornamental Florentine draughtsmanship, help create his familiar style, full-fledged by 1700.

Luti was a lovely and careful artist; and he is rather a rare one. His originality was appreciated, but not without reservations and misunderstanding. Highly intelligent, solitary, melancholy, and sickly, Luti was a great collector of drawings and prints, and not overfond of the act of painting—at which he was more brilliant and easy than any Roman colleague of the day. His honors and his fame in Europe were considerable; his relationships with the French are important for the history of European painting, and lack useful examination. His perfectly considered paintings, his drawings of exquisite quality (including the famous pastels usually of nubile girls and boys), are one of the finest and most formative achievements of the century.

REF.: Vittorio Moschini, "Benedetto Luti," *L'Arte*, **XXVI**, 1923, pp. 89–114; Francis H. Dowley, "Some Drawings by Benedetto Luti," *The Art Bulletin*, **XLIV**, 3, Sept. 1962, pp. 219–236.

84

Christ and the Woman of Samaria
Copper: 37 x 30 cm.; 14½ x 11⅞ inches
Private Collection, U.S.A.
Not signed
DATE: 1715–1720

EX. COLL.: Said to be from Benjamin West's collection; inscribed in ink on the verso *Mr. West* and an illegible catalogue number or price (*W* 18 ?); Arthur Appleby, London 1960.

REF.: Unpublished

The view behind the Samaritan (who might be considered a typical Trasteverina) is characteristic of the edges of Rome looking toward the Alban Hills, or could be a view in those hills. The composition is rather traditional and derives generally from the Carracci; a painting by Conca, aware of this particular example, was sold at Florence by Sotheby, 18 October 1969, lot 132. Luti's chronology is not yet certainly known but the painting may be dated 1715–20.

A Roman, Masucci studied first with Andrea Procaccini, one of Maratti's best pupils (1671–1734, left Rome for Spain, 1720) and then with Maratti himself (died 1713). This last fact was emphasized throughout Masucci's career by the artist himself. Giuseppe Chiari (*q.v.*) laid claim to the authority—and to the explicit leadership of the Roman school—that the heritage of Marrati gave. At least at the time of Chiari's death (1727) Masucci claimed to be Maratti's successor with an open implication of his leadership of Roman painters. Despite the obvious preeminence of older painters—such as Trevisani and Luti, both in this exhibition—and the popularity of painters nearer Masucci's own age—such as Conca (*q.v.*) and Francesco Mancini (see the entry on Mariano Rossi), Masucci was almost able to get away with his pretensions. His brains and talents were great enough and the heritage of Maratti (*and* Carracci *and* Raphael—which were also implied by Maratti's name) valuable enough.

Born in Rome, Masucci won academic prizes in 1706 and 1707, exhibited first about 1715 and a year or so later had on permanent view the earliest of his delicate, profoundly sound and lucid church altarpieces. At the same time in the second decade he was known for portraits, at first in chalk and then in oil; the early portraits are vigorous and intense, somewhat less cold than they later became. With excellent support from the Roman aristocracy and court, by 1722 (when Masucci was elected to the Academy and painted the portrait of the new pope) the young Roman had become the fashionable portrait painter for the Grand Tourist. On Chiari's death (1727) Masucci was known in the city and abroad as the preëminent serious painter in Italy. A decade later he was the President of the Roman Academy.

By 1740 (the intention is clear by the 1720's) Masucci's style was clear, gracious, and (according to Mariette)cold; the order and lucidity of his painting is extraordinary, beautiful, and prophetic of actual neoclassical painting of sixty years later. Masucci purified the High Baroque style of Rome and returned it to its sources. That the effort was excessively academic can be argued and even shown—in the disastrous comparison of the portraits of Pope Benedict XIV (1740) by Subleyras (Versailles) and Masucci (Academy of St. Luke, Rome). Masucci lost the contest, but in the last decade of his life another intelligent Frenchman, the artist Cochin, listed him with Mancini, Giaquinto, and Batoni as the best Roman painters. Cochin ignored Subleyras (who died in 1750) and Benefial, Pannini, Conca (all in this exhibition), and also such only slightly lesser lights as Costanzi, Mazzanti, Pozzi, and Zoboli.

85

The Annunciation
Canvas: 98.5 x 68.3 cm.; 38¾ x 26⅞ inches
The Minneapolis Institute of Arts, The Ethel Morrison van Derlip Fund
Not signed

DATE: C. 1742

EX COLL.: Palazzo Parisani Ascoli Piceno (from c. 1750); Hayward, London (October 16, 1816 by label of Baker's Depository, Kensington, London); Old Masters Gallery, London, 1962 (as Maratti).

REF.: *The Minneapolis Institute of Arts Calendar*, December, 1962; Anthony M. Clark, *op. cit.*, 1967, p. 264, fig. 16; *Catalogue of European Paintings in The Minneapolis Institute of Arts*, forthcoming.

A *modello* for the painting in mosaic in the chapel of S. Roque, Lisbon, which was commissioned for John V of Portugal and made in Rome (1742–47, the paintings; to 1752 the mosaics). The models for this and Masucci's other two pictures for the chapel were sent at the end of 1742; the full-size oil paintings (which may exist in Portugal) were shown in 1747. There are a number of large and poorer versions, especially of the popular *Annunciation* composition, by which Masucci obviously profited. The present painting closely resembles the life-size Valenti picture in the Copenhagean Gallery (1748) and could be considered its preparation, whether or not predating Cardinal Valenti's composition.

REF.: Anthony M. Clark, "A Conclusion and a Reformation of the Roman Baroque," *Essays in the History of Art Presented to Rudolf Wittkower*, London, 1967, pp. 259–264.

The most celebrated and popular of the 18th-century land-scapists in the century itself, Giampaolo was born in Piacenza and came to Rome in 1711. He trained with scenographic architects and landscape painters and in the drawing academy of Luti. In 1716 the Earl of Oxford bought from Andrew Hay "a fine piece of architecture by Chisolfi (Ghisolfi) and a companion by Sr. Jo. Pabolo"; in 1724 his pictures were in London auctions. During these early years he established himself as an architect (Cardinal Valenti's villa; the chapel in S. Maria della Scala, 1728) and a fresco decorator of Roman palaces that demanded architecture, views, and even allegorical figures. These decorations include work at Villa Patrizi (1719–25), Seminario Romano (1721–22), Palazzo Alberoni (1722?), Palazzo Quirinale (the first decoration, 1722, Stanza dei Mezzanini), Palazzo de Carolis (1720), Palazzo Albani (1720 commissioned by a Cardinal Albani; noted in the 1765 Roisecco Roman guide; reported as "Galleria Famosamente Dipinta" in Pio's biography of P. P. Cennini, who added the floral decoration here and in Quirinal I). In 1719 Panini was in the exclusive Roman Academy (he was President 1754–55) very well backed not only by Roman grandees but by the French art colony. Panini married the sister of Vleughels, director of the French Academy in Rome (1727–37), where he taught perspective, and whose parent organization in Paris elected him to membership (1732).

By 1729 the "*pittore di prospettive parmigiano*" was working hard for the cardinal-protectors of France and Spain, producing vast firework machines and other temporary architectural decorations, and painting magnificent records of them. A large number of real views of Rome (in a more worldly version of Vanvitelli) and of "*vedute ideate e rovine*" (fantasy views of Roman ruins) was also being produced for both native and foreign patrons. His production was, and remained, tremendous and, while quality does not exactly suffer (for Panini is both a very eloquent and very polished painter), one finds studio reproductions in large number. Canvas painting in spate also ended the fresco decorations.

Panini's success tended to sweep other Roman landscape painters under the rug; his influence on the French dominates most of the century, from Vernet through the pupils of Robert. While the sources of Panini (the Bibieni, Vanvitelli, and other Lowlanders, Ghisolfi, Orlandi, etc.) are fairly obvious and entirely to be expected perhaps his assurance with French taste is not; one wonders if Panini learned a great deal from the French or taught them all, figure painters included, a very

great amount more. Luti, Conca, Locatelli, Vanvitelli, all may have taught Panini something, but at some point he must have looked at Rome with the eyes of a very grand French dancing master.

REF.: F. Arisi, *Gian Paolo Panini*, Piacenza, 1961; E. Brunetti, "Il Panini e la monographia di F. Arisi," *Arte antica e moderna*, 26, 1964, pp. 167–199.

86

Piazza Farnese Decorated for the Dauphin's Marriage
Canvas: 117 x 239 cm.; 46 x 90$\frac{1}{8}$ inches
Collection Walter P. Chrysler, Jr., New York
Not signed
DATE: 1745

EX COLL.: Earl Howe, Penn House, Amersham, Buckshire (1930); Christie's 7 December 1933, Lot 49; David Koetser, New York (1953).

VERSIONS: Drawings for the painting rest in the British Museum (see bibliography, p. 38).

REF.: *Painting from the Collection of Walter P. Chrysler*, Portland 1956, pp. 37–38, no. 49, ill. p. 97 (with bibliography before Arisi); F. Arisi, *Gian Paolo Panini*, Piacenza, 1961, pp. 177–178.

The seventy-foot-high fireworks machine with the Marriage of Love and Hymen in Minerva's Temple was set up in Piazza Farnese to celebrate the first marriage of the Dauphin, commissioned by the French minister, Abbé de Canillac. The festival took place in June, 1745. Panini designed the architecture and one of his sons drew the machine for an engraving of May 1745. The fireworks lasted three hours after sunset and were seen by twenty cardinals. In the painting perhaps it is Panini directing the scurrying workers by the monument, right of center, with left fist raised.

The painting has added excitement in not being fully achieved, although fully sketched out. Panini painted the *Theatre Festival for the Dauphin's Second Marriage*, 1747 (Louvre), as well.

87

The Palatine, the Arch of Constantine, the Colosseum (a)
The Campo Vaccino from below the Capitoline to the Arch of Titus (b)

Canvas: a) 74 x 134.7 cm.; 29⅛ x 53 inches. b) 73.4 x 134.7 cm.; 28⅞ x 53 inches

The Detroit Institute of Arts. Gift of Mr. and Mrs. Edgar B. Whitcomb

SIGNED AND DATED: a) *I. P. Panini/Roma 1735;* b) the same

VERSIONS: dated variants or versions of b) from 1725–1750 see Arisi, p. 147.

EX COLL.: Duke of Norfolk, Beech-Hill, Yorkshire.

REF.: F. Arisi, *Gian Paolo Panini*, Piacenza, 1961, a.) p. 148, no. 99; b.) p. 147, no. 98.

The Roman Forum, still a cow pasture in the 18th century, was one of the most popular views of the ancient city; the Detroit view is perhaps the finest of many Paninis. Another, dated 1747, in the Walters Art Gallery, Baltimore, moves farther back and shows the monuments at the left, except the Arch of Septimius Severus. The Walters' view is mated to a more usual viewpoint of the Colosseum, from the other side of the Arch of Constantine. The Detroit pair instead follow a good part of the ancient Sacred Way.

Both views are faithful but definitely *"vedute ideate."* The Colosseum landscape has borrowed several famous antiquities and arranged them appetizingly about. The pair of pictures are also contrasted: one is meant to be more urban, the other more rural.

Michele Rocca 1666–ca. 1730(?)

This rococo artist was born in Parma and came to Rome (*c.* 1682) to study and flourish. He studied with Ciro Ferri, the fine academic administrator of the style of Pietro da Cortona. According to Nicola Pio (1724), Rocca studied Raphael in Rome and, long and steadily, Correggio, for whose work he returned home. Pio also notes that the landscapes in Rocca's pictures were praised. There is no sign of Raphael in Rocca's works, but there is of Ciro's, the decorative qualities of which he stirs into mannered rococo preciosity. Rocca is plainly a colleague of Sagrestani in Florence (the Parmesan worked in Tuscany), and must have known Pellegrini (Rocca was reputedly in Venice in 1715, and is even said to have died there in 1751, a surprisingly similar date). The first phase of the Italian and Parisian rococo style must have been well known to Rocca, and influenced by him. Rocca clearly remains a Parmesan painter (and was called Parmigianino, thus explaining the odd attribution on some 18th-century drawings), but for decades was an established Roman painter. Fond of 16th-century Mannerism (not least for its classicism and eroticism), Rocca was a rococo Cortonesque painter; his work parallels the more ambitious Conca (*q.v.*), his palette transformed by the bright blond and acid colors of his exact contemporary Luti, and of Pellegrini.

His Roman career includes a large high altar (1698 in the Maddalena) and election to the Academy (1719). While the numerous semiprecious cabinet pictures are familiar, and dominate the memory of Rocca's work, the fact of a few other large commissions for French and Italian churches ought not to be forgotten, as also the circulation of Rocca's pictures throughout Europe, including Paris.

Rocca is last noted (as far as the cataloguer has ever found) in Rome in 1727, when he holds office in the Academy, and has a painting belonging to the Academy engraved. Perhaps this was the year he left Rome; Rocca is dead well before 1740, as far as the yearly lists of the Roman academicians knew.

REF.: Hermann Voss, "Michele Rocca," *Zeitschrift für Bildende Kunst*, 1921, April, p. 69s; G. V. Castelnovi, "Settecento Minore," *Studies in Art History Dedicated to William E. Suida* . . . , New York, 1959, pp. 333–337.

88

The Toilet of Venus
Canvas: 49.7 x 36.9 cm.; 19½ x 14½ inches
Museum of Art, Rhode Island School of Design
Not signed
DATE: (*c.* 1710)

EX COLL.: Boston, 1915; French private collection; Julius H. Weitzner, New York (1955).

VERSIONS: see below

REF.: A. M. Clark, "A Mythological Subject by Rocca," *Museum Notes, Bulletin of Rhode Island School of Design*, 42, November, 1955, p. 13, ill. on cover.

It is possible, but unlikely, that this may be the slightly wider version published in Voss in 1921 as in the Brunsvik collection, Vienna, with a pendant *Venus and Adonis*. A much wider version was in a Berlin auction, 24 February 1930, no. 37, with a pendant *Choice of Paris*. Rocca often repeated his pictures even to a number of autograph versions (the studio seems to have been small), and the same composition can survive from his early, brown period to such a painting as this, which is unlikely before the 'teens of the century. The unusually fine Providence example, in size, kind of subject, and number of figures, is typical of the majority of Rocca's cabinet pictures.

Born in Sciacca, Sicily, he was a pupil of Benefial in Rome where he then settled. He was elected in 1766 to the Academy of St. Luke together with the distinguished Calabrian painter, Lapiccola (c. 1730–90); in 1770–71 in Turin on the recommendation of Alessandro Cardinal Albani (the patron; also the protector of Savoy) doing frescoes in the Royal Palace and other work for the Turinese king. From 1754 he produced religious works for his home town; by his return to Rome in September, 1771, he was a well-known painter. There are altarpieces in a number of Roman churches (from 1765), commissions for Prince Yusupov and other Northerners (1780's), frescoes for the Royal Palace at Caserta and elsewhere (1790's). The artist died in Rome, where he could be seen in plentiful works; he spent some of the difficult period at the end of the century in Sicily (1800, frescoes in Palermo Cathedral, etc.)

Mariano Rossi's style is that of a typical South Italian artist—with the usual dominating knowledge of Sebastiano Conca—who has formed himself in Rome. The influence of Benefial (by whom Rossi probably was influenced only in the situation of a drawing academy) shows itself in preference for classical subjects and cognizance of the great Bolognese-Roman academic tradition. There is more influence, indeed, of the superb painter, Francesco Mancini (1679-1758; impossible to represent in the present exhibition) who was trained by the Bolognese and adapted their style (especially that of Cignani) to Roman and original needs. Rossi's grace and lovely handling, and something of his broad drawing, comes from Mancini. His intense dramatic ability is Southern and his own; it is cooled and increased by intellectual courage from Benefial, the aloof and fresh tones of Giaquinto, something of Conca's inventiveness and depth, as well as by Mancini's most impressive personality. Mariano Rossi is always recognizable: he survives his stylistic parentage.

REF.: G. Veneto, *Elogio Biografico di Mariano Rossi*, Palermo, 1864; M. M. Tropea, *Mariano Rossi e i suoi affreschi di genere storiche*, Catania, 1908; G. Ceci and F. Noack, Entry, Thieme-Becker, *Künstler Lexikon*, Leipzig, 1935, XXIX, pp. 67–68.

88a

Camillus Defeating Brennus; Romulus Before Jupiter Pleading for Rome; Allegorical Scenes of Time Discovering Truth; Fame; Abundance; and The Power of Rome; etc.
Ceiling fresco (Illustrated by photograph in the exhibition)
Entrance Hall, Casino of the Villa Borghese, Rome.

DATE: 1782

M. Furius Camillus was one of the greatest Roman generals, and after his defeat of the Gauls he was hailed as the second Romulus. The part of the fresco one sees on entering the Casino shows Camillus lifting the occupation of Rome by the Gauls (389 B.C.) having picked a quarrel with the leader of the Gauls and driven them out—as Plutarch describes.

The entire ceiling is one of the largest 18th-century decorations in Rome, and one of the most spirited and best. After Giuseppe Chiari's 1700 *Olympus* in Palazzo Colonna there were constant Roman palace (and church) decorations by native-born and foreign painters, but on a more modest scale. The frescoes and ceilings in the downtown Palazzo Borghese (1770's) and at the Villa (1780's) are not large in format because of admiration of the 17th-century Baroque, but to fill the large 17th-century spaces. For these two important Borghese sets of commissions the leading Roman painters (including Cades, Corvi, and Pecheux, to mention the few included in this exhibition) were carefully selected and assigned suitable tasks. Mariano Rossi worked in both buildings; the Villa Salone fresco is his masterpiece.

The principal frescoed works before and after in his career are in the following places: Royal Palace, Turin (1771); Biblioteca Classense, Ravenna (1779); Royal Palace, Caserta (c. 1795); and the apse of Palermo Cathedral (1800). There are also Rossi frescoes in Roman and other churches, and his career in Rome as a fresco painter was surpassed or equalled only by Tommaso Conca (Sebastiano's nephew), Cristoforo Unterberger, Bernardo Nocchi, Ermenegildo Constantini, Coccetti, and Giani (the latter three were fresco specialists). Of these Rossi is superficially the least "advanced," the Villa Borghese fresco is part of a revival of interest in Baroque grandiloquence at the very moment when pure neoclassicism is meant to be arriving and taking over. From the time of Maratti's supposed restraining of the High Roman Baroque a century before, there have been a number of energetically *barochetto* moments in Roman painting, even into the mid-19th century. These moments, in a sense, might also be called the only 18th-century rococo moments of a city with a very weighty and perpetually rather Baroque style.

Trevisani was born in Capo d'Istria, studied in Venice (where his younger brother remained as a painter), and arrived in Rome c. 1678. In Venice he studied with Zanchi, the Late Baroque master who, with Loth and Langetti, managed a *scuola tenebrosa*, a dark, dramatic manner which Trevisani brought with him to Rome, as well as some compositional usage of the great 16th-century decorator, Veronese. Strong drama and chiaroscuro were supported by Roman sources as well: Caravaggio, Lanfranco (whose cool and blond colors also appealed to Trevisani), Giacinto Brandi, and the Dutch *bamboccianti* or genre painters (it was not by accident that the Grand Duke of Tuscany commissioned of Trevisani the 1682 Jan Miel portrait).

In Rome the Venetian artist was constantly employed by two cardinals, Flavio Chigi (1682–92) and Pietro Ottoboni. The latter was the great Roman patron of the period (d. 1740); Trevisani lived on a large monthly pension from him and had his studio in the cardinal's palace. A smaller pension was to support Sebastiano Conca (*q.v.*), but Trevisani was the great Ottoboni artist, producing the cardinal's portraits (from the great 1689 portrait at Bowes Castle through the cardinal's life, at least into the 1720's), and a large number of the fine pictures hanging in his palace (including the pendant of the van der Werff, a surely significant commission for another aspect of Trevisani's art).

Ottoboni was not alone in his attention. Although at least until 1715 Maratti and his pupils were the official Roman painters, from 1696 (the S. Silvestro in Capite chapel), Trevisani was the most important and popular. His intense and rich style, with its intimacies and swooning ecstasies, was revolutionary, and perfectly apropos to the new needs of the rising century. Trevisani had an immediate influence upon the Italian schools as well as the German and French. Commissions also went in large numbers to Great Britain, not least his portraits: such full-lengths as Lord Leicester at Holkham and the Duke of Beaufort at Badminton are sourcebooks for British portraits. Altarpieces, subject pictures, and portraits went in a steady stream to Portugal, Spain, and the Italian and German cities. To the Roman clerics and princes Trevisani was the most popular and notable of artists. Totally independent of the academy, his pictures were in every Roman collection, in many Roman churches, and, the crowning honor, in St. Peter's.

One year older than Solimena (*q.v.*), and as long-lived, Trevisani's European importance is comparable. He was a more advanced painter than Solimena; and the rococo style depends absolutely upon him.

89

Apelles Painting Campaspe
Canvas: 72.5 x 58.6 cm.; $28\frac{1}{2}$ x 23 inches
Norton Simon Foundation
Not signed

DATE. C. 1725

EX COLL.: Julius Böhler, Munich 1959; Morris I. Kaplan, Chicago; Sotheby, London, sale 12 June 1968, no. 99.

REF.: "Mostra del Settecento a Roma", Rome, 1959, no. 620, p. 219, pl. 6 "La Peinture Italienne au XVIIIe Siécle," Paris, 1960–61, no. 160, pl. 12.

This exquisite small painting was first identified by the late Hermann Voss, and ought to be compared to the other painting in this exhibition of the same genial scene from the life of Alexander the Great by the much younger G.-B. Tiepolo (cat. no. 43). The two pictures are probably not far apart in date (c. 1725). Both have something to do with Veronese, although Trevisani forgets most of his Venetian heritage in his Roman archeological and academic correctness. Trevisani is more intense, realistic, rococo and "French" (unlike Tiepolo, he influenced the French). Tiepolo's Apelles' portrait of Campaspe is as if of, or by, Rosalba, a light and brilliant decoration. Trevisani's portrait of Campaspe shows her as Diana, a strongly drawn Diana appropriate to Veronese, to Correggio, and yet other admired old masters. Tiepolo's world is sloppy, idle-minded, and rather dyspeptic; Trevisani's miniscule, sensual, and ecstatic.

REF.: D. Gioseffe, "L'Opera di Francesco Trevisani," *Pagine Istriane*, 4, 1950, pp. 107–116; A. Griseri, "Francesco Trevisani in Arcadia," *Paragone*, 153, 1962, pp. 28–37; Frank R. Di Federico, unpublished Ph.D. dissertation, New York University, The Institute of Fine Arts; and "Francesco Trevisani . . . in S. Silvestro in Capite," forthcoming in *The Art Bulletin*.

"*Il pittore della Roma moderna*" was born in a small town near Utrecht in the part of Holland most affected by recent Italian culture and especially that of Rome. The pupil of a noted local landscapist, Mathias Withoos (who had done the usual training in Italy), the young man entered the Dutch artist's organization in Rome, the 'Bent, in 1675, probably having arrived the year before. He worked as a draughtsman with the famous engineer (and his compatriot) Cornelis Meyer on projects dealing with the navigation of the Tiber and Rome's obelisks as meridians. By 1681 the great Colonna family had become patrons of his landscape paintings (by his death they owned about 100 landscapes); his style was formed and his success insured.

In 1690 he visited Lombardy and Florence and in late 1694 went to Bologna and thence to Verona and Venice, returning to Rome at least by 1696. Under the patronage of the Duke of Medinaceli, Spanish Viceroy of Naples, Vanvitelli moved there in 1700, and in Naples his son, the famous architect Luigi (who was to build Caserta), was born. By 1701 the Viceroy's great plans had collapsed and Vanvitelli returned to Rome with many Neapolitan views of a brilliance and heritage not to be seen or used there until Joli's visit (*c.* 1762–77) or the work of Fabris and Hackert, true inheritors of Vanvitelli at the end of the century.

Vanvitelli in the new century was an academic success as well as a commercial one and was elected to the Roman academy in 1711. His eyesight began to fail soon after ("*Gasparo degli Occhiali*" because of the huge glasses for his cataracts), and his last pictures from his last decade are worked more cursively and were seen with only a single eye.

What he had seen changed European painting. Venetian 18th-century landscape painting depends upon Vanvitelli, through his influence on Carlevaris (who would have known his work 1685–90) and Canaletto (probably in Rome, 1719). His style was also spread far beyond Rome through grand tourists for whom his concrete evocations of their favorite places were most desirable. Vanvitelli's crystalline transparency, unpretentiousness and objectivity were especially sympathetic to the British. He helped to determine the 18th-century's anti-rococo, realist position which was to be rigorous in style yet—as Professor Briganti puts it—"not for that reason neoclassical."

REF.: Giuliano Briganti, *Gaspar van Wittel*, Rome, 1966.

90

View of Marino Towards Villa Colonna and the Alban Mount
Canvas: 72 x 96 cm.: $28\frac{3}{8}$ x $37\frac{3}{4}$ inches
Galleria Palatina, Palazzo Pitti, Florence
INSCRIBED AND DATED: *G. V. W. 1719*

EX. COLL.: bears lower right the crowned column of the Colonna, Rome, for whom it was painted.

VERSIONS: Colonna collection, Rome, nos. 434, 555 (larger and smaller versions). The preparatory drawing exists in the Biblioteca Vittorio Emmanuel, Rome.

REF.: Giuliano Briganti, *Gaspar van Wittel*, Rome, 1966, pp. 106, 107, 220, and no. 132.

For such a painting as this Vanvitelli made a patient, perspectively sound drawing the size of the painting, while seated at a good viewpoint. This drawing would be used as the basis of all further replicas large (as this) or small (as the little gouaches), with very small changes to update the human and sometimes, architectural figures. The fixed viewpoint, the optical care and perspective authority, the rationality and direct simplicity of style are typical. Vanvitelli writes (1707) of his patience and care. What is especially notable is his modesty before a world seen with crystalline clarity and naïve love. His patience and care render the views as if first seen through very good new glasses. There is no more "personality" in Vanvitelli's paintings than in Claude's, yet they are equally recognizable.

The Dutchman's natural heir in Rome is the Fleming, van Lint, whose own heir was Anesi. These artists are also faithful, pure, and—in van Lint's case—microscopic. The grand imaginative style in Roman landscape was to be supported not by Vanivitelli's ravishing optics and reportage but by van Bloemen (and his mediocre heir, Busiri), as well as Locatelli and Panini. Of these only Locatelli appears to admire Vanvitelli's realism and Panini his knowledge of perspective and of good viewpoints. But Panini is quite willing to repaint, so to speak, Vanvitelli's painting in his own more worldly style.

69.

Naples and Southern Italy

by Michael Stoughton

Born in Castellamare, where it is speculated that he received his earliest artistic training, Bonito later went to Naples where he studied with Solimena (*q.v.*). His success as a pupil resulted in his first commission, two pictures for S. Maria Maggiore (Pietrasanta) in 1730. He was responsible for decoration in other churches (sacristy of Monte di Pietà, 1742; S. Chiara, 1752 (destroyed); Ss. Giovanni e Teresa, all in Naples; ex-Duomo, 1787, Vico Equense) and in the royal palaces at Caserta and Naples. His fame, however, rests today as it did during his own lifetime primarily on his genre pictures (often confused with Traversi, *q.v.*) and portraits, praised by de Dominici for their lifelike quality and the naturalness of the sitters' gestures. By the early 1740's, Bonito had come to the attention of King Charles VII who commissioned portraits of the visiting ambassadors of Turkey and Tripoli (Palazzo Reale, Naples). So convincing was the likeness of the latter, as de Dominici relates in an amusing anecdote, that the sitter went to inspect the back of the canvas, convinced that his very soul had been taken by the artist. In 1751, Bonito was nominated *pittore di camera* of the King and the next year he was elected to membership in the Accademia di S. Luca, Rome. He became the director of the Naples drawing academy in 1755, the year of its creation by the King, and later was placed in charge of the royal tapestry works. Bonito's pictures do not have the facile elegance of the rococo, but are characterized, nonetheless, by a decorative and spirited vivacity.

REF.: G. Cosenza, "Giuseppe Bonito," *Napoli nobilissima*, XI, 1902, pp. 81–87, 103–109, 122–127, 154–158, 180–188; XII, 1903, pp. 12–14; R. Longhi, "Di Gaspare Traversi," *Vita artistica*, 1927, pp. 145 ff. (reprinted in *Saggi e ricerche 1925–1928*, Florence, 1967, pp. 189 ff.); F. Bologna and G. Doria, *Mostra del ritratto storico napolitano*, Naples, 1954; R. Mesuret, "Le portrait de Charles IV par Giuseppe Bonito," *La revue des arts*, VI, 1956, pp. 116–117.

91

Portrait of Ferdinand IV
Canvas: 247 x 140 cm.; $97\frac{1}{4}$ x $55\frac{1}{8}$ inches
Gripsholm Castle, Sweden
Inscribed on verso: *Giuseppe Bonito Pittore di camera di Ferdinando IV Re delle due Sicilie ec:ec: Direttore*
DATE: 1784?

EX COLL.: In Gripsholm Castle before 1790.

REF.: P. Napoli-Signorelli, "Gli artisti napoletani della seconda metà del secolo XVIII," *Napoli nobilissima*, II, 1922, p. 150; *Katalog över Statens Porträttsamling på Gripsholm*, I, Stockholm, 1951, p. 96.

Several portraits by Bonito of Ferdinand IV of Naples (III of Sicily, and later I of the Two Sicilies) are known to have existed (S. Anna di Palazzo, 1768; inventory of possessions of the last Bonito heir, 1803; Ss. Giovanni e Teresa). The present example is part of a series of portraits of the rulers of Europe ordered by Gustaf III to decorate a room in Gripsholm Castle. All are full length and the patron himself is included. Gustaf was in Naples in 1784 and the picture was presumably commissioned at that time. The portrait is perhaps the one described by Napoli-Signorelli in his manuscript completed in 1798: "*Singolarmente merita ogni applauso la gran tela del meraviglioso ritratto al vivo di Ferdinando IV in piedi in maestosa posizione vestito coll'abito dell'ordine costantiniano.*" Ferdinand (1751–1825) succeeded his father, Charles VII, as King of Naples when the latter ascended the Spanish throne as Charles III in 1759. After the regency presided over by Tanucci, Ferdinand reached his majority in 1767. He married Maria Carolina, sister of Marie Antoinette, and, with his consort, maintained a position of power through purposeful corruption and terror.

It is only because de Caro signed certain of his pictures that his existence is known at all. His birth and death dates are unknown; there are no biographical notices about him, and he is not mentioned in Neapolitan literature. It seems logical to assume that de Caro was lost among the many followers of Solimena (*q.v.*) and not given particular notice by his contemporaries. Voss has published the only study on de Caro and brings together a nucleus of the artist's authentic paintings: the *Judith* in the exhibition and its pendant; *Expulsion of Heliodorus*, Pinacoteca Nazionale, Bologna; *Education of the Virgin* and *Adoration of the Magi*, Museum, Solothurn; *Judith and Holofernes*, on the market in 1965, Lucerne; five scenes from the Old Testament, private collection, Contù (Como); and the *Adoration of the Magi* and *Holy Family*, on the market in 1957, Florence. All of these examples are small in scale, suggesting that they were used as private devotional pieces, and not one is dated.

De Caro adopts the lightness and grace of Solimena, for the most part without his usual chiaroscuro modelling, and the capricious drapery patterns associated with de Mura (*q.v*). In certain cases, there is also a reference to Traversi's kind of specific facial type.

REF.: H. Voss, "Lorenzo de Caro, Ein vergessener Maler des Neapler Settecento," *Festschrift Ulrich Middeldorf*, Berlin, 1968, pp. 494–96.

92

Judith Showing the Head of Holofernes
Canvas: 76 x 50.5 cm.; $29\frac{7}{8}$ x $19\frac{3}{4}$ inches
Collection Maestro Francesco Molinari Pradelli, Bologna
Not signed
DATE: *c.* 1750?

EX COLL.: R. Bastianelli Collection, Rome, 1922.

REF.: *Mostra della pittura italiana del sei e settecento in Palazzo Pitti*, Florence, 1922; Voss, p. 494.

The pendant to *Judith Showing the Head of Holofernes* (*Conversion of Saul*, also Molinari Pradelli Collection) is signed. The present example bears a close relationship to the Contù picture of the same subject (Voss, plate CCX, fig. 7). The format of the latter is horizontal and the composition is reversed. However, drapery configurations, positions assumed by the figures (especially Judith, her maid, and the horseman), as well as the general arrangement of the turreted fortress, rocky outcrop and distant battle scene are very similar in both works. The use of a figure, cut off by the frame, in the immediate foreground is common in de Caro's pictures and Judith is characteristic of his elegant female type.

Born in Gaeta and trained under Solimena (*q.v.*) in Naples, Conca settled in Rome in 1707 and remained there, except for brief periods (notably 1731–32, when he produced the huge fresco in the Ospedale, Siena), until his return to Naples and Gaeta in 1752. He achieved the greatest prominence of any of his Neapolitan compatriots in Rome, where he found immediate success. Conca was patronized by Clement XI (1700–21), Benedict XIII (1724–30), various important Cardinals, as well as Roman and foreign patrons throughout Europe. With the success of the S. Cecilia in Trastevere ceiling (1721–24), the Duke of Parma gave the artist apartments for his studio and school in the Palazzo Farnese where the private academy he established flourished. He was President of the Accademia di S. Luca from 1729–32 and from 1739–40, three times longer than usual. The masterpiece of Conca's last period, after the move south, was the ceiling of S. Chiara (1753, destroyed). Conca's small easel pictures reveal a personal, intimate approach to his subject and in his larger altarpieces and frescoes there is a recognition of the established, Marattesque Roman tradition with virtuoso rococo flourishes. During his long, prolific career, Conca became one of the most influential artists of the century.

REF.: A. M. Clark, "Sebastiano Conca and the Roman Rococo," *Apollo*, XXCV, 1967, pp. 328–35; G. Sestieri, a two-part article to appear in *Commentari*, 1970.

93

The Baptism of Christ
Copper (oval): 61 x 73.7 cm.; 24 x 29 inches
Collection Joseph R. McCrindle, London
Not signed

DATE: 1725–35

EX COLL.: Sangiorgi, Rome, 1960; Hazlitt Gallery, London, May 1963.

REF.: *The Burlington Magazine*, CV, 1963, p. 227 and fig. 37.

There is a preliminary drawing, not oval in format but shaped below as if for an overdoor, in the Victoria and Albert Museum. With the reversal of Christ's legs and other changes and additions, another rectangular composition exists in an engraving. (The state known to the cataloguer bears only the artist's name. It could, nevertheless, be from an early drawing by the artist, and a state of Stephanoni's engraving which the cataloguer has not seen.) Although the figures are more apart and more calmly adjusted, Christ, the Baptist, and the kneeling angel at the left are taken from Maratti's *Baptism* (1710) in the Certosa di S. Martino, Naples. Conca's admiration for the dominant High Baroque Roman master is known; it is interesting that he chose the Naples *Baptism* as a source rather than the better known, earlier Maratti of the same subject in St. Peter's. The Naples *Baptism* might be called Maratti's most rococo painting. Conca (who would have first seen the Naples picture in Rome, shortly after his arrival there) has cooled the rococo compositional ardor of Maratti even though his own physical types and the delicate and imaginative manner of painting are very rococo.

The painting may probably date to the decade between 1725 and 1735. The back of the copper is painted (the long way upright) with a half-length, blessing, bearded bishop saint.

A. M. C.

Falciatore, called Filippetto because of his small stature, studied first with Paolo de Matteis (*q.v.*) before becoming a student of Domenico Antonio Vaccaro (1651–1750). The artist has been little studied until recently. He was, as far as is known, active only in Naples and his dated works are from the middle of the century: frescoes (badly deteriorated) in the sacristy S. Maria del Carmine, documented 1741; *Holy Family Adored by Angels* and its pendant, *Flight into Egypt*, 1741, Romano Collection, Florence; and a sketch, *Adoration of the Shepherds*, 1754, S. Martino, Naples. (In 1746, Falciatore was responsible for restoring 287 paintings for the monastery Trinità delle Monache, Naples.) As de Dominici relates (*Vite*, IV, 1846, p. 278), Falciatore executed works for various churches and private patrons as well as *capricci* of assassinations, fires and *fêtes galantes* (two of the last have been identified; see Bottari). However, his most distinct honor, according to de Dominici, was being chosen to paint the decorative panels for the sedan chair of the queen, which were praised by Solimena (now in the Floridiana, Naples).

Falciatore emerged from the circle of Vaccaro to carry on a personal interpretation of his master's style. The lively colors and decorative accessories of Falciatore's *petite manière* pictures contribute to the delicate elegance which is characteristic of his style.

REF.: A Fiordelisi, "La Trinita delle Monache," *Napoli nobilissima*, VIII, 1898, p. 147; S. Bottari, "Filippo Falciatore," *Napoli nobilissima*, III, 1963, pp. 97–102; S. Bottari, "Aggiunte all'opera di Filippo Falciatore," *Napoli nobilissima*, V, 1966, pp. 102–104; W. Vitzthum, "Filippo Falciatore, petit maître oublié du style rocaille à Naples," *L'oeil*, no. 145, 1967, pp. 18–23.

94

Joseph and Potiphar's Wife
Copper: 26 x 38.2 cm.; $10\frac{1}{4}$ x 15 inches
E. B. Crocker Art Gallery, Sacramento
Signed left center: *Falcitore*

EX COLL.: Acquired by E. B. Crocker about 1874 in Europe.

The arrangement of the figures in relation to their setting relates the Sacramento painting to the *Holy Family Adored by Angels* in the Romano Collection, signed and dated 1741. (The *Finding of Moses* in the museum at Linz must also be from this time.) Indeed, the pose of Joseph, with one foot placed firmly on the floor, is identical with that of the small angel in the lower left of the Romano picture. On the other hand, the spirited drapery patterns, more gentle, diffused light, as well as the delicacy of the features of the two figures in the Sacramento work, would suggest a slightly later date, closer to that of the *Adoration of the Shepherds* (S. Martino, Naples, signed and dated 1754). Therefore, around 1750 seems appropriate for the date of *Joseph and Potiphar's Wife*. By this time, Falciatore had developed the graceful figure type and ornamental elegance characteristic of his sedan chair panels.

Born at Molfetta, Giaquinto moved to Naples in 1719 where he studied first with Nicola Maria Rossi and then with Solimena (*q.v.*). He settled in Rome in 1723 as a pupil and assistant of Sebastiano Conca (*q.v.*), where he remained until 1753, with two stays in Turin (1733 and 1735–39). By invitation in 1753, he succeeded Jacopo Amigoni as court painter to Ferdinand VI and director of the Academy S. Fernando. After the arrival of Mengs, Giaquinto left Spain in 1762 for Naples, where he spent his last years. Although born in the South where he received his earliest training, Giaquinto is not to be considered a Neapolitan painter, but a member of the school of Rome, where he spent the greatest part of his life. He was Conca's most inspired follower. In Spain, where an emphasis on drawing and discipline could not fetter him, Corrado applied his first Neapolitan lessons, and his special talent as a genuinely rococo decorator flourished.

REF.: M. d'Orsi, *Corrado Giaquinto*, Rome, 1958; M. Volpi, "Corrado Giaquinto e alcuni aspetti della cultura figurativa del '700 in Italia," *Bollettino d'arte*, XLIII, 1958, pp. 263–282; A. Videtta, *Considerazioni su Corrado Giaquinto in rapporto ai disegni del Museo di S. Martino*, Istituto di Storia dell'Arte dell'Università di Napoli, Saggi e ricerche, 4, Naples, 1965.

95

The Visitation
Canvas: 287.1 x 177.9 cm.; 113 x 70 inches
The Montreal Museum of Fine Arts. Purchased 1968, Horsley and Annie Townsend Bequest
Not signed
DATE: *c.* 1762–65

EX COLL.. S. Luigi di Palazzo, Naples; private collection, Bedford, Mass.; Castagno Gallery, Boston; purchased by Montreal Museum of Fine Arts, 1968.

This painting was once an altarpiece in the church of S. Luigi di Palazzo, Naples. At least the four main altarpieces of this church—all by Giaquinto—entered the Curtis Collection in Boston in the mid-nineteenth century, bought, according to family memory, from a ship which had come from Spain (see the forthcoming catalogue of the Harvard University Collections of Italian Paintings by Everett Fahy). Of these paintings, a *Holy Family* and a *Marriage of the Virgin* remain in the family (a sketch for the former is reproduced by L. Dania, *The Burlington Magazine*, CX, 1968, p. 143, fig. 39); and a fourth picture, the *Presentation*, is in the Fogg Art Museum (published by A. M. Clark, "A Presentation by Corrado Giaquinto," *The Annual Report of the Fogg Art Museum*, 1957–58, pp. 40–45).

A sketch for the present painting exists in the Pinacoteca Comunale, Fano (published by L. Dania, *Paragone*, no. 235, 1969, p. 65, fig. 49, 75 x 50 cm.). It is apparent that all the altarpieces are very late works and were probably produced upon the artist's return from Spain in the last several years of his life.
A. M. C.

96

The Holy Trinity with Souls in Purgatory
Canvas: 99.2 x 74 cm.; 39 x 29⅛ inches
The Minneapolis Institute of Arts, The Putnam Dana McMillan Fund
Signed on base of cross: *C. G. / Inv. F.*
DATE: *c.* 1742

EX COLL.: Christie's, London, Feb. 24, 1967, lot 50; Julius H. Weitzner, London, 1968.

VERSIONS: formerly Vangelli Collection, Rome; S. Cassiano, Grugliasco.

REF.: A. M. Clark, "Corrado Giaquinto's Trinity with Souls in Purgatory," *The Minneapolis Institute of Arts Bulletin*, LVII, 1968, pp. 54–55.

This is not the version formerly in the Vangelli Collection, Rome (d'Orsi, fig. 54), which appears to have been a studio copy. Another version in the church at Grugliasco, near Turin, is variously described as an altarpiece and a sketch. In the upper part of the composition, Giaquinto has reused his ceiling fresco tondo of the *Trinity* in S. Giovanni Calibita, Rome (*c.* 1742).

The rarity of signed, highly finished devotional pictures in Giaquinto's production is well known; most of the examples seem to be early.

A landscape painter, he was born in Naples, worked in Rome, the Marches, and Perugia, where he died. Nicola Pio writes (*Vite* 154) that de Marchis came to Rome at seventeen (*c.* 1701), studied for a year and a half with Rosa da Tivoli, the animal painter, and was drawn to the landscapes of Gaspard Dughet. Lanzi (the main, but secondary, period source) gives the story of the artist's jail term and exile from Rome for setting fire to a hayloft "wishing to paint fires more accurately"; a complicated law suit, possibly pyromania, and the protection of Clement XI's family are involved. His main Roman patrons were Marchese Theodoli, the Albani (decorations—accompanying the also untraced Panini frescoes—in their Roman and, later, in their Urbino palaces), and the Ruspoli (two rooms painted *c.* 1720 in competition with others, mainly such genre and landscape painters as Amorosi, Reder, and Locatelli). Urbino pictures exist (the five Albani overdoors; in S. Giuseppe; in Casa Santini) as do a horde of unstudied (partially unattributed) landscapes in the Nationalmuseum, Stockholm.

His delicacy, lucidity and spirit (and his fires) made de Marchis a celebrity. His use of Dughet was not towards a pleasant rococo classicism (as Locatelli and Orizzonte), but towards a rococo romanticism, delicate and haunting.

The attribution (oral) is due to Professor Chiarini.

REF.: L. Lanzi, *Storia pittoreca della Italia*, II, 1809, p. 169; M. Chiarini, "Alessio de Marchis as a Draughtsman," *Master Drawings*, III, 1967, pp. 289–291.   A. M. C.

97

Landscape with Herdsman
Canvas: 114 x 143 cm.; $44\frac{7}{8}$ x $56\frac{1}{4}$ inches
Galleria Nazionale d'Arte Antica, Rome (on deposit in Villa d'Este, Tivoli)
Not signed

EX COLL.: Quadreria del Monte di Pietà, Rome, 1895.

REF.: (N. di Carpegna), *Villa d'Este, Tivoli, La Quadreria*, Rome, n.d., p. 12, no. 50 (as Jan Both); N. di Carpegna, *Pitture fiamminghe e olandesi del '600*, Rome, 1954, p. 11, no. 14.

The evocative sky, against which the herdsman and his cows are silhouetted, juxtaposed with the suggestive obscurity of the rock formation creates the romantic mood of the scene.

After convincing his father that he should be allowed to go to Naples to study (Paolo was born in Cliento), de Matteis entered the school of Luca Giordano, the most celebrated Neapolitan artist at the turn of the century. Taken to Rome by a friend of Luca, he continued his studies with G. M. Morandi. His career, however, was launched by the Marchese del Carpio, Spanish ambassador to Rome, who found the young artist sketching altarpieces in St. Peter's. The ambassador ordered several copies from Paolo and gave him quarters in his palace sometime before 1682 when del Carpio went to Naples. De Matteis then left for Naples himself where he again studied with Giordano after the latter's return from Florence in 1686. Paolo was taken to Paris in 1702 by the Duc d'Estrées where he remained at the court of the Dauphin until 1705. Upon his return to Naples, de Matteis was patronized by the Austrian commander, Count Daun, and Admiral Byng, commander of the British fleet in the Mediterranean. He was also commissioned by the remarkable Lord Shaftesbury to translate into visual terms his dogmatic essay, the *Choice of Heracles* (1712, City Art Gallery, Leeds). Another project for Shaftesbury was completed in 1713.

Late in his life, de Matteis was in Rome a second time (three years) where he received commissions from Benedict XIII.

De Matteis was noted for his rapidity of execution (faster even, according to de Dominici, than Luca) and he was the most important rival of Francesco Solimena (*q.v.*).

REF.: B. de Dominici, *Vite*, IV, 1846, pp. 313–358, D. C. Miller, "The Gallery of Aeneid in the Palazzo Bonaccorsi at Macerata," *Arte antica e moderna*, no. 22, 1963, pp. 154–55.

98

Martyrdom of St. Catherine of Alexandria
Canvas: 45.2 x 36.3 cm.; $17\frac{3}{4}$ x $14\frac{1}{4}$ inches
Collection Mr. and Mrs. Milton J. Lewine, New York
Signed (*verso*): *Paulus de Matthei F. 1708 Neapoli*
DATE: 1708

De Matteis had treated the subject of St. Catherine when he was in France. De Dominici refers to a *Marriage of St. Catherine*, tondo, half-length, and its pendant (perhaps a *Martyrdom*) which were in the collection of Cardinal Polignac. The artist's ceiling fresco of 1712 in S. Caterina a Formiello, Naples, is devoted to the two Sts. Catherine.

The Lewine picture was executed after Paolo's return from France to Italy and reveals the influence of his major teacher, Luca Giordano, in the use of robust figures and in the sense of drama.

De Mura was one of the important pupils of Solimena (*q.v.*) actually born in Naples, where he was active for the greatest part of his career. The frescoes in the church of the monastery at Montecassino (chapel of S. Bertario), among his earliest important works in the late 1720s, are destroyed. In 1732, de Mura began the apse fresco at the Nunziatella a Pizzofalcone (finished 1734); he returned to the church almost twenty years later to decorate the nave vault (signed and dated 1751). By this time, the artist had successfully completed additional work at Montecassino, frescoed the vault of SS. Severino e Sossio, Naples (*c.* 1740), and, on the invitation of Charles Emanuel III of Savoy, decorated with allegorical scenes several ceilings of the royal palace in Turin (1741–43). While there, he was singularly favored with a deer hunt held in his honor at Stupinigi. De Mura's late works in Naples include the altarpieces in the Annunziata and the frescoed chapels in SS. Apostoli.

In his early works, de Mura's coloring and, in certain cases, chiaroscuro reveal a profound influence of Solimena, who is ultimately the source of the sense of spaciousness and vastness in de Mura's compositions. His development was towards a classicizing of his scenes, treating them with simplicity and a sense of quiet.

REF.: A. Griseri, "Francesco de Mura fra le corti di Napoli, Madrid e Torino," *Paragone*, no. 155, 1962, pp. 22–43; R. Enggass, "Francesco de Mura alla Nunziatella," *Bollettino d'arte*, XLIX, 1964, pp. 133–148.

99

The Woman from Samaria at the Well
Canvas: 104.2 x 156.3 cm.; 41 x 61½ inches
Seattle Art Museum, gift of Dr. and Mrs. Richard E. Fuller
Signed (*verso*): *Francesco De Mura Pingebat Anno 1752*
DATE: 1752

EX COLL.: Rome; Jack Baer, London; on the market, New York.

The *Woman from Samaria at the Well* was painted during the artist's period of full maturity. The apostles at the left, swathed in abundant drapery and performing elegant, rather affected gestures, could have left the scene of the *Assumption of the Virgin* (ceiling fresco, 1751, Nunziatella a Pizzofalcone, Naples) to take their position in the Seattle picture. The men cut off at half-length by the hill are related to a similar grouping in the fresco and there is the same effect of an airy scene bathed in light.

The present example is also related to the canvases in the chapel of the Assumption in the church of the monastery of S. Martino, Naples. In similar fashion, the *Visitation* in that chapel is fixed with heavy forms at strategic points in the composition. The use of such details as the dogs and rocks as transitional elements into the space of the canvas is common in de Mura's pictures.

Solimena was the successor of Luca Giordano (1634–1705) as the undisputed leader of the Neapolitan school during the first half of the eighteenth century. Born in Nocera, Solimena arrived in Naples in 1674 where his style was formed primarily under the influence of Giordano. This is most evident in the masterpiece of his first period, the frescoes in the sacristy of S. Paolo Maggiore, Naples (1689–90), where his facile arrangement of groups of figures and lively colors depend upon the elder master for their inspiration. About the time of Giordano's departure for Spain in 1692, however, an influence from Mattia Preti (1613–69) can be noted in the generally darker palette of his easel pictures and the shadows used in modelling figures, a hallmark of Solimena's style.

Although he worked almost exclusively in Naples, Solimena became one of the most eagerly sought after painters of his time. He was responsible for major frescoes in many churches in Naples (S. Maria Donnaregina, S. Paolo Maggiore, S. Domenico Maggiore, Gesù Nuovo, Gerolomini) and he sent paintings to patrons throughout Europe. His many pupils, taught in his own academy in Naples, include Sebastiano Conca (*q.v.*), Corrado Giaquinto (*q.v.*), Francesco de Mura (*q.v.*), and Giuseppe Bonito (*q.v.*). For the Neapolitan school, Solimena serves as the transitional artist between the late Baroque and the full rococo.

REF.: F. Bologna, *Francesco Solimena*, Naples, 1958; F. Bologna, "Aggiunte a Francesco Solimena, I, La giovinezza e la formazione (1674–84)," *Napoli nobilissima*, II, 1962, pp. 1–12.

100

Rape of Orythia

Canvas: 114 x 86.5 cm.; $44\frac{7}{8}$ x 34 inches

Kunsthistorisches Museum, Vienna

Not signed

DATE: 1700

EX COLL.: Belvedere, Vienna, before 1735; Kunsthistorisches Museum, before 1783 (Mechel inventory, p. 72, no. 21).

VERSIONS: Galleria Spada, Rome (horizontal format with variations); formerly private collection, Leningrad (identical, but probably not autograph).

REF.: see F. Bologna, *Francesco Solimena*, pp. 274, 282.

Solimena painted the version in the Galleria Spada when he was in Rome for a month in 1700 and the Vienna *Rape of Orythia* probably dates from the same time (Bologna places it *c.* 1730). The compositions of the two works are very similar and there is the same use of chiaroscuro light effects and specific figures. The Vienna picture was presumably executed for Eugene of Savoy, an important foreign patron of Solimena; it was in the Belvedere by 1735 when an engraving was made. (Eugene later ordered a *Rape of Cephalus* from the artist which arrived in Vienna in 1729.)

Boreas, the North Wind, had been frustrated in his earlier, subtle attempts to woo Orythia and is shown as he carries away the unfortunate maid who had been playing with her companions on the bank of the Ilissus. The drama of the scene is created by agitated drapery patterns, flickering light, movement of the figures and the compositional diagonal.

101a

The Holy Trinity, Dominicans and Heretics
Ceiling Fresco (Shown by photograph in the exhibition)
Sacristy, S. Domenico Maggiore, Naples
DATE: 1709

The commission for the sacristy ceiling fresco was given first to Domenico Antonio Vaccaro (1681–1750), but passed to Solimena with the death of the Prior (Vaccaro's sketch is probably the one in the Busiri-Vici Collection, Rome. See S. Bottari, "Filippo Falciatore," *Napoli nobilissima*, III, 1963, p. 101, note 6). A sketch by Solimena for the project is in a private collection in Florence and a preliminary drawing, very close to the finished work, has recently gone to the University of Colorado ("College Museum Notes"). Another drawing, supposedly showing an earlier version of the composition, is located at Windsor (see Offerhaus).

The grandiose, spiral composition includes the Trinity above, the Virgin, who directs the angel placing the aureole on St. Dominic's head, various virtues, Dominican saints, and heretics, expelled from the celestial realm. It is in essence a glorification of St. Dominic and celebration of the works of the Dominicans' promulgation of the Faith.

101

Massacre of the Giustiniani
Canvas: 227 x 164 cm.; $85\frac{3}{8}$ x $64\frac{1}{2}$ inches
Museo e Gallerie Nazionali di Capodimonte, Naples
Not signed
DATE: 1715–17

EX COLL.: Acquired from the Canessa Collection, 1907.

VERSIONS: Collezioni Comunali, Genoa (shop).

REF.: see F. Bologna, *Francesco Solimena*, pp. 111, 191, 268.

The sketch showing the massacre of the eighteen sons of the Giustiniani family at Scio was done in preparation for the major of the three large canvases commissioned by the Republic of Genoa to decorate the ceiling of the Sala del Consiglio of the Senate Palace. The other two represent the *Arrival of the Ashes of St. John the Baptist at Genoa* and the *Arrival of Christopher Columbus in the Indies* (the sketch for the latter, Musée des Beaux-Arts, Rennes, is signed and dated 1715). All three works were completed in Solimena's studio in Naples, installed by 1729 and later destroyed by fire.

The scene of the massacre (the central section is taken from Mattia Preti's *Martyrdom of St. Catherine*, S. Pietro a Maiella, Naples) takes place in a vast architectural setting with a convoluted composition related to his virtuoso performance in the sacristy ceiling of S. Domenico (*q.v.*).

102

The Naming of St. John the Baptist
Canvas: 40.4 x 32.3 cm.; $15\frac{7}{8}$ x $12\frac{3}{4}$ inches
Walker Art Gallery, Liverpool
Not signed
DATE: *c.* 1715

EX COLL.: Said to have come from a collection in Ireland. Sotheby's, 1953; Colnaghi's, 1953, where it was purchased by the Walker Art Gallery.

VERSIONS: Museo Civico, Teramo (autograph, but weaker).

REF.: see F. Bologna, *Francesco Solimena*, pp. 112, 255; and *Italian Art in Britain*, Royal Academy, London, 1960, no. 439; *Neapolitan Baroque and Rococo Painting*, Bowes Museum, Barnard Castle, 1962, no. 65; *Foreign Schools Catalogue*, Walker Art Gallery, 1963, p. 186; G. Carandente, *Il Museo Civico di Teramo*, 1960, p. 21, no. 40; *Le dessin a Naples du XVIᵉ siècle au XVIIIᵉ siècle*, Musée du Louvre, 1967, p. 44, no. 77.

The *Naming of St. John the Baptist* was painted around the time Solimena was at work on his commission for the Senate Palace, Genoa, (*q.v.*). A picture of this subject is mentioned by de Dominici (*Vite*, IV, 1846, p. 427), one of two ordered by the Cardinal Ottoboni. The biographer, however, speaks of *rametti* and the present example is painted on fabric. A preliminary drawing for the work is located in the Louvre.

The touching, intimate scene shows Elizabeth as she reaches for her son while the father establishes the child's name in order to bring back his power of speech. The seriousness with which the drama is handled and the chiaroscuro modelling are inherited from Mattia Preti.

Practically nothing is known about the life of this artist who produced some of the most intriguing pictures of the eighteenth century. Indeed, before the fundamental article of Longhi (1927), his existence was scarcely recorded. The year 1769 is perhaps correct for his demise, but 1732 seems too late for his birth since the artist would have been only seventeen years old when he completed his first works.

The earliest dated pictures by Traversi are the *Birth of the Virgin*, the *Annunciation* (both inscribed "*Gaspar Traversi P. 1749*"), and the *Immaculate Conception* in a chapel in S. Maria dell'Aiuto, Naples. These works show Traversi to have been a provincial exponent of the rococo style and suggest that he had studied with Solimena (*q.v.*), and, in gesture and drapery pattern, knew the work of Francesco de Mura (*q.v.*). However, a slightly later series of five pictures in a corridor of S. Paolo fuori le Mura, Rome (the *Annunciation* is signed and dated 1752), shows that the artist has reverted to Neapolitan examples primarily from the early seicento for his inspiration. The remainder of Traversi's known religious pictures are related stylistically to the S. Paolo works and were executed by the artist in Rome, where he probably remained until his death. They include a series of the fourteen Stations of the Cross (the *Deposition* is signed *Gaspare Traversi napoletano dipinse*), S. Rocco, Borgotaro; five pictures in the Galleria Nazionale, Parma; three scenes of the Passion (the *Pietà* is monogrammed *GT*), Collegiata and its museum, Castell'Arquato; and the *Pentecost*, 1758, S. Pietro d'Alcantara, Parma. The number of religious pictures now known by Traversi would indicate that his importance as a genre painter has been overstressed. It is, however, on his genre scenes (several portraits have also been identified) that his fame today primarily rests.

REF.: R. Longhi, "Di Gaspare Traversi," *Vita artistica*, 1927, pp. 145–167; R. Longhi, "Un'aggiunta al Traversi," *Vita artistica*, 1927, p. 197 (both republished in R. Longhi, *Saggi e ricerche 1925–1928*, Florence, 1967, pp. 189–216 and 217–219); R. Longhi, "Traversi: un'opera e nuove notizie," *Paragone*, no. 1, 1950, pp. 44–45; A. Ghidiglia Quintavalle, "Inediti di Gaspare Traversi," *Paragone*, no. 81, 1956, pp. 39–45; M. Gregori, "Tre opere di Traversi a Castell'Arquato," *Paragone*, no. 81, 1956, pp. 45–49; A. Ghidiglia Quintavalle, "Ancora un Gaspare Traversi," *Paragone*, no. 209, 1967, pp. 27–29.

103

The Arts—Music
Canvas: 151.5 x 204.2 cm.; $59\frac{5}{8}$ x $80\frac{5}{8}$ inches
Nelson Gallery—Atkins Museum (Samuel H. Kress Collection), Kansas City
Signed lower left: *Gaspar Traversi P.*
DATE: *c.* 1750

EX COLL.: R. Herzka, Vienna, *c.* 1928; David M. Koetser's, New York; Samuel H. Kress Collection, 1953.

REF.: R. Longhi, *Saggi e ricerche 1925–1928*, p. 218 and plate 183; N. Pevsner and O. Grautoff, *Barockmalerei in den romanischen Ländern*, Potsdam, 1928, p. 206 (the pendant of the present example is reproduced); S. O., "Gaspare Traversi," in U. Thieme and F. Becker, *Allgemeines Lexikon*, XXXIII, Leipzig, 1939, p. 361; F. Shapley, unpublished entry for a catalogue of later schools of Italian painting in the Kress Collection.

Not one of his known genre pictures is dated; however, Longhi places them at mid-century on the basis of a comparison with dated religious works. The present example (its pendant, *The Arts—Drawing*, is in the same collection) is one of several by the artist showing musical entertainment. A young lady is at the harpsichord while two gentlemen play the flute and viola da gamba. The text of the music is *Cantata a Voce Sola / Sorge la bel aurora / i vaghi prati indora / e rende*. . . (Song for a Single Voice / Beautiful aurora rises / gilds the lovely meadows / and renders . . .). Among the girl's admirers are several stock types. The man standing at the right and the inevitable old page-turner are common in Traversi's pictures and de Dominici's description (*Vite*, IV, 1846, p. 611) of the *cicisbeo* in a similar scene by Giuseppe Bonito (with whom Traversi was formerly confused, *q.v.*) exactly fits the man who rests his chin and hands on the knob of his walking stick. The frequency with which these characters with their specific physiognomies appear would suggest that they were stock figures from the theater and that Traversi was perhaps inspired by the vivacious writings of the Neapolitan playwright, Barone de Liveri (see R. Bacchelli and R. Longhi, *Teatro e immagini del settecento italiano*, Turin, 1953, pp. 194 ff.).

243

104

Allegory of Clement XI
Copper: 70.3 x 52.1 cm.; $27\frac{5}{8}$ x $20\frac{1}{2}$ inches
Walters Art Gallery, Baltimore
Not signed

EX COL.: Marcello Massarenti Collection, Rome; purchased by Henry Walters, 1902.

REF.: E. van Esbroeck, *Catalogue du musée de peinture, sculpture et archéologie au Palais Accoramboni*, Rome, 1897, no. 355 (as S. Ricci); *Italian Baroque Paintings 1600–1750*, Walters Art Gallery, Baltimore, 1969.

This generalized allegory shows the Catholic Church as a female figure wearing the papal tiara protecting with her cloak the tabernacle, symbolic of the dogma of the Faith. A portrait of Clement XI (1700–21) is displayed at the side as Fame proclaims the Pope's virtuous deeds. Below, enemies of the Church are bound in chains. The allegory is possibly in reference to the efforts of Clement XI against the Jansenist heresy, which occupied him for many years, and his action in the struggle against the Turks for the safeguarding of Christendom.

For this anonymous Neapolitan picture tentative attributions to Filippo Falciatore (*q.v.*) and Paolo de Matteis (*q.v.*) have been suggested. Employment by Clement XI of de Matteis is known. However, the resemblance to certain works by de Matteis might be considered superficial and no more telling than similarities with works by de Matteis' younger rival, Domenico Antonio Vaccaro (1681–1750).

Technical Note

Original with the planning for this exhibition was the desire to include in the catalogue a discussion of the technical aspects of 18th-century Italian painting. Obviously, the ideal project would have been to have a body of conservators give each picture in the exhibition a thorough examination, thereby providing a basic vocabulary and set of references for our knowledge in this field. However, given the impossibility of this (both physically and temporally), it was decided to limit the investigation to a detailed examination of two pictures. While the conclusions to be drawn from this presentation can only, at best, imply some of the basic attitudes in the 18th century toward painting technique and, perhaps more so, give some sense of the variety of techniques used in different regions, it is hoped that—even at this level—the information will be useful as an introduction to a new method of technical examination and serve as a beginning for essays of this type for the 18th century, a period which was as innovative and complex in technique as in style.

The materials and techniques of two paintings, *The Grand Canal, Venice* by Francesco Guardi and *St. Benedict Joseph Labre* by Antonio Cavallucci were investigated in the conservation laboratory of The Art Institute of Chicago. The methods of examination included polarized-light microscopy, chemical microscopy, and the use of the stereo microscope. In several instances information gathered by these means was corroborated by electron microprobe. The goal of this investigation was to learn as much as possible about the materials and techniques used by these artists to create their particular visual effects.

To this end, not only were pigments identified, but the ranges of particle sizes in which they were used were noted, and the proportions of various pigments used to achieve a particular tone were recorded. A key technique here was mounting a 25 μm (1/1000″) crushed sample from a particular area being studied and viewing it through the polarized-light microscope at about 100 to 1000 magnifications.

In addition, the technique by which the painting was created was investigated by studying the structural order of layers. This was done both by viewing the painting through the stereo microscope at about 25 magnifications and by taking 50 μm (1/500″) sectional samples and studying them under the polarized-light microscope with the addition of reflected top light. From these sectional samples one could learn the order of layers of paint, gain an approximate picture of the materials and particle sizes used in each layer, and measure the thickness of each layer, using an ocular micrometer.

By using these minute samples and the polarizing microscope to gain a complete picture of the materials and techniques used in constructing a painting, one can gather enough information to compare a particular painter's work with that of other painters of the same period and of different periods. Thus one can ascertain the similarities and differences between one period and another and, in this instance, discover some of the special characteristics of examples of eighteenth century Italian painting from two different schools of painting.

Samples	Fragments	Crushings
	[1 μm [micrometer] = 1/25,000 inch]	(range of particle sizes) % by volume, estimated
1 Ground h. 0.400 M w. 0.680 M		*Ground* 10% lead white 1–4 μm; 6–12 μm agglomerates[1] 40% red ochre 0.5–1 μm; 5–10 μm agglomerates 10% raw sienna 2–7.5 μm 40% calcium carbonate (calcite) 6–20 μm
2 Sky, gray-blue clouds h. 0.440 M w. 0.061	*Top view* lead white 1–4 μm; 8–40 μm agglomerates bone black 1–6 μm ultramarine, 1 particle, 94 x 120 μm vermilion 1–10 μm Van Dyck brown 16 μm *Sectional* (from painting's surface down to ground) white-gray layer 12 μm blue layer 15 μm ground 20 μm	*White-gray layer* 70% lead white 1–4 μm 1% ultramarine 2 μm 28% vermilion 2–20 μm 1% bone black 4 μm *Blue layer* 70% lead white 1–4 μm 20% ultramarine 2–6 μm 9% vermilion 2–6 μm 1% bone black 2–6 μm
3 Sky, bright blue h. 0.618 M w. 0.015 M	*Top view* lead white 8–4 μm agglomerates ultramarine 0.5–8 μm 1 particle 120 x 200 μm 1 particle 32 μm Naples yellow 8 μm *Sectional* blue layer 20–30 μm ground 30 μm	*Blue layer* 75% lead white 2–6 μm 23% ultramarine 1–6 μ 1 particle 100 μm 2% bone black 1–12 μm
4 Sky, yellow clouds h. 0.392 M w. 0.393 M	*Top view* 89% lead white 5–70 μm agglomerates 5% ultramarine 1–60 μm 0.5% vermilion 4–6 μm 5% Naples yellow 2–10 μm; 70 μm agglomerates 0.5% bone black 2–4 μm *Sectional* yellow-white layer 50–60 μm thick blue layer with red particles 50 μm blue layer 50 μm gray-white layer 25–50 μm ground 75–100 μm	*Yellow-white layer* 70% lead white 1–4 μm ultramarine 2–8 μm 10% vermilion 4–6 μm crimson latke 6 μm 10% Naples yellow 8–28 μm 10% bone black 4–8 μm *Blue with red particles layer* 90% lead white 1–4 μm 8% ultramarine 2–12 μm 3% vermilion 3–6 μm *Blue layer* 90% lead white 1–3 10% ultramarine 3–10 μm *Gray-white layer* 90% lead white 0.5–2 μm 4% ultramarine 1–2 μm 1% raw sienna 4–8 μm

Samples	Fragments	Crushing
5 Water h. 0.039 M w. 0.570 M	*Top view* 50% lead white 30–90 μm agglomerates 5% ultramarine 4–40 μm 25% green earth 3–10 μm, 130–160 μm 1% raw sienna 6–8 μm 1% burnt sienna 1 agglomerate of 4 μm particles 10% Van Dyck brown 4–12 μm 5% bone black 4–40 μm	same as fragment
6 Buff steps h. 0.100 M w. 0.852 M	*Top view* lead white 1–5 μm vermilion 2–5 μm Naples yellow: pale yellow particles 6–12 μm dark yellow agglomerates 4–60 μm bone black 1–4 μm 1 particle 140 μm	*Buff layer* 75% lead white 1–5 μm 2% green earth 5–12 μm 1% vermilion 1–4 μm 20% Naples yellow 1–8 μm 2% bone black 4 μm
7 Red cloak h. 0.090 M w. 0.933 M		*Red cloak* 20% lead white 0.5–1 μm 80% vermilion 1–10 μm
8 Brown cloak h. 0.098 M w. 0.863 M		*Brown cloak* 30% lead white 1–4 μm 32 μm agglomerate 1% green earth 16 μm 1% vermilion 2 μm 65% Van Dyck brown 1–10 μm 2% bone black 3–15 μm
9 Blue costume h. 0.088 M w. 0.771 M	*Top view* lead white 1–4 μm ultramarine 3–5 μm, 20–30 μm vermilion 2–5 μm	*Blue costume* 40% lead white 1–3 μm and 4–12 μm agglomerates 50% ultramarine 2–16 μm 5% vermilion 4–6 μm 5% Van Dyck brown 4–6 μm
10 Church roof, gray blue h. 0.503 M w. 1.009 M	*Top view* lead white 8–32 μm agglomerates green earth, 1 particle 200 μm, 6–8 μm vermilion 2–4 μm Naples yellow, 1 agglomerate 100 μm Van Dyck brown 4–12 μm bone black 4–12 μm, 1 particle 60 x 120 μm	*Church roof* 80% lead white 1–4 μm in 8–32 μm agglomerates 8% ultramarine 4–12 μm 1 particle 16 μm 4% vermilion 1–8 μm 1 particle 16 μm 2% raw sienna 2–4 μm 2% Van Dyck brown 6 μm 4% bone black 2–12 μm
11 Pink building h. 0.176 M w. 0.680 M	*Top view* lead white agglomerates 10–40 μm vermilion 2–10 μm red lead agglomerates 10 μm Van Dyck brown 2–10 μm bone black 2–20 μm, 1 particle 80 μm *Sectional* pink layer 40 μm thick ground, incomplete	*Pink layer* 50% lead white 1–4 μm 1% ultramarine 2–5 μm 25% vermilion 2–8 μm 10% red lead 1–8 μm 10% bone black 3–6 μm

[1]Agglomerate: "A cluster of individual particles". W. C. McCrone, R. G. Draftz, and J. G. Delly, "The Particle Atlas", Ann Arbor, Michigan, 1967, p. 347.

Samples	Fragments	Crushings
		(range of particle sizes) % by volume, estimated
1 Ground h. 0.315 M w. 0.001 M		*Ground* 10% lead white 1–4 μm; agglomerates to 8 μm 70% anhydrite 5–40 μm 20% gypsum 16–20 μm
2 Background h. 0.315 M w. 0.001 M	*Sectional* black layer 30–40 μm thick ground 20 μm (incomplete)	*Black layer* 5% lead white 3–5 μm agglomerates 5% red ochre 2 μm agglomerates 20% yellow ochre 1–6 μm 70% bone black 1–8 μm
3 Hand, light flesh tone h. 0.071 M w. 0.242 M	*Sectional* flesh tone 20–40 μm ground 120–130 μm	*Flesh tone* 95% lead white 1–6 μm agglomerates 20 μm 0.5% red ochre 0.5–1 μm agglomerates 1 μm 2.5% yellow ochre 0.5–2 μm 2% bone black 2–4 μm
4 Hand, flesh shadow tone h. 0.046 M w. 0.174 M		*Flesh tone* 60% lead white 1–2 μm 30% yellow ochre 0.5–6 μm 10% bone black 2–8 μm
5 Hand, pink tone on thumb h. 0.100 M w. 0.313 M		*Pink tone* 40% lead white 1–2 μm 20% red ochre 0.5–1 μm, agglomerates 2–5 μm 40% yellow ochre 0.5–5 μm
6 Hair, light tone h. 0.513 M w. 0.186 M		*Hair–light tone* 15% lead white 1–2 μm 4% red ochre 0.5–1 μm, 1–5 μm agglomerates 80% yellow ochre 1–6 μm, 6–10 μm agglomerates 1% bone black 2–8 μm
7 Hair, mid tone h. 0.514 M w 0.189 M	*Sectional* hair tone 20 μm ground 80–90 μm	*Hair, mid tone* 50% lead white 1 μm to 12 μm agglomerates 2% red ochre 5–10 μm agglomerates 40% yellow ochre 0.5–5 μm 8% bone black 5–9 μm
8 Coat, light tone h. 0.003 M w. 0.026 M		*Coat, light tone* 50% lead white 1–4 μm 35% yellow ochre 0.5–4 μm 15% bone black 2–8 μm

Samples	Fragments	Crushing
9 Lip tone h. 0.351 M w. 0.175 M		*Lip tone* 10% lead white 0.5–5 μm 2% red ochre 8 μm agglomerates of 1 μm particles 40% yellow ochre 0.5–2.5 μm 40% burnt sienna 1–6 μm 8% bone black 2–3 μm
10 Beads, yellow h. 0.138 M w. 0.180 M		*Beads, yellow* 15% lead white 1–4 μm 80% Naples yellow 1–4 μm 5% bone black 2 μm
11 Beads, brown h. 0.102 M w. 0.148 M		*Beads, brown* 15% lead white 1–3 μm 75% yellow ochre 1–5 μm 5% burnt sienna 2–3 μm 5% bone black 5–8 μm
12 Shirt front, mid tone h. 0.145 M w. 0.175 M		*Shirt front* 75% lead white 1–2 μm 24% yellow ochre 0.5–6 μm 1% bone black 2–5 μm

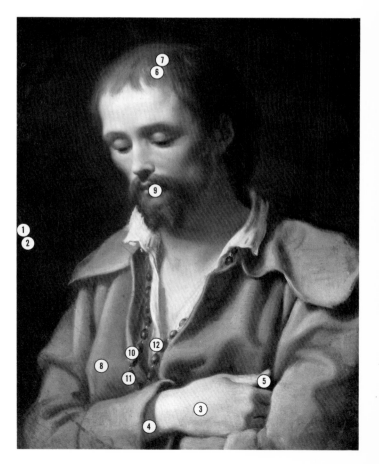

SUMMARY

The two paintings offer a marked contrast in number of pigments used with Guardi using an extensive palette and Cavallucci using a very limited palette:

F. Guardi	Cavallucci
lead white $2PbCO_2 \cdot Pb(OH)_2$	lead white
bone black $C + Ca_3(PO_4)_2$	bone black
ultramarine	Naples yellow
$\quad 3Na_2O \cdot 3Al_2O_3 \cdot 6SiO_2 \cdot 2Na_2S$	
green earth	yellow ochre
$\quad$ Fe, Mg, Al, K hydrosilicate	$Fe_2O_3 \cdot H_2O$
vermilion HgS	red ochre
red lead Pb_3O_4	burnt sienna
red ochre $Fe_2O_3 \cdot nH_2O$	
crimson lake, unidentified organic dye	
Naples yellow $Pb_3[SbO_4]_2$	
raw sienna $Fe_2O_3 \cdot H_2O$	
Van Dyck brown, bituminous earth	
burnt sienna Fe_2O_3	

These differences in palette are in keeping with other contrasting characteristics found in the two paintings.

Guardi used complex mixtures of pigments in some areas. For example, in the water he used lead white, green earth, ultramarine, Van Dyck brown, raw sienna, and black. Similarly, in the church roof's gray-blue areas, he used lead white, green earth, vermilion, Naples yellow, Van Dyck brown, and black.

Adding to the complexity of materials, one finds the special characteristic of Guardi's having used two ranges of particle sizes of a single pigment in several tones. In the blue sky tones ultramarine is present in a small particle range of $0.5-8$ μm and in a large particle range from $32-160$ μm average diameter. Likewise, in the water one finds green earth in a range of small particles from $3-10$ μm, and in a range of larger particles from $130-160$ μm. The large particles are visible to the naked eye and are dark in color. The small particles are a less intense color, yet when mixed with highly refractive and reflective lead white particles, result in a bright color.

Often, as in the sky tones, the predominant pigment present is lead white, and the hue is achieved by the presence of relatively few particles of a colored pigment. For example, in the sky yellow cloud areas, the pale blue layers consist of 90% lead white and 10% ultramarine. Likewise, in the bright blue areas one finds 75% lead white and 25% ultramarine.

Another special characteristic of the Guardi proved to be the presence of agglomerates, particularly of lead white, in nearly every tone. These agglomerates were viewed and measured from the top in minute fragments of the paint surface. In the water tone sampled, one finds $30-90$ μm agglomerates of lead white comprising 50% of the total pigment used. In the gray-blue clouds of the sky one finds $8-40$ μm agglomerates of lead white comprising 70% of the total. These agglomerates give the paint surface quite a special quality when viewed under the stereo microscope and probably contribute to the muted blending of varied tones when the painting is viewed with the naked eye. The Guardi paint layers were found to be very crumbly, making it difficult to take sectional samples. This could suggest the use of comparatively less medium combined with the extensive use of agglomerates and large particles of pigment.

In the areas sampled, Guardi was found to have used from one to four distinctly different paint layers. Individually, these ranged from 12 and 15 μm relatively thin layers to 20 μm to 60 μm layers of average thickness.

In summary, Guardi used an extensive and complex palette with varying ranges of pigment particle size, agglomerates of lead white, and varying numbers of layers of paint. These special characteristics result in much variation of color and texture in the surface of the painting.

In contrast, Cavallucci's technique appears to consist of quite a different set of characteristics from those of Guardi. Cavallucci used a limited palette of just six pigments as compared with Guardi's twelve. This provides a framework in the Cavallucci for a more subtle set of tonal relationships.

Likewise, for a given tone, one usually finds comparatively simple pigment mixtures in the Cavallucci painting. Often only two pigments predominate within a tone, with a few particles of a third or fourth pigment also present. For example, the flesh shadow tone on the hand is mostly lead white and yellow ochre with a few particles of bone black. The yellow on the beads is mostly Naples yellow, with a little lead white and bone black.

Cavallucci consistently used a more limited range of particle and agglomerate sizes than Guardi. For example, his pigment particles range from 0.5 μm to 8 μm and agglomerates, when found, measure from 2 μm to 10 μm and one occasion, 20 μm. Guardi's particles measure up to 200 μm and agglomerates to 90 μm. Cavallucci's limited particle size range results in a more uniform paint surface which probably enhances the subtlety of the limited palette.

One finds a simpler layer structure in the Cavallucci. Usually one layer is used; sometimes a second layer, usually a highlight, is applied over the first, as in the hair. Never does the structure become as complicated with Guardi's multiple layers.

One special characteristic of the Cavallucci is the use in several tones of yellow ochre as the predominant base pigment rather than the more frequently found lead white. For example, the light tone of the hair is 80% yellow ochre and the brown of the beads contains 75% yellow ochre. The hair mid-tone contains yellow ochre almost equal in amount to the lead white present. This could be expected to give a warmer tone than had the predominant tone been the usual lead white. Yellow ochre may also produce a more muted tone due to lower birefringence and therefore less refraction of light of yellow ochre particles as compared with lead white particles.

In summary, Cavallucci has used a limited palette, relatively simple pigment mixtures for a particular tone, a very narrow range of pigment particle and agglomerate sizes, and a simple structure of layers. The resulting visual effect is one of great uniformity of surface and subtlety of tonal relationships.

Marigene H. Butler

Index of Artists

(References are to page numbers)

Amigoni, Jacopo, 46
Amorosi, Antonio, 164
Anonymous Neapolitan, 244
Anonymous Tuscan, 158
Bacciarelli, Marcello, 166
Balestra, Antonio, 48
Batoni, Pompeo, 168
Bazzani, Giuseppe, 18
Beaumont, Claudio Francesco, 20
Bellotto, Bernardo, 50
Benefial, Marco, 176
Bianchi, Pietro, 180
Bigari, Vittorio, 142
Bloemen, Jan Frans van, called Orizzonte, 182
Bonechi, Matteo, 146
Bonito, Giuseppe, 218
Butafogo, Antonio, 52
Cades, Giuseppe, 184
Canal, Giovanni Antonio, called Canaletto, 54
Carlevaris, Luca, 58
Carlone, Carlo Innocenzo, 22
Caro, Lorenzo De, 220
Cavallucci, Antonio, 188
Ceruti, Giacomo, called Il Pitochetto, 24
Chiari, Giuseppe, 190
Cignaroli, Giambettino, 60
Cipper, Giovanni Francisco, 28
Conca, Sebastiano, 222
Corvi, Domenico, 192
Crespi, Giuseppe Maria, 116
Creti, Donato, 122
Damini, Vincenzo, 62
Diziani, Gaspare (de Ciano), 64
Falciatore, Filippo, 224
Ferrari, Gregorio de, 42
Ferretti, Giovan Domenico, 150
Franceschini, Marcantonio, 126
Gabbiani, Anton Domenico, 154
Gandolfi, Gaetano, 132
Gandolfi, Mauro, 134
Gandolfi, Ubaldo, 128

Gherardini, Alessandro, 156
Ghezzi, Pietron Leone, 194
Ghislandi, Fra Vittore, called Fra Galgario, 30
Giaquinto, Corrado, 226
Graziani, Erocle, 136
Guardi, Francesco, 66
Guardi, Giovanni Antonio, 72
Guglielmi, Gregorio, 196
Guidobono, Bartolemeo, 32
Locatelli, Andrea (Lucatelli), 198
Longhi, Alessandro, 74
Longhi, Pietro (Falca), 76
Luti, Benedetto, 200
Maggiotto, Domenico, 78
Magnasco, Alessandro, 34
Marchis, Alessio de, 230
Marieschi, Michele, 80
Masucci, Agostino, 202
Matteis, Paolo de, 232
Milani, Aureliano, 138
Monti, Francesco, 140
Mura, Francesco de, 234
Panini, Giovanni Paolo, 204
Pecheux, Lorenzo (Laurent), 38
Pellegrini, Giovanni Antonio, 82
Piazzetta, Giovanni Battista, 84
Pittoni, Giovanni Battista, 92
Ricci, Marco, 96
Ricci, Sebastiano, 96
Rocca, Michele, 208
Rossi, Mariano, 210
Rotari, Pietro, 100
Solimena, Francesco, 236
Tiepolo, Giovanni Battista, 102
Tiepolo, Giovanni Domenico, 110
Traballesi, Giuliano, 40
Traversi, Gaspare, 242
Trevisani, Francesco, 212
Vanvitelli, Gasparo (Gaspar Van Wittel), 214
Zuccarelli, Francesco, 112

from Zanotti, *Storia dell' Accademia Clementina*, Bologna, 1739

Design by Everett McNear

Composition by The University of Chicago Printing Department

Printed and bound by The Veritone Company, Chicago

Colorplates by Collins, Miller & Hutchings, Inc., Chicago

The map of Italy is from the collections of
The Newberry Library, Chicago

Date Due

DEC 7 1988		ILL : 274 1850
		EVI : 8/26/97
		Due : 3/27/97

Demco 38-297